THIRTEEN MOONS

Conversations with the Goddess

Peter Knight

Including the *Thirteen Insights* –
to help restore planetary balance

Stone Seeker Publishing
Wiltshire, UK
Honouring ancient wisdom and the Earth

www.stoneseeker.net
stoneseeker@waitrose.com

Published in the UK by
Stone Seeker Publishing,
Calne, Wiltshire, England
Website: www.stoneseeker.net
Email: stoneseeker@waitrose.com

First published 2007
Reprint 2010 (with additions) and in 2012 (with additions).

ISBN 978 1 905553 15 0

Other books by Peter Knight

Sacred Dorset - On the Path of the Dragon
Dorset Pilgrimages - A Millennium Handbook (with Mike Power)
Earth Mysteries - An Illustrated Encyclopaedia of Britain CD-ROM
The Wessex Astrum – Sacred Geometry on a Mystical Landscape
    (with Toni Perrott)
*West Kennet Long Barrow – Landscape, Shamans and the
    Cosmos.*
The Cerne Giant – Landscape, Gods and the Stargate.
Calne – Gateway to Ancient Wiltshire (with Sue Wallace)

This edition cover design: Peter Knight

Line drawings © Peter Knight, unless otherwise stated

Printed on FSC paper in the by CPI Antony Rowe, Chippenham.

Contents

Dedications, acknowledgements and some reviews   4

1. Genesis - February: Arbor Low   5
2. First Moon - March: Knowlton. Lesson - All is Consciousness   15
3. Second Moon - April: Men-an-Tol. Lesson - The Human Experience   29
4. Beltaine Clogs   44
5. Third Moon - May: Avebury.
                        Lesson - Connecting With the Land and Self   48
6. Newgrange and a Meeting with Einstein   64
7. Fourth Moon - June: Loughcrew, Ireland. Lesson - The Play of Wyrd   75
8. Chasing Rainbows - Fourknocks, Tara and Castleruddery   88
9. Fifth Moon - July: Wiltshire Crop Circle. Lesson - Sacred Geometry   93
10. Dreaming a Crop Circle   111
11. Dartmoor, Deer and Dowsing   116
12. Sixth Moon - August: Dartmoor. Lesson - Walking the Land   122
13. Shamanic Moon - Wolf and Stag   131
14. Dartmoor - Open and Closed   141
15. Seventh Moon - September: Stonehenge. Lesson - Sacred Sites   154
16. Drumming, Didges and Diana   169
17. Eighth Moon - October: Wayland's Smithy.
                        Lesson - Leys and Earth Energies   176
18. Strolling with Mary and Michael   196
19. Stones, Secateurs and Samhain   204
20. Ninth Moon - November: New Forest.
                        Lesson - Spirit of the Green Man   214
21. The Coven and the Dragon Tree   227
22. Tenth Moon - December: Carnac, France.
                        Lesson - Connecting with Ancestors   236
23. Madeleine, Prêtres and Prejudice   253
24. Returning my Father to the Land   267
25. Eleventh Moon - January: Rosslyn Chapel.
                        Lesson - The Grail and Mary Magdalene   275
26. Finding Mary   290
27. Twelfth Moon (Part 1) - January: London.
                        Lesson - Towards an Earth-Conscious Future   295
28. Twelfth Moon (Part 2) - Visions from the All-Seeing Eye   307
29. Reunited in Londinium   317
30. Thirteenth Moon - February: Glastonbury. The Thirteen Insights   323

Resources

Thirteen Moons Localities and Further Reading   338
About the Author   347
Thirteen Moons Tours and Workshops   348
Stone Seeker Tours   349
Other Books by the Author   350
Dorset Earth Mysteries Group   351
The Wessex Research Group   351

Dedications

To Mother Earth
To my mother and late father
To my children and granddaughter
and to all those people, known and unknown,
who have helped me along the Path

Acknowledgements

First and foremost, may I thank Sue Wallace, who
proof-read this new edition, spotting the deliberate mistakes I
had planted (that's my excuse and I'm sticking to it). I would also
like to thank all those individuals, and there were many,
who furnished me with information and gave of their wisdom.

(Wiltshire, Spring 2012)

*'I came to realise that for all my travelling to ancient places,
over many years, in my insatiable quest for the Goddess, I
needed only look into the eyes of my 5 yr-old daughter,
Leela Zen, to find Her. And that any of us, for that matter,
need only look in the mirror. She is there, returning our gaze.'*
Peter Knight (from *Earth Mysteries* - CD-ROM)

Some reviews of *Thirteen Moons*

*"… a profound and profoundly excellent book… it deserves
to become a widely read classic… Parallels with The Celestine
Prophecy and The Da Vinci Code will inevitably be drawn, but the
truth is that this is a far, far better book… Superb – buy it now!"*
Merry Meet Magazine

*" Peter writes with perceptive humour… woven deftly into this lively
narrative are important esoteric threads… it has a solid ring of truth
which kept me reading."*
Sacred Hoop Magazine

"… a passionate attempt to connect us with Nature."
Western Daily Press

*"This humorous, semi-autobiographical novel makes
brilliant reading."*
Pauline Johnson, Society of Ley Hunters.

1. Genesis -
February: Arbor Low

© P Knight

Tell me of the landscape in which you live,
and I will tell you who you are.
(Jose Ortega Gassett, 1883 -1955)

'What the hell am I doing here?'

A good question that, and one I didn't even begin to have the answer to. The wind was whistling around my increasingly chilled ears, sunset had been and gone, and darkness was closing around me like a menacing Dementor. And yes, it had arrived – it was raining! I was sitting midst a pile of old stones, miles from anywhere, and it was raining. And the weird thing was this; in the past I'd never really felt drawn to visit prehistoric sites. OK, as a child I had been dragged along to Stonehenge by my parents, and had stood there, quite bored, whilst dad pointed out to me how clever our ancestors had been to build such a mighty, enduring edifice all those thousands of years ago. But to me it was just a load of old rocks, and I wondered what it would look like when it was finished! It had the look of an abandoned construction site. The highlight of the day was the refreshment kiosk and the gift shop afterwards.

Yet there I was, miles from anywhere, sitting on top of a block of cold limestone in the Derbyshire Peak District. Arbor Low didn't feel too inviting and seemed to barely tolerate my presence, as it contrived to periodically spit darts of rain into my eyes with the venom of a cobra. The *Low* element of the name seemed more than fitting, as my feelings plummeted toward the suicidal. I wondered if there was an *Arbor High* somewhere. Now that place at least sounded a bit more upbeat.

'Well. What the hell *am* I doing here, my friend?'

'Beats me.'

Well, it's finally happened – I'm talking to myself.

As the raindrops became more persistent and my nose finally plunged to sub-zero, I teetered on the brink, before plunging into some Gollum-like state as my mind fought itself; *We are getting cold… yes, but we'd better stay… Master doesn't care about us… Master will be pleased if we stay… but we are getting wet… it is a small price to pay for finding the Precious…*

'… What bloody Precious!'

My words of anguish were ensnared by the wind and scattered across the desolate, ever-darkening landscape. I didn't recall Robert Langdon sitting cross-legged on a rock on a rain-sodden Derbyshire hill. Oh no, he found locations like Paris, Rosslyn and London. No, my saga was more like the Da Vinci *Cold!*

As I sat there, I mentally retraced the steps that had led me to that ancient, back-of-beyond place on that wet, windswept evening. I won't bore you too much, save to say that in the immediate past, at the tender age of forty five, I had been made redundant from my job as senior editor for an alternative lifestyle magazine, following a takeover by a rival company. I decided to take six months off on the proceeds, do a bit of travelling, see the world, relax in the sun, that sort of thing. The severance pay was indeed generous and I felt like a Lotto winner when the dosh appeared on my bank statement. I was soon offered a position by another cool magazine, but I needed a well-earned break to recharge my batteries. Well, that's the mundane stuff in a very small nutshell.

As for my spirituality, I had been dipping my toes in the ever-confusing pool of spirituality and inner growth for some fifteen years. From an early rush of positive thinking (*God bless Louise Hay*), I went on to Buddhist chanting (*God bless me*), before being attracted to Hinduism (*God bless my cow*). Then I studied the Hare Krishna movement (*God bless open-toed sandals and George Harrison*), Sufism (*God bless everyone*), Judaism (*God bless my bank*) and even, gulp, Christianity (*God bless me although I'm just a miserable sinner on the Alpha Programme*). I toyed with the idea of becoming a follower of Osho, spending some weekends at their retreats, but found I couldn't stay awake for the discourses and meditations after all the *free love* I'd had the night before (seemed worth it at the time though!)

At one point I had even had the realisation that I myself was indeed God, or a facet of the Divine. *I am God. Nice one.* But it slowly dawned on me that if I was God, then perhaps the Planet was well and truly screwed!

So for some time I had been just ambling along with my spirituality, playing with it I suppose, a workshop junkie, a fully paid-up member of the ranks of frustrated spiritual seekers, with arguably more money than sense. I had chanted millions of Oms in groups, whilst sitting cross-legged (which always gave me cramp, as well as letting out occasional embarrassing wind), had purchased enough crystals to sink the Titanic, and had tried circular breathing into a hollowed-out tree trunk until I'd turned purple. The only noise I ever produced from a didge sounded like a flatulent elephant the night after a good curry! And through all this, my ego desperately wanted the assurance that I *could* make a difference in the grand design of the Universe. *Oh yeah? So you think a tiny speck of a human being such as you has any relevance in an infinitely vast Universe? Think again, pal!* Finally I had begun to get disillusioned with the whole concept that there even was a God.

But then… one day, just two weeks previous on a bright winter's day in January, some odd things happened (and bear in mind that the following all took place in a single day). First off, I checked my e-mails, as I do religiously every morning (I hate that phrase - 'religiously', although I suppose it is apt if you are compelled to do something out of mindless duty!). A press release had been forwarded to me about a pilgrimage some Druids were making to an ancient henge called Arbor Low, in Derbyshire. Nothing much appealed. Second up, a friend of mine rang me to see if I wanted to join him and some of his mates youth-hostelling in Derbyshire. He added they would visit a cool ancient place nearby called Arbor Low, to build a campfire, have some drinks and indulge in a few spliffs. *Arbor Low again. Now there's a coincidence.* And then, and this is when it started to get seriously weird, there was a *Meet the Ancestors* programme on TV that night about prehistoric Derbyshire, which included Arbor Low! Three separate instances on the same day about a place I had never heard of before.

Now I was a believer in some sort of fate, a process working behind the scenes of the visible Universe connecting everything and everyone. Carl Jung had called it synchronicity (catchy

7

phrase, five syllables, nice one Carl), whereby meaningful coincidences occur in our lives and link us to everything else. So I thought and I thought some more. *Arbor Low*. I somehow felt drawn to it. I was soon on the Net finding out all the info, the where, what and how of it all. Neolithic - *that's old, isn't it?* Over four thousand years old. A henge – bank on the outside of a ditch. An ellipse-shaped circle of megaliths – all lying scattered on the ground. The henge was over 1000ft above sea level and it looked like a nice part of the country – quaint cottages, open spaces, wayside inns and all that. *That's cool.*

So there I was, sitting in the wind and spitting rain, all on my lonesome, squinting across an ever-darkening moor, perched on a rock. Well it hadn't been too bad when I'd arrived, about an hour before – there had been plenty of light then, for me to explore the henge and its stones. At its centre was a ruined 'cove' of seven megaliths, one of which was the largest survivor. It was prone now but on one side of it was a wonderful face in stone, peering timelessly across Middleton Common. It was in fact looking toward Gibb Hill, a Neolithic mound about half a mile away, which may have marked ancient astronomical events. It was indeed an impressive site in an equally impressive landscape.

But all that had changed. The sun had gone down and the weather had well and truly closed in.

'Well? What the hell *am* I doing here?'

Done that one. OK, let's try this one. How long am I going to be doing whatever it is I am doing here? God, I'm starting to sound like Winnie-the-Pooh now, and I haven't even brought along any honey pots to sustain me!

Well, I sat there for what seemed like the whole of the Neolithic, until I could stand it no more. I was getting chilled to the bone and was wondering where the nearest pub was. My hands scratched away at the stone on which I was balanced and I could just make out the lichen-covered surface. My mind wandered again, and in desperation I speculated at what a certain detective would have made of the stones:

Well, Holmes, what do you think of the stones?

Sedimentary, my dear Watson, sedimentary!

OK, but give me a break. I was cold, tired and my warped sense of humour was holding my mind together. And then came the moment. *ENOUGH!* I rose from my cold, hard seat and turned to walk back to Upper Oldham Farm, through which meandered the path back to my car.

But no sooner had I got to my feet than I was frozen to the spot. Across the other side of the henge stood a tall, dark figure, faintly silhouetted against the last strands of light of the dusk sky. I could just make out a black hood and an equally dark matching full-length cloak. The figure stood motionless, save for the cloak, which rippled and billowed in the wind.

Shit, where did he come from? And how long has he been watching me?

I stood stock-still, no quite sure what to do next. He was clearly returning my gaze; there was no denying it. Eventually I could stand it no more. *Well, here goes.* I started towards the entrance of the henge, close to where he stood. My heart was pounding in my ears and despite the cold my hands were now perspiring. I tried to comfort myself. *Look, this dude is not the Yorkshire Ripper, is he? We are in Derbyshire after all.* On the other hand, he bore more than a passing resemblance to Silas, the psychopathic, self-flagellating monk in *The Da Vinci Code* – GULP!

I just had to keep walking, straight past him, looking straight ahead. As I approached, my heart was pounding so loud that he might have heard it. I was now level with him. He was silent. *Don't look back. That's it. He's just one of those gothie dudes, the ones who dig Marilyn Manson and think they only look cool in black leather with matching nail varnish.*

I got to the grass bank that marked the edge of the henge. I thought I'd made it.

'Who is he that walks on this hallowed ground, the temple of ancestors, on such a wearisome night?'

I was frozen to the spot. His voice was soft, yet deep and powerful, easily carrying in the wind and echoing around the whole site.

Damn - now I'll have to talk to him. I turned to face the stranger.

'Hi, there! How are you?' I replied.

How are you? Dead original that - nice one!

'I am well. And I can see from your presence here on this Night of Ewes that you too are walking the right path.'

I'm confused. What's he on about?

I replied, more out of courtesy than genuine curiosity.

'Night of the Ewes? Is that one of those pagany festival things?'

'A pagany festival thing?' he continued, 'Well you could say that. More precisely it is Imbolc, the festival of the lactation of lambs, the first of the annual celebrations of the Old Ones, revered

9

long before the people of the one prophet came to these shores. It dates back to times when people lived close to the Land, times of fairies, giants and dragons, times when magic was afoot.'

Relief. He **is** *a bloody Druid!*

He wasn't going to kill me after all, for I had never heard of a Druid being convicted of anything more than lying down in front of a JCB at anti-bypass protests. And I had certainly never heard of anyone being garrotted by a golden sickle.

He approached me, slowly, stopping just a few feet away. He pulled off the hood that had hidden his features. His pupils shone like diamonds, with an honesty and integrity that made me ashamed that I had labelled him as the Grim Reaper just moments before. A grey beard betrayed his years and around his neck hung a silver pendant in the design of a dragon. I introduced myself and after a short pause he did likewise.

'I am Bel, Guardian of this place, otherwise known as the Keeper of the Stones.'

Weirdo alert!

'You are puzzled, I can see. Let me explain, my friend. Many ancient sites have Guardians. Our task is an ancient and vital one. We ensure that places such as this remain pure and safe and that we are here to guide people such as yourself.'

'Do all ancient sites have Guardians?' I queried, '… for I have never heard of such people.'

He continued in a slow and measured voice.

'Few know we exist. Yet our lineage stretches back thousands of years. We are chosen, for we are selected when previous Guardians return to the Great Mother.'

'Selected by whom?' I enquired.

'By the Great Mother, of course, whom do you think?'

A smile appeared on his face as he surveyed me intently for my reaction.

OK, I'll go with this. He seemed genuine and the interchange was taking my mind off chilled fingers.

The worst that might happen is that he might run me through with a squeaky plastic replica of Excalibur!

'The Great Mother?' I enquired.

'Yes', he answered, 'She who is everything. She who is the Universe…' His hands gesticulated in swathes that swept out across the Land, '… Is all that has ever been and will ever be. She is the Goddess, your Mother, and my Mother. She is the Land. She is all.'

You're a heavy dude – I bet you go down a storm at parties, mate, creating Stonehenge out of balloons.

But then he came right up to my face, stopping within inches, as if the words *'you're a weirdo'* were tattooed on my forehead in day glow. His eyes burnt into mine like lasers.

'And She has been calling you, my brother. She comes for you... for you have been chosen.'

I'm starting to get freaked out now. Beam me up, Scottie!

I tried to marshal my thoughts, replying in a voice that seemed distant, as the wind scattered my retort across the moor:

'Chosen - me? Hey, I don't think so. Look, man, I came up here to check out this circle, nothing more. I'm not into all that witchy, naked-pagans-around-the-bonfire stuff.'

'Oh, really? Perhaps this be so – up 'till now. But look at the signs that led you to this place, led you to me. You may doubt for a while, but chosen you have been all the same. I have seen the signs for many moons. I knew you were comin'. You are to bring new messages to the world of men, messages from the Mother, from the Land. A book, yes, I have seen a book. She will contact you over the next thirteen full moons, at thirteen sacred sites, most in Albion. She's acomin' for you, my friend. She's gonna scare you shitless at times. But She will also fill your heart with such love that few have ever experienced. You are blessed beyond your wildest dreams, brother. I am honoured to have met you on this sacred night.'

He bowed his head ceremoniously, before resuming his penetrating stare.

Come in, Scottie - I said to beam me up!

I again retorted at his ridiculous statement:

'Hang on a minute. Why... er... what are you on about and what is it *She* going to say to...?'

'Listen to me, my friend,' he interrupted, '... that is between She and you. *You* have been chosen, not I. But I know it will affect many, many people. Magic is again moving across the Land. She is stirring once more, breathing her grace over us, and we will do well to heed her words. And you are blessed indeed to be a part of this enchantment. For tell me, my friend, haven't you felt for sometime that there was a space, a void, within you, a feeling that you have been living but a small part of who you really are? You feel like a jigsaw puzzle with a piece missing? Is this not true?'

His eyebrows rose, for he already knew the answer.

11

He took a few steps backwards, and reached out in a sudden movement that made me jump, as he grasped both my hands and outstretching them towards him.

'You are truly privileged, my brother. I can see it all now. She has chosen someone who is spiritual, but who has not been into the Old Ways. That way people will take on board what you will say. A bit like how UFO's are usually seen by policemen, vicars and doctors, rather than those who race around lookin' for 'em. People will believe you because you do not go around in tie-dye, have dreadlocks, or wear a purple shell suit. Yes, I see it. You are just a normal, run-of-the-mill bloke, no one exceptional.'

Thanks for nothing!

I countered once more: 'Well, if all this were true, just for argument's sake like, wouldn't a woman be better for all this Goddess stuff? Aren't those feminist, witchy women gonna reject me 'cause I'm a bloke?'

'True', he replied, '… you make a good point, but it seems to me that it is happening like this for two reasons. Firstly, the Goddess is in danger of being hijacked by certain sisters who, although well intentioned, are excluding men from her. Are they not potentially setting up a similar imbalance as we have had for the past 2000 - odd years? Nature has equal male and female, yin and yang, and to deny either spells trouble, as we have seen for centuries past. Secondly, it is men more than women who need to change their ways in this world, for men still run most religions, businesses and governments. Coming from a man, I feel that those who need '*converting*' will be more receptive. The lessons you will be putting out into the world are for the uninitiated, not the believers. I feel this is how She wants to help the world this time around.'

He let go of my hands, which fell lifeless to my sides. For a few moments we stood facing each other in silence, our eyes mutually transfixed. Then, with a wry smile and a wink, he turned his back on me and, pulling his hood back over his grey locks, began to walk slowly away.

'Hey. Hang on a mo'…' I cried out, '… you can't just swan off like… like Obi-Wan Kenobi, leaving me standing here. What do you mean 'a book'? Who will contact me and why… who the hell are you?'

He did not answer any of my questions. But after dozen paces he turned to face me once more.

'But a word of warning, my friend,' he said, with another piercing stare. 'There may be those who will not want the ancient ways to become common knowledge again. They may try to, how shall I say, *distract* you from your quest and may even wish to harm you...'

Sharp intake of breath - lump in throat. I had sudden visions of Opus Dei assassins, hotfoot from the Vatican. My skin crawled and a tsunami-sized shiver swept through me as his words cut me to the bone.

'... But keep faith. Be strong. Much depends on your integrity and determination, and your innate belief that the Truth must come out and become widely known, as it once was.'

'Be harmed by who? And why? Hang on... please!'

He turned once more and resumed his retreat from the henge. I watched open-mouthed as he melted into the inky blackness of the night.

I yelled into the darkness whence he had disappeared:

'And may the Force be with you too, mate!'

Once again I stood alone. My head was spinning with all he had said and my brain wrestled to recall every word and gesture, in case I forgot something vital.

A book? The Goddess? Oh, come on!

This reject from Hogwarts had said I was to be contacted by the Earth Mother, Planet Earth no less. What planet was *he* on?

Get a grip man. What was his name? Oh yes, Bel – well ring the other one! This is absurd. It is, isn't it? Mad... right?... mad... yes!

'Now let's get back to the car, find the pub I'm staying at, and get ever so slightly drunk.'

Not twenty minutes later I was sitting in front of an open fire sampling the landlord's finest real ale. I could feel my fingers again and was considering that perhaps the stranger had been some poor soul who had escaped from a local psychiatric hospital. Yes, that would explain it. After all, even places of extreme mental suffering have spiritual inmates - take the Vatican, or the White House for example, not to mention the Houses of Parliament! I chuckled aloud at my comforting, if forced, humour.

I approached the bar for a refill.

'Same again, please mate.'

'Been up to Arbor Low, I 'ear', said the barman as he handed me my change.

'Yes. It's quite a place... very atmospheric.'

'Oh, you can say tha' again', he said with a half-smile that was designed to arouse my curiosity.

'Sorry? What do you mean?' I enquired between sips.

13

'Oh, nothing really. Just tha' the older locals 'round these parts tell of a shadowy, bearded man who always wears black, see, and who appears this time of year. He's often seen in the distance walkin' around the stones, but no one can ever get close to 'im. He melts away into the moor, like a ghost. They says 'e is guardin' the place against evil. Some call 'im the Keeper of the Stones.'

The Keeper of the Stones!

I stood at the bar, unable to speak. With a grin all over his face, the barman moved off to serve another thirsty soul, and I was left staring at my reflection in the mirror tiles behind the bar. There was a lump in my throat that hadn't been there before and my heart raced towards meltdown.

I downed my pint in one, as the enormity of the barman's story sank in.

Bel, it was you.

'Bloody hell!'

2. First Moon – March: Knowlton, Dorset
Lesson – All is Consciousness

© P Knight

He who sees the Infinite
in all things sees God
(William Blake)

So come on, be honest. What would *you* do if you were at a sacred site one night and some guy resembling Gandalf said you were to receive lessons from the Goddess over thirteen full moons at thirteen ancient places? Would you give up your day job? Bel the Weird One had mentioned Albion. I knew this was an old name for Britain, and straight away felt a bit cheated. How come the heroes of *The Da Vinci Code* and *The Celestine Prophecy* got dispatched all over the world to exotic places, admittedly getting shot at, whereas as I was stuck here in good old Blighty, where the biggest perils to my welfare were likely to be frostbite and 'losing my marbles'. Perhaps I'd end up in the same padded cell as this Gandalf, or Bel, or whoever he was.

I returned to Dorset and over the next week tried to forget the events of that night in early February. But the more I tried to put it on the back burner, the more I found myself replaying what had happened on that rain-swept night. I did find myself, however, increasingly curious about sacred sites and our ancient spiritual heritage. I bought some books and surfed the Net. It was as if something was pulling me toward these places. *'Thirteen moons* at thirteen sacred places across Albion'. I found myself increasingly wondering where the first place would be. But that was nuts, I'd remind myself. *The Planet, I mean the Earth, talking to me?* I felt I had more chance of a Supermodel selecting me from a line up of hunky lifeguards than being chosen to converse with Planet Earth. I mean, what do you say to Mother Earth? *Hi there, how you doing? How you feeling Down Under? Don't those smiling, clicking dolphins drive you nuts? Why don't you let the penguins meet the polar bears? And what about Crop Circles – are you having a laugh?* Do you tell her a joke: *Have you heard the one about the Buddhist who goes up to a hamburger stand and says to the vendor, 'Can you make me one with everything?'* Hardly.

But deep inside me a little voice kept asking where the first sacred site would be. I even circled in all the full moons for that year in my diary, noting how one month had two full moons - thirteen in one year. But what if the dude at the henge *was* a little deranged. He seemed genuine enough and sincere in his beliefs. But so was Adolf Hitler and, OK, so was Gandhi, but which one was more akin to the soul at Arbor Low? My brain tossed and chewed over all that had transpired on that evening in the Derbyshire Peak, but I knew that only one thing would resolve things for sure – and there was a Full Moon approaching!

Then the dreams started; just vague recollections on waking at first - images of me sitting in some sort of rock chamber, with beams of light penetrating the darkness from an unknown source. But then came the biggie. Picture the scene. I dreamt I was in a dark enclosed stone chamber, ancient and damp from dripping water. It felt like a prehistoric tomb or something similar. I could feel the cold and see my breath in the light that shone from a single candle, which illuminated ancient symbols on some of the stones. Then the voice came. It was female, yes, definitely that of a middle-aged woman - whispering softy.

'I am coming… I am coming.'

'Who are you?'

'You know me.'

'Who are you?'

'I am that which you seek.'

'Please let me see you.'

'Even if such a sight would blind you with my brilliance and magnificence?'

'Yes, yes, show me, show yourself!'

Instantly a blinding light illuminated the chamber, and flashing iridescent rainbows strobed my eyes, causing me to retreat behind my hands. Then the loud roar, and then lightning! And finally, the same voice shouted into my ears from very close range…

'I AM HERE!'

I sat bolt upright, sweat pouring down my face and body, my bed saturated. My breathing was fast, and my heart raced as if I had just jogged up Glastonbury Tor. Those words echoed around my head. *I am coming... I am here!*

Hey man, this is beginning to get seriously weird.

I toyed with the idea that some psychosomatic process might be going on in my muddled head, whereby I had taken on board the ramblings of that dude Bel, and my imagination was working double time. I knew from delving into the Human Potential Movement that the mind could be programmed to override old patterns and replace them with more relevant, positive thoughts. So had the idea that I was to be some Saviour bearing a Divine gift for all mankind struck some cord with me? Had my ego got hooked, welcoming with open arms the concept that I was to be a messenger from God? Was I conditioning my mind to believe the unbelievable? Well, one thing was for sure - after a week of such dreams I needed to go shop for new bedding.

It was now early March. The buds on the trees were turning into tiny leaves, the unfolding hope of spring. Full moon was only four days away. There had been a run of three consecutive clear nights and I had sat outside watching the silver orb slowly ripen to full, squinting to find the hare on its features. Who was coming? Where was it to be? I had been given no clues. Perhaps none would come. Huge doubts stampeded through my mind, and several times, under the moon's watchful gaze, I burst out laughing. She seemed to get the joke as I thought I detected a smile on her face.

'Do you know the answer', I called up.

The moon did not answer, but I felt she knew more than she was letting on. *God, I'm talking to the moon now!* I tried to get a grip. Yet despite my doubts, deep inside I sensed something was unfolding. In fact, if truth were told, I was hoping it was.

Be really cool if the dude on the moor was for real. Can I even begin to imagine it? Forget winning the Lottery! Only four days to go. OK, Mother Earth, if you're for real, come and get me!

So the day of the Full Moon arrived. But there were no signs, no messages - nothing, not a dickie bird - zilch. I must admit I was a bit downhearted. I even felt a bit of an idiot. How could I have got sucked up into that head stuff, all based on a weirdo in a stone circle, a ghost story, and a few bizarre dreams? It was about an hour before sunset and I had to go for a drive. I headed off, not knowing where to - I just had to drive.

'OK, Mother Earth...' I challenged aloud from behind the wheel, '... show me what you got!'

I left behind the lights of my Dorset hometown and headed across Cranborne Chase, an area of rural beauty and rolling hills. I had often been walking along its chalk ridges, which were littered with ancient burial mounds. After about twenty minutes of aimless driving along country lanes I spotted the top of a church tower peeping over the hedgerows, and further on it became clear that it was ruined. The hairs on the back of my neck suddenly prickled and my mouth went dry. Around another bend and there it was. I pulled into a small lay-by, next to an iron gate. The sun had still not set as I opened the gate, the creaking of which echoed across adjacent empty fields. An English Heritage sign told me it was a sacred site called Knowlton, a Neolithic henge that had later been Christianised with the erection of a Norman church. The church was fairly complete, although it lacked a roof and some sections of wall. The tower was still fine and was decorated with glistening flint. Surrounding the church was the deep Neolithic ditch and outside that a grassy bank, constructed thousands of years before the coming of the cross.

It was so quiet, save for the call of crows in the trees that covered a nearby mound. I entered the ruins through an archway and stood midst its ruinous skeleton, looking west towards a sky that was becoming increasingly colourful. I could not see the sun for low cloud, but knew it was close to setting and I stood mesmerized by the light show that was unfolding, for my benefit alone it seemed. A palette of reds, purples and oranges danced before my eyes, and I suddenly felt good to be alive. All trepidations seemed to fade away and I felt that I was exactly where I was meant to be.

Then it dawned on me. *The Full Moon!*

I turned around to look for her silvery face, but was disappointed to see a bank of dark cloud hugging the eastern horizon. *Damn.*

'Where are you then?'

This wouldn't have happened in The Celestine Prophecy or that incredible movie Avatar! Come on Planet Earth, you gotta give me the bloody Full Moon!

'But you know it is there.'

I was stopped dead in my tracks. *Who said that?* A voice, a woman's voice, of middle years. More than that, it was the voice of my dreams! But it was all around me. I spun around in every direction. No one.

'Who's there?' I shouted.

There was no reply. I raced back out through the archway and walked around the exterior of the church, surveying the ancient, silent banks and ditches as I scurried around the ruins, looking for someone, anyone. There was no one. But the voice had been very close, as if someone were but inches from me. Within the ruins there was a carpet of crunchy gravel, so how could anyone have got away from me that quickly without a sound? I felt in my pocket for the comforting shape of my car keys.

Get ready to beam me up again, Scottie.

'Who's there?' I shouted again, this time at the top of my voice. The reply was immediate and took my breath away.

'No need to shout.'

Again I looked around, spinning like a top, trying to catch a glimpse of anyone in the fading light. Feeling somewhat giddy, I stopped and tried to compose myself as best I could, with little success. I enquired again, this time in a softer voice, even though part of me hoped there would be no reply.

'Who are you?'

'Who Am I? Well now, let me see. People have been trying to answer that question for thousands of years. It really depends on your point of view, culture or preference. To some I am Athena, to others Demeter, Quan Yin, Great Spirit, Epona, Persephone, Brigit, Kali, the Virgin Mary, Sophia, Isis, Hecate and Mary Magdalene. Take your pick, for I am all of these and a thousand others. But I am also Cernunnos, Pan, Merlin, Zeus, Apollo, Jesus the Christ, Buddha, Archangel Michael. Need I go on?'

'Look, this is freaking me out. Please, show yourself. I can hear your voice, real close to me, but I see no one. Please, show yourself, before I have an accident!'

'Humour. That is good. I too dance to the joy of life. People so often take life and themselves too seriously. Many will

19

listen to me through you because you are not pretentious - people will laugh with you.'

'They will probably laugh *at* me!' I replied, still hoping that someone might appear from behind the gnarled walls. Even Bel the Weird One would have sufficed.

'You must trust me. Unless you yourself create it, no harm will come to you. You are free to go now and I will not contact you again. You must decide. You can return to your car and drive away, or you can stay. If you choose to remain, I can promise you but one thing; your life will never be the same again. You are standing at a threshold. Few are invited to cross the bridge to the realms of ancient knowledge, in fact few wish to be. Magic or mundane, new life or old? Which is it to be?'

Talk about laying it on the line. OK, when in doubt ask questions.

'But who or what are you? What would I be saying *yes* to, if I did?'

'Trust me.'

'Trust who?'

'It is I.'

Trust someone I can't even see – good God!

'You could say that!'

'Hey, hang on. I didn't say anything out loud then. You read my thoughts.'

'Did you think I would not to be able to?'

'Yeah but… but… that means…'

'… That I am real. Indeed I am. I am here. I am everywhere. I am around you and inside you. You have no secrets from me. I know all you know, for we are one.'

I felt as if my privacy had been breached big time.

This, whatever it is, has just been inside my mind.

'You better believe it!'

'But how can you do that? Hang on a minute, perhaps you are just in my head, that's it.'

'But you are hearing my words now through your ears, are you not?'

That's true!

'Look, this is really freaking me out. I am standing in a ruined bloody church, on the night of the Full Moon, hearing voices that do not seem to have a body. What is happening?'

'You are happening... I am happening... everything is happening. Right now, at no other time, just now. All else is illusion. I only do now, you see. And so it is with you. Time is simply the eternal unfoldment of Now moving on from Now to another Now!'

'We only do now? OK. OK. But, er, what about history and time, and... hang on a minute, you haven't really answered my question yet. Who are you?'

'That is a good question. But it is one that will take thirteen moons to answer, and even then not fully. You see, even I do not know the answer to your enquiry.'

'But that's nuts! You are, what... Planet Earth, Mother whatever Goddess? How can you not know what's going down?'

'First things first... Right. For thousands of years wise men and women around the world have known a secret that most people were not able to grasp. Those in authority sought to deprive the masses of this knowledge, even though it would have individually empowered the people. Tell me, what do you see around you right now? You see a world of hard and soft, light and dark, life and death, solid and liquid, animate and inanimate, a physical world with hard and fast physical laws, do you not?'

'Of course.'

'Yet you also feel that there is more than this. For many years now you have known that part of you will go on beyond your physical body. You might call this your Spirit, your Higher Self or your Soul.'

'Yes, I guess so. I believe I have some sort of Soul, a consciousness that will live on when I die... in principle anyway.'

'Ah yes, your Soul. Well, the Earth too has a Soul. But it is more than you think. To imply that the Earth has a soul behind physicality immediately creates the concept of duality, this being separate from that. But try to comprehend, if you will, that the physical planet you know is not just an extension of Consciousness, but that the Earth IS Consciousness. Every atom that you see, feel, sense, taste, smell or touch, is pure Consciousness.'

'You mean all of this is a result of Spirit. I can go with that.'

'No. That is not what I said. Everything that exists in physicality is not just an outward indication of some Spiritual Law or process, for everything IS Consciousness. For one cannot be separated from the other. The apparent

21

separateness is merely a convincing illusion. Many great spiritual masters have said this over many millennia. It is not new knowledge, even if relatively few fully realised the enormity of the concept. The majority of these wise souls were not able to impart this message adequately. But the time has come for me to relate these spiritual truths to the masses, in an accessible way that will help preserve the Planet so that our mutual evolution is assured, at least long enough for us to reach our full potential.'

'This is still freaking me out. OK. You say *our* potential. But you are, I presume, the Earth Mother, the Goddess. Surely you have divine control over all that is to happen in the future.'

'Why should you think that? For I too have never been this way before. As you learn, I learn. As you feel joy and sorrow, so do I. All that you experience, I experience. It is true that I see a bigger picture than you. I am higher up in the balcony of life, so to speak, whereas you are in the front row and are thus too close to the screen; it is too big for you to take in. You are totally immersed in the movie of Life. I see the overview, yet I do not control its destiny, for I too am learning with you. For in the entire physical universe I have never created two identical things. No two ants, no two people, no two clouds, no two crop circles, no two grains of sand have been identical, or will ever be. What would be the point of duplicity? I am here to learn who I am, and I am achieving this by creating – just as you are.'

'You are here to learn who *you* are?'

'Yes. I too have separated myself from pure love and Spirit in order to know myself. It was at the moment you call the 'Big Bang' that I created and entered into physicality. It has often been said amongst your wise people that we are just remembering what has been lost. Well, this is another way of looking at Creation. I too have immersed myself in physicality and I am gradually returning to pure Spirit. So, for now anyway, I do not know what is to come in the medium you call future time.'

'But you are Divine. You must know all there is to know, and therefore be in control of it. I'm not sure if I can cope with a God, sorry Goddess, who doesn't know what the hell's going on.'

'I did not say I did not know what is happening. I know every detail of every butterfly wing, of every physical cell, and see and understand all that happens as it is created. I am

22

aware of every event that is manifesting and can remember everything that has ever manifested. But I do not know what is to come, for I simply create, observe and experience. How could I know what is to be, when you and I are creating every unique manifestation for the first time as it happens? I understand all that has been and all that is. I can dream, as you do, but the future is a blank canvas.'

'I think you might have that one wrong. You must know more than me, so you must be able to control the future. You're the Goddess, aren't you?'

'Yes, I am She. But this is the point, my son - you are also She.'

'Pardon me? Could you run that one by me again, please?'

'You are I. And I am you. You are the Earth and the Earth is you. You are my Consciousness and I yours. You are the Land and the Land is you. Can you not see that everything, every person, every animal, every grain of sand, is I, but is also you? You are as Divine as any God or Goddess, saint or prophet. You are pure Consciousness, you just haven't realised it! Few have. You are not a physical being with a Spirit guiding your way from the wings. You are 100% pure consciousness.'

'Are you saying I am a God or Goddess, that I am Divine?'

'But of course you are. Everything is. How can there be exceptions? There are no exemptions to this rule. If it exists, then I am there. I cannot fail to be. Everything is energy and light. I am, in fact, the I AM mystics speak of.'

'This is heavy stuff.'

'Actually it's light.'

'Very funny. You have a sense of humour.'

'Of course we do!'

'But how about this book Bel went on about? You said that lots of people, much wiser than me, have for thousand of years been telling the world that spirit underpins the physical. What new message can you pass on for me to write about? What will be new?'

'This time it is to be different, for it has to be. This time the lessons are purely about interacting with the Land, the Planetary Spirit – my spirit. In the past, even wise sages have not paid heed to the way human beings have treated the Earth. As a result, you as a species are in danger of closing the human experience before we have reached our full

23

potential. Your religions and various spiritual movements have complicated what was once so simple. The Truth has been veneered within layers of impenetrable distractions and controls, leaving people bewildered by the complexities of dogma, ritual and theosophy. In seeking deeper knowledge you have lost the purity of the message. Everyone now needs to be more aware than ever before of the Spirit in the Land, of ley lines, of earth energy, of sacred sites, of the inhabitants of other dimensions who share the Land with you. The lessons this time must reach the masses, not just philosophers and learned men. I am not here to preach to the converted.'

I crouched down against a nearby wall to steady myself. My head was still spinning as I tried to tackle the enormity of it all.

'Over thirteen moons I will speak with you about all these issues and more, in a dialogue that all can comprehend, and at the end shall bestow unto you the Thirteen Insights, to help Man to heal. The overriding message this time is to see yourselves not just as a body with a Spirit, but as part of the Spirit of the Land, of the Planet, inseparable and umbilically linked. Many well-intentioned seekers have been looking for Ascended Masters, UFO's, Heaven, Worm Holes, portals, Angelic Hosts, Prophets, the Second Coming and various other means of salvation and enlightenment. But those are all 'up there' or 'out there', always out of sight and out of reach. Your intellectualising of these issues makes this inevitable. But all along, the Truth was all around you. The Divinity you have all sought is here and is now. It is contained within the Land.'

'Within the Land? By this do you mean everything physical on the Earth?'

'Yes, good. But in particular the Land, for this is your theatre of exploration, the stage on which you have all agreed to play a role. Geography is sacred. Every hill, sea, valley, river, rock and waterfall, tree and flower is Divine. More than this, I did not make them per se, rather they ARE ME, as are you. You may see here a great irony. For I will teach you that the more you venture out and connect with the Land, the more you will recognise the divinity that is your own true nature. The more you go outwards, the more you are in truth journeying inward. Mankind has complicated the simplicity of the Universe almost beyond recognition, and the results are for all to see. But life can be so simple for you.'

24

'Simple, perhaps, if you are the Goddess.'

'That's what I said – simple for you. Your only major hurdle is for you to realise that you and the Land are one. Shamans have known this for thousands of years. For your species to truly advance spiritually, you must ultimately be as one with the Land, as you once briefly were thousands of years ago. Religions since have taught their adherents that the Earth is simply an object to use and abuse as they wish, and is of no real consequence to God's plans. Wrong! The Earth IS the Divine plan, not a sideshow. And the Earth is indeed a school, for it holds the lessons, the teachers and the students. As you learn so the Earth learns, so I learn.'

'You learn? But what do *you* need to learn about?'

'Everything that is to come.'

'So you really haven't got a clue how this story is going to end?'

'Not an inkling! How could I? You and I and the rest of creation have not yet dreamed it into existence. This will come as a shock to many, who wish to be guided by an omnipotent all-powerful God who is leading his children back to some Promised Land. Some may feel disempowered, in that there is no longer a God guiding them, as a shepherd would lead his flock. But the opposite is the truth; the realisation that you and I are on the same journey, a Divine quest to know ourselves, is to empower you beyond your wildest dreams. For you are all divine beings.'

I needed a break as my thoughts swam uncontrollably around my head. I stood up, suddenly realising that the church now stood in almost total darkness. Shadows were everywhere and my imagination went into warp factor. I turned to face the east and was greeted by the Full Moon, which had snuck over a nearby wooded hill and hung low in a misty sky.

'Its beautiful!' I exclaimed aloud.

'It is. Now how does the poem go? Ah yes:

Slowly, silently, now the moon,
Walks the night in her silver shoe;
This way, and that, she peers, and sees
Silver fruit upon silver trees.'

'That's cool. Did you write it?'

'Well, you could say that, although it was the part of me manifesting as Walter De La Mare at the time.'

'Looking at this scene I can see how he, or you, was inspired.'

'Yes, we did a good job dreaming the moon, didn't we?'

'What do you mean *we*?'

'Don't you realise that you have been with me since before what you call time even began, since before Sister Moon was created. Nothing has been added to or subtracted from the physical Universe since I dreamed it into existence. I couldn't have done it exactly the same without you. Every single atom determines the outcome of the whole. You were there with me at the beginning, my son, and we will be together at the end.'

'The end? Tell me; will there be an end? I've never really felt easy with all that end-of-the-world, Book of Revelations, Mayan Prophecy stuff.'

'Oh yes, long into the distant future of what you call time, I will know who I am. I am determined to accomplish this. Then you and I will not need to create any more. We will be able to say, 'This is who I am. This is I. I am this'. I am just trying to discover who I am. Just as you are - no more, no less.'

Suddenly I panicked. How could I possibly remember all that had been said? My thoughts were again read.

'Do not worry, for you will remember all I say - every single word, without fail. After all, I am only talking to myself! I offer this dialogue as a means toward planetary survival, for mankind to reconnect to the Old Ways, to interact with sacred sites and the Land. Together, we will grow. Together, we may again become one. Worry not, for you will remember. I will return to you at the next Full Moon. Look for the signs. They will guide you to another sacred site left to you by your ancestors. You will learn about many wondrous things over the coming year, and will be drawn to experience the true nature of sacred sites as you receive the lessons. The medium of the message will vary. Some of these heralds may at first appear alien, even terrifying, but be assured that no harm will come to you, save for that birthed by your own fears.'

'But at Arbor Low, Bel said that some people would harm me if I went ahead with the book and if I spread whatever it is you want known across the world.'

'That is not exactly what our beloved brother said. He warned that there may be some who may TRY to stop the new wisdom being spread, and that some people may WISH to harm you. That is not the same as them succeeding, is it? I

26

cannot physically stop you being harmed, for that would breach the Laws by which the Universe turns. People must be free to actualise that which they believe, be they manifestations of what you call 'good' and 'evil'. But signs will be laid before you to help you avoid, or deal with, such confrontations, and it will be up to you to recognise such portents, and act on them as you see fit. And in time, your personal power and wisdom will grow beyond the stage where such assaults could even take place.'

'You're telling me that it all hinges on me being able to spot obscure signs and other weird stuff. That is not exactly putting my mind at rest you know. After all, Jesus and Ghandi didn't succeed, and were killed when people...'

'... You think they did not succeed? You assume that premature death is not part of Divine purpose. My friend, there is no such thing as premature death, for there is no death on a soul level. So do not worry. When you attune to the Earth, the Land, and your own innate wisdom, the signs will be as clear as daylight and your way will be illuminated as if by a million candles. Do not fear, for you are never alone, as I am always with you – we are one. And as I know all there is to know, that makes YOU pretty clever, don't you think?'

'Put like that, I guess so.'

'I feel that is enough for now. You need time to take in what has happened this night. We will work harder and longer on future occasions. Good night, my messenger. We have chosen well. And, by the way, I've heard the one about the Buddhist and the hamburger stand!'

'That figures!'

There was a gust of wind that tossed leaves around my feet, and then I could feel that the connection had gone. I stood alone again, as I had done at Arbor Low after my encounter with Bel. My mouth was still agape, and it took a dribble of saliva trickling down my chin to bring me to my senses. Well, I guess I was allowed a dribble - it was my first day at school after all! My God, it had really happened to little old me. Not to David Icke, or the lovely Estelle Carr-Gomm, or some leader of a coven, or Dan Brown, Paul Devereux, or some other famous researcher into earth mysteries. No, it was me that had been chosen.

Bloody hell! This is all too much. I shook my head in disbelief.

'Why me?' I shouted at the top of my voice.

But the only reply was a brief echo from inside the ruined tower. I stood facing the moon and at that moment I knew that Scottie was never going to beam me up, and that the Enterprise was probably not even in orbit around the planet I was now on. Yet moments later, I found myself smiling at the moon, beaming in fact, as a feeling of unbridled bliss swept through me, filling every niche of my body with a lightness and joy I had never felt before. Focusing on the Full Moon sent me into a trance-like state, and I did not want the feelings I had to end.

I can live with this!

I don't know how long I stood there before I started gathering my senses again. I think it was the cold night air that brought me back.

How the hell am I going to drive home?

But drive home I did, even though I was on autopilot. It had begun, and I had no idea where it was going to end, and neither, if what She said was true, had the Goddess. By the time I reached home, there was only one thought occupying centre stage in my muddled head - powering up my laptop!

3. Second Moon – April: Men-an-Tol, Cornwall
Lesson – The Human Experience

© P Knight

Your daily life is your temple and your religion.
(The Prophet, Kahlil Gibran)

When the Goddess said I would remember every word, She wasn't kidding. And it was effortless too, there never being any doubts in my mind that I had omitted any dialogue. *Uncanny.* One problem for me, however, was reverting to a normal life. Just how do you integrate yourself into the checkout scrum at Waitrose or Wal-Mart when you have had a conversation with an invisible entity professing to be the Spirit of the Planet? I was tempted to start up conversations as I waited in line, but where would I have started? *'Hello, there. Do you know that we are all pure consciousness, and so too, for that matter, is that cabbage sitting in your trolley'.* Or, as the checkouts trilled all around, how about, *'Did you know that you and I were here at the beginning of time, when the Universe was formed?'* I felt I would soon have been led out the door by Security. Or perhaps my fellow shoppers may have even tolerated me with some amusement, thinking that I was some overzealous Doctor Who fan, or some anorak groupie of Patrick Moore or Steven Hawking. As I did not want to be regarded as any of those, I kept my mouth shut and was content to simply open my wallet.

But day-to-day living was not the same, and never would be again. For one thing, I spent most of my free time either surfing the Net for anything to do with sacred sites, ley lines, crop circles, Paganism and ancient cultures, anything that I felt would put me in good stead with my divine teacher. *I must impress her, show her I am serious and that I will 'do the right thing'.* But occasionally the words of Bel would echo in my ears:

They will believe you because you do not go around in tie-dye, or have dreadlocks, or wear a purple shell-suit. Yes, I see it. You are just a normal, run-of-the-mill person.

Would I spoil some grand universal plan by excessively delving into all that stuff? Perhaps all I needed to know would be given to me directly. *OK, that seems cool.* If it could be read in a book or on the Net then it could not be the new knowledge She had spoken of. She would tell me all I needed to know. Well, that was a relief. Instead of spending hours wading through weird and wonderful websites with names like *Starship Earth, Intergalactic News* and *Pagan Naturists* (OK, I did do a bit of research on the last one!) I simply had to turn up at an ancient site, on the Full Moon, and listen to a voice without a body. *Now isn't that a relief!* As you can gather, this whole thing was freaking me out, although She had said that no harm would come to me.

She is the all-seeing, all-knowing Goddess all said and done. Man, this is nuts!

Throughout April I watched the moon grow as it ripened towards full, which was to occur during the last week of the month. Spring was now upon us, and I watched with a renewed wonder at the growing leaves, the spring flowers, the prancing of lambs and calves in the fields, and the lengthening days now that Equinox had passed. I also had the innate feeling that all things were exactly as they were meant to be and that everything was happening at precisely the right moment. The Land seemed more alive than I had ever perceived it before. Even flattened road-kill seemed to be meaningful, as I watched other creatures scavenging on the compressed remains. The apparent savagery that I had previously witnessed, such as cats catching birds, birds eating beautiful butterflies, or the sight of a dead infant bird fallen from its nest, all seemed to have their place in the big scheme of things. I somehow really knew that everything had its purpose. I was learning who I was. And in doing so, apparently, She was learning who She was too. *Is life really that simple?*

Cornwall. All through the week before the Full Moon I kept on getting Cornwall. On TV adverts, documentaries, in newspapers, even from my friends. For instance, there was a shipwreck off

Penzance, and a programme about the rebuilding of Boscastle following the flood of 2004, another on the sale of Land's End, as well as a programme on Tintagel and its connections with King Arthur. Cornwall, Cornwall, Cornwall.

OK, Ma'am, I get the message!

The day before Full Moon I travelled down to St Ives, and booked into a nice B&B overlooking the harbour. It was pleasant around the town, and a welcoming spring sun warmed the harbour promenade. I had done enough research to know that there were heaps of sacred sites in the area, and that the famous St Michael Line started there. This alignment ran across Southern England, calling at sacred places such as St Michael's Mount, the Cheesewring, Glastonbury, Avebury, Royston Cave, and a host of others. Was the Goddess to lead me to some of these in the coming months? I knew not the answer. She certainly seemed to be keeping her tarot cards close to her chest, so to speak! Perhaps even She didn't know where we were to meet! *Now there's a thought.* Perhaps it all depended on earth energies, planetary alignments, and all sorts of weird things, including me. *Cool.* All this gave the Land and the Earth a sense of freshness and spontaneity. She really *was* living in the now! And She seemed to trust me to pull it off, so how could I dare doubt her? It wasn't *her* I doubted course, but myself. Occasionally, I felt it was either a dream, or that one day I would wake up in a padded cell, with speakers churning out Radio Two music hosted by Ann Robinson. God, what a thought! I think I'd rather have watched endless replays of party political broadcasts, and that's saying something! After all, even politicians were part of the Goddess' plan to know herself. I hoped, however, that politics and the need for politicians was a lesson She would learn sooner rather than later, to put us all out of our misery!

It was early evening as I sat on the old harbour wall of St Ives, my legs dangling over the bobbing boats below. People were still milling around, and my nostrils informed me that unseen tourists nearby were consuming chips heavily soaked in vinegar. *Right, so where are we going then?* Full Moon was at 1.05pm tomorrow afternoon, more or less midway between the two midnights. So would I be drawn to somewhere that night, the following night, or during the day? Although my encounters at Arbor Low and Knowlton had taken place at dusk, nothing had led me to believe that the contacts would all be made at night. Something then compelled me to close my eyes and just listen.

I could hear the sea lapping the harbour walls, and noisy seagulls overhead, and the chattering of small children on a nearby jetty, and the smells of the sea and the harbour also vied for my attention. Every now and again people would walk by and I would get snippets of conversations. Nothing that seemed relevant, however, unless Man Utd drawing with Arsenal was somehow significant, or a conversation concerning the operation on a ladies' troublesome verruca. I was just about to open my eyes when I picked up, '... and Men-an-Tol was quite good. We dowsed there and found a female current going through the hole in the stone, and then we went ...' I did not hear the end of the sentence for the speaker had gone out of earshot. But I had heard enough.

Men-an-Tol. Of course! I opened my eyes and looked in the direction from whence the last of the conversation had come, but no one stood out as obvious perpetrators.

'Thank you, whoever you are. If you only knew...'

OK, I know where - but when? OK, it worked once, so I'll try it again: please give me the time, Mother.

I felt the urge to get up and investigate, whilst remaining free to follow my intuition and let it lead me to wherever. I walked further around the promenade, watching and listening for signs. But this time it was not with any sort of urgency, for I knew that an answer would come - I absolutely knew it. Something drew me to a blackboard a few yards in front of me. On it was chalked the times of high tide, low tide, the heights of these, and, wait for it, the phase of the moon! It read *Full moon: 1.05pm tomorrow*. I had already said it to myself on the wall earlier. I did not heed it, so here it was again. *What a twit. OK, Goddess, I'm still a little slow at times, you'll have to bear with me.* I could sense that She was quietly amused by what had happened, but I also hoped She was pleased that I had sorted the place and time out, and using processes of the mind that I had never fully utilised before.

Back at the B&B I had time to do some research on Men-an-Tol, using books I had brought with me. The site was only a few miles to the west, not far from Penzance. A photo showed two pillar-like stones and a centre stone with a hole though it, giving it the appearance of a huge ring doughnut! The stone had healing folklore; stories of how sick or injured children or adults had passed through the orifice to initiate a cure. One story told of how, as late as 1966, a crippled child had passed through the hole and then walked for the first time in her life. I also learned how holed stones right across the world had similar curative folklore.

The ancients knew more than we've given them credit for.

I arose after a great night's sleep. I was not aware that I had dreamt at all, but I remember half-waking during the night and realising that the moon was shinning on my face, and that I felt bathed in a wash of love and healing light. After a hearty breakfast I set off to Men-an-Tol. I had noted that there were a couple of good ancient sites on the way. The first was Zennor Quoit, an incredible Neolithic structure, consisting of a tomb-like chamber covered by a huge 9½ ton capstone, which had slipped and was now precariously perched at an angle of about 45°. Apparently this was due to the mindless efforts of a 19th Century farmer, in his desire to turn the quoit into a cowshed! The dolmen was saved through the intervention of a local vicar, who purchased it. I stood in front of the ancient stones, wondering who had built them and for what purpose. I also felt a feeling of my stomach, like I were a balloon being inflated. I realised that I may have been standing midst one of the energy flows that dowsers spoke of.

Next up was Lanyon Quoit, another Neolithic dolmen of equally spectacular proportions. It stood magnificently right next to the road, defiantly resisting both Man and time. I was able to stand beneath the stones, as the underside of the capstone was over 6ft high. As I sat beneath the 13 ton, 17ft long stone (the largest in Cornwall) I somehow felt at home. *I know this place, I know it.* Yet I hadn't been that way before, which prompted me to think that I may have in a previous incarnation. I sat within the nurturing protection of the huge stones until my watch told me it was 12.40pm. *Time to go! Men-an-Tol beckons and who knows what else?* I knew someone held the answer.

It was a short walk to the stones from the dirt track where I had left the car. And there they were, the holed vulva stone, flanked by her two, very phallic-shaped suitors. The time was 1.00pm, almost the precise moment of the Full Moon. I knew I had to do it - I had to pass through the orifice, so I went over and stood before the stone. *Well, this doughnut is certainly too big to munch.* But it reminded me of something, and I couldn't quite put my finger on it. I walked around to the other side, hoping the change of direction would jog my memory, and peered through again. Then it hit me. *Stargate!* Yes, it was just like the big ancient portal of the SF film and TV series, the device that shot people along a wormhole to the other side of the Universe.

Cool. I wonder where I'm about to journey to.

Just as I had this realisation, I started to perceive a faint shimmering, like a heat haze, within the hole. Then more obvious ripples started up, but ripples of what? The air was being disturbed somehow, but it was more than that. I could then see waves of colour and, yes, faint pulses of light, which gradually became more lucid, until I could make out translucent rainbow patterns. The display of waves and pulses got brighter and more frenzied until I could also detect a faint humming. Before long the inside of the hole was filled with a beautiful exhibition of colours and ripples of light. At times the manifestation moved in an organic-like manner, whilst at other times it resembled a fluorescent river.

I knelt in front of the pyrotechnics and marvelled. It was the exact moment of Full Moon. It was awesome and mesmerising, yet I was not afraid, for I knew that the display was perfectly natural. On my hands and knees I approached the lights and tentatively immersed my hand into them. The waves of light interacted with my fingers, as they produced a ripple, and the energy seemed to explore, even caress my outstretched hand. I knelt before the hole, poised to enter.

'Well, here goes!'

I entered the opening headfirst. Whoosh! My eyes were filled with all the colours of the rainbow, all dancing and gyrating around me, cascading in a ballet of dance, beautiful and alive. *That's it – alive! The energy is alive!* The noises of the outside world, the wind and the birdsong, ceased instantly, replaced by a silence that was deafening in its immensity. I was immersed in a field of living energy that was passing through every inch of my body.

After a few moments I had clambered through the hole and out the other side. As I emerged, the sounds of the breeze and birdsong burst into my head. I scrambled to my feet and, like a naughty schoolboy, looked around to see if anyone had seen me. But I was alone. I looked back through the hole, and almost immediately the lights faded until they were no more.

'Now you too are reborn.'

Even her comforting tones made me jump. She had returned.

'Yikes! You never give me any warning do you?'

'Don't I? The signs were all around you if you had but eyes to see. You saw them yesterday at the quay. You sensed my pulse at Zennor, and again at Lanyon. You have just passed through the light of my love, which is particularly powerful here at Full Moon. And look, I am there too.'

34

I gazed to my left, just in time to see a huge buzzard take off from the top of one of the pillar-like stones.

You hadn't been there before, had you?

'Signs are all around if you look at the world with your heart rather than your mind. But more of that next moon, when we will talk about connecting with the Land. Did you enjoy the journey just then?'

'Wow, you bet ya'. What was all that about? Those colours, they moved as if they were… alive.'

'But they were alive, as everything is. The energy was always there, but your eyes perceived that which once you could not. You are opening up to the Land, and the Land welcomes you back. I welcome you on your voyage Home. It is the start of a new journey for me, as well as for you.'

I sat down against one of the upright stones, gazing up to the sky as the buzzard circled above, riding the thermals.

'I need to talk to you about the human experience today, about what it means to don a material body and return to physicality. All I speak of later will be meaningless if you do not learn some basic truths about your place on Earth and why you are here. For Man is the only creature on this planet who refuses to be what he really is.'

'OK.'

I got comfortable against the stone, facing the hole through which I had passed.

'You are infinite Divine energy, my son, which has chosen at this time the temporary finite experience of this planet, for the purpose of experiencing the full potential of physicality. You have needed to take on the illusion that you are separate from your Soul, your higher self, separate even from me. But never forget that you are spirit first, and human second. You are not only the shadow that dances on the wall, but you are also the hand that creates it, and even more than this, you are the source of the light. Within you, you already know all there is to know about life on this planet, you just need to remember. You can recall it all because you and I are one, and I know all that has ever been. Tell me, have you not spent much time and effort in recollective meditation, or past life regressions and so forth, to recall something you felt you needed to heal?'

'You can say that again!'

'Well, I can now tell you this; the best healing you can receive on this planet is to live in the now. To embrace this moment, to cherish it and realise that now is all there is. At such a moment of realisation you will be free of your worries, ills, stresses and anguish. For living in the now is living as the Land does. To live in the now is to experience as the Earth experiences. The Land does not experience history, or have any fear of the future, or have any regrets, or hold grudges, or feel guilt, nor indeed can it. Now is the only condition the Land can experience, for it is creating now, and only now. In fact, I can do nought else.'

'So by staying in the now, as you say the Land does, as you do, how can that help me live a more conscious everyday life?'

'A good question. And the answer is a simple one, and one that is the foundation of the Universe. Experiencing the now is to experience love. And I don't just mean romantic love, or love for a pet, or a sibling or child, although these are all beautiful facets of the whole. Living in the now is to experience that which you are – pure love. For you are part of me, and I too have stepped out of a state of pure love in order to seek to know myself. I am creating every possible scenario in the Universe in order to eventually return to that state of pure love, where I shall say, 'I am this'. And you are the same, and even in your microcosm you can experience and appreciate a loving Oneness on Earth. And as you do, I too will experience it and reclaim it as my own. To live in a Taoist way, in close harmony and peace with the Planet, living with the Earth not against her, is perhaps the best chance mankind has to reach that state of pure love it has so desperately been seeking for so long.'

'But this feeling of Oneness; how can we keep this feeling when all around is anguish, war, famine and the injustices of the world?'

'I do not judge. I do not administer retribution. I see the bigger picture of all that is manifest and therefore have no need to judge as everything happens for a very good purpose. I am not Man's judge. I simply am. I create and I experience. And you too can learn to be like this. Whilst you are pointing fingers, will not someone else judge you? Whilst you are angry, so you attract anger in return along the strands of the Web of Life. What you send out comes back. I cannot stop this process, for it is indeed beautiful in its simplicity and efficiency. The way out of this cycle of non-

love is to realise that you do not have to fear life; you do not have to solve life; you do not have to avoid life; you are not being 'trained up' towards something. You are here to experience and appreciate life to the full. Period.'

'Hey, hang on. So I do not have to learn anything. Doesn't that make a mockery of all the New Age stuff, as well as Buddhism and other spiritualities who value knowledge?'

'I am not saying that it is bad to attain knowledge; in fact you cannot stop yourself in this pursuit. What I am saying is that intellectual accomplishment will not necessarily help you achieve the 'enlightenment' you seek. You are already enlightened – you just don't remember! And there is a good reason for this – you don't need to! And the reason for this is because all the knowledge and wisdom of Mankind can be bottled into the simple act of living in the now, for therein is enlightenment, there sits pure love. You are on Earth not to learn per se, but to experience – to experience and appreciate the miracle of life. Experience death, experience love, hate, and everything else that you attract your way. It is the way you choose to perceive your experiences that is the key. You can choose love or fear. Fear tells you that you need to keep safe. Love tells you that you ARE safe.'

'But that sounds so simple. Surely that cannot be the answer to all the world's problems.'

'In principle it is very simple. But the waters have become muddied by your immersion into the human experience. Fear was born. Darkness was born. Limitations were born. But when you choose love, then fear, darkness and limitations dissolve like a morning mist under the warming rays of the sun. The key is to find love even in the 'darkest' situations, seeing love amidst the apparent injustices in the world. Everything is a journey back to love, back to Oneness. And the Land is your greatest teacher here. It does not judge. It does not have fears. It simply is. It experiences every happening and does so out of pure love. At times you witness things in nature that may appear cruel to you, with no apparent purpose. Be assured that every single event in nature is part of my journey, our journey, back to Oneness. If it does not have purpose then it cannot manifest.'

'I'm never going to take all this in. OK, don't say it – I will.'

'Indeed. As long as you live you will never obtain all the answers to the apparent suffering on the planet. Look back at

your own life, for example. I am sure you will recollect wonderful things that have developed from apparently negative situations. So apply the same to the Planet. You will never know the higher picture of everything, for that is not your purpose here. But the nearest you will get to an understanding is by living in the now and thereby eradicating fear. Fear is the illusion. Fear witnesses only its own expectations. Just remember that nothing transpires that your soul has not already authorized. Every day you choose between fear and love. It is the only issue you ever have to make a decision about. Simple really. Love or fear? Truth or Illusion?'

'But the ills of the world are so persuasive, so real. I want to believe in pure love and that everything happens for a reason, but the physical reality is overwhelming. And are you saying that we should not show compassion, empathy and charity, and we should be indifferent when confronted with tragedies because we know there is a higher purpose?'

'Of course not. You take a step nearer towards pure love every time you show charity and compassion. And you may indeed continue to seek to eradicate poverty, disease and famine. In doing so you are expressing love, and as a by-product you will attract love and compassion in return. But remember that there is a higher picture to all that manifests in the world. Do not forget that no one dies. The Soul is eternal. Death is a release from the constraints the Soul has been experiencing whilst in your body. The individual soul breathes a sigh of relief at the moment of physical death, believe me, as if it has taken off a pair of very tight fitting shoes. Physical death is simply a door closing as another simultaneously opens. Death is a celebration, a returning to Home. Death is like a caged bird being released – if you could only see yourselves sing and soar moments after your physical demise. Therefore, seek to acknowledge the shadow side of yourselves and of Nature, for you cannot look too long at the sun. Don't be mesmerised by the light, for there must also be the dark. This is the balance, the yin and yang, the polarities that turn the Universe. So when you think you are encountering negative situations, do not judge, nor add the kindling of anger to an already raging fire. Remember, you add just as much negativity to the world when you take offence as when you are offensive to others. Every day you

38

choose between fear and love. This is the Divine freewill religions speak of. To withdraw this from humanity would be to punish myself. Even if I could, why would I wish to withdraw love from myself?'

'I am beginning to see what I should do.'

'Well, I will add that there are no 'shoulds' and 'should-nots' in a loving Universe. These are phrases born out of the vocabulary of fear. How about replacing them with 'coulds', which do not dictate orders, but instead point towards infinite possibilities.'

'OK. I know what I *could* do. Please cut me some slack, will you?'

'I having been doing that for Mankind for the past two thousand years!'

'Point taken. So, in a nutshell, we should, sorry could, choose love over fear, live in the now, and look to nature for our inspiration.'

'I couldn't have put it better myself.'

'But you did … er, didn't *we*?'

'Very good. You learn quickly. Oh my dear son, try to realise that you create your own reality. I see through your eyes, together we create your beliefs, for we cannot help but do so. I do not judge, nor do I know fear, for I see the bigger picture. I will create whatever you ask for, I have no choice; if I have not created a particular scenario before I must create it sooner or later, in the quest to know myself.'

'You, the Goddess, the Great Mother, the Planetary Spirit has no choice? How so?'

'Because I am compelled by my desire to know myself, to once again exist as absolute pure love. What I do is to create, for I am the Creator religions speak of, and I create as a means to progress to Oneness. The sooner you as a species realise your potential and your Divinity the quicker we'll be done. I will create whatever you believe – I am your Cosmic Kitchen no less. So be careful what you order, for sooner or later it will land on your table of experiences.'

'So what is the bottom line? What can I order from the Cosmic Kitchen that will help me live more harmoniously?'

'Another good question. Studying Nature and living in harmony with the natural forces of the world is the main schooling you need, for within the Land are two important lessons for you. The first gift my natural world offers you, by

way of example, is patience. Nothing happens on this world unless the timing is perfect. Every flower opens at the right moment, every bird hatches only when ready, every baby arrives at the time it wants to. There is no room for error. I can't do error, for I know all there is to know, remember? So you can relate this to your own individual lives. You say that patience is a virtue, but it is this and more. Patience is love. Patience is an acknowledgment that all is well in the world and that all is where it is meant to be. City-dwellers especially, and other people living under stress, would do well to learn that. Only fear can upset this beautiful process.'

'And the second lesson?' I said with the enthusiasm and impatience of an eager young schoolboy.

'Patience, my son!'

'Sorry.'

'The second important natural principle is that of balance. I eternally strive for balance; if it is winter on one part of my body, then it is summer on the other; a flood in one area of the world will be countered by a drought in another. Although short-term changes may appear to be quite startling, overall the balance of nature will prevail. Yin and yang, female and male, night and day, moon and sun, animus and anima, Mary and Michael energies, positive and negative magnetism, light and dark. The existence of polarities is what makes the Universe revolve. This is a wondrous gift to mankind, and one that you can all relate to your everyday lives. Any extreme in nature causes upheaval, and so too with people. Strive for balance in your life, avoid the stagnation of imbalance, for therein lies your fears and your blockages to love.'

'That sounds beautiful. And it seems so simple.'

'It is.'

'So why can't we all do it.'

'You can.'

'But will we?'

'I have given you free will and the means, the rest is up to you. But the quicker Mankind learns this, the quicker we can all move on to something even more magical. Wait... someone is coming.'

I instantly stood up. 'I can't see anyone.'

'They are approaching all the same. Have faith.'

'But we were in the middle of something really fantastic.'

'Perfect timing. Remember?'

'OK. I get it. If something happens it's meant to - at exactly the optimum time.'

'But of course!'

'Then I guess that's it for today, is it?'

'Well, you could say that. Or else your perception could be that this moment is just the start of the rest of your life. Every day I am with you, I cannot help but be with you. Your heart is my heart. What you experience between now and the next Full Moon so do I. Look for signs all around you, to guide your life. Let these portents steer you along the rivers of change, for nothing is constant except change, so go with the flow. In future months our dialogues will become longer, deeper and you will interact with the Land in magical ways. The next lessons will be about how to connect with the Land, and how the web of life is spun. The principles of Wyrd, spelt w-y-r-d, and pronounced 'weird', will be revealed to you.'

'Wyrd? Sorry, but this whole thing's bloody Wyrd!'

'How right you are... how right you are. Farewell for now.'

At that precise moment a middle-aged couple bearing backpacks and hiking boots approached the stones. It *was* perfect timing. But why should I have expected anything less? I surveyed the skies overhead to find that the buzzard had gone. The couple approached the stones but did not speak any greeting or give any acknowledgement of my existence. They stood a few yards to my left and I could feel their eyes burning into me. I suddenly felt uneasy and threatened by their presence. The warning words of Bel rang through my head. The man suddenly started up a conversation with his female companion, which was loud enough for me to be sure it was also for my ears. His well educated, middle-class voice echoed around the stones, jarring my senses.

'Very ancient site this, my dear, Neolithic, they think. You have to admire their stone-building techniques, for certain, but in those days people worshipped many gods and goddesses, and stone idols. They probably performed hideous rituals and sacrifices at this very spot, I'll wager. Thank goodness people now know better, in that there is but one God and Jesus is his only son and our Saviour. You know there are wretched people, Pagans, Devil-worshippers and such, who still come to sites like this to practice their deluded, wicked beliefs...'

He turned to look in my direction and our eyes met.

'... But the Almighty knows who they are, and they *will* be punished. Oh yes, they *will* be punished, you mark my words.'

The energy changed from that of love and beauty to darker vibrations and I suddenly hoped that Scottie still had the transporter charged up. I got to my feet and, without looking towards the unwelcome gatecrashers, walked away from the stones, making sure not to appear hurried. Was this unwelcome encounter a taste of what was to come, that of which Bel and the Goddess had foretold?

It was only after I got back to my car that I wished I had been stronger and had said something to the ignorant toff. But I felt I had done the right thing. I did not yet feel confident or knowledgeable about all this ancient stuff to engage in debate. I felt sure, however, that there would come a time when I would hold my own.

Back in St Ives, I inputted all the events of the day into my laptop. Every word flowed freely, every detail recalled with perfect clarity. She said it would be so. I had to be back in Dorset that night, and although I would have to start back soon, I wanted to visit more sacred sites en route. It was still the day of the Full Moon after all, and I was eager to soak up anything magical that might yet occur. I was soon on the road, following my guidebook of Cornwall's prehistoric wonders.

Bodmin Moor is a beautiful, semi-wild, upland region at the east end of Cornwall, an area strewn with ancient sacred sites. Two caught my eye; the Hurlers stone circles and Trethevy Quoit. The Hurlers was my first stop. The monument originally consisted of three complete adjacent stone circles, but time and Man had taken their toll, and only forty-two out of the eighty original megaliths remained. Nevertheless, it was still a powerful place, and my guidebook told me that the Mary and Michael energy flows of the St Michael Line converged at the circles. Standing in the centre circle I tried to see if I could sense anything. After just a few moments I became aware of a strange sensation in my stomach, as if I were again being inflated like a balloon. The feeling was good though, and I soon noticed that my fingers were tingling. The Goddess said that She would cover earth energies and ley lines at some stage and I felt encouraged that I could already feel those forces. Standing in the circles, with the late afternoon sun shining on my face I was, fleetingly, totally at one with the Land. The feeling was gone in an instant, but for a split second I seemed to literally melt into the very ground I stood on. There seemed to be no separateness between the Land and myself. The feeling left me with an appetite for more, and I knew that this thirst would be well satisfied in the months to come.

Close by the Hurlers is the legendary Cheesewring, an outcrop of granite blocks. They were piled up like roughly hewn, gigantic playing cards, so precariously stacked that they might topple at any moment. A spectral Druid was associated with the area and this folklore reminded me of Bel, back at Arbor Low. As I circled the rocks I could make out huge weird heads and faces from certain angles. I could see how our ancestors believed that spirits and otherwordly creatures inhabited the Land. Looking at the forms before me I felt that they still did – for these were surely the giants of myth and legend.

Trethevy Quoit was a short drive from the Cheesewring, and stood seemingly forgotten in a field behind stone cottages. The sloping capstone reminded me of Zennor Quoit, although the huge stone, thankfully, was less slumped. At over 15ft tall, the stones towered above me, like some rearing rodeo horse. A gap between the supporting uprights allowed me to enter its hallowed interior. *Wow!* I seemed to be in some sort of time capsule, as the huge stones blotted out the outside world. The wind sang to me as it whistled through the gaps between the stones, and I blissed out. That's the only way I can describe it – I was blissfully happy. I knew I was in exactly the right place at the right time, just as She said we always were. But the difference was, I now knew it. I wondered who else had sat in that spot before me, over thousands of years. Priest, shaman, sheltering shepherd and courting couple – I bet the stones could tell a few stories! I thought about the countless people who had come and gone, over a hundred generations, yet how the stones still remained – seemingly eternal. I patted one of the huge uprights, and looked up to the giant capstone.

'Will some part of me survive even after you crumble to dust, my stone brothers?'

Dare I believe it, I mean really believe it. God knows I wanted to. Goddess knows I wanted to. She knew the Truth. And so did I, somewhere deep within. I just had to believe it.

I am an eternal being of light? Funky!

4. Beltaine Clogs

© P Knight

The nine men's morris is filled up with mud,
And the quaint mazes in the wanton green
For lack of tread are indistinguishable.
(*A Midsummer Night's Dream,* Shakespeare)

It was May. The apple blossom was out, the air was getting warmer by the day, and I continued to wonder at the magnitude of events of the preceding months. In between the full moons there was no apparent contact from the Goddess, but I knew this to be for a good reason. These were times for me to make contact with *Her.* By this I mean going out to local Dorset sacred sites, experiencing the countryside, reading up on Pagan things that I felt drawn to, and going over the contents of the file in my laptop entitled *13 Moons.doc.* I still found it incredible that it was I who was to relate the story, and still do for that matter! And my once-wounded ego had got over the fact that I had been chosen because I was Joe Bloggs, Mr Average Human Being. Well, almost!

At the beginning of May was the old festival of Beltaine, now May Day. This ancient fertility celebration marked the beginning of Summer, once a time of maypoles and Morris Dancers. I noticed in the local rag that on the evening of May 1st, the Saxon Inn in the village of Child Okeford was host to a troupe of hanky-waving Morris dancers. It all sounded great fun, and was based, so I gathered, on ancient Pagan practices. *Let's go see!*

They had already begun the evening revelry by the time I'd arrived. The courtyard at the front of the pub was awash with onlookers consuming ale, all gathered around the dancing men,

44

whose emblems identified them as the Wessex Morris. The jingle bells on their ankles reminded me more of the impending arrival of Santa's sleigh. The music was catchy and upbeat, yet it was ancient and hid the memories of country ways many hundreds of years past. The drums beat a steady rhythm and a fiddle gave it a Celtic feel. I bought my pint in the bustling bar and returned outside to watch the men in white and green continue their routines under a turquoise dusk sky.

My mind drifted off midst the music and commotion, as I found myself wondering where the next Full Moon revelation would be. *Now Macchu Picchu looks nice, darling, or how about at the feet of the Sphinx!* But I somehow knew it would be somewhere far less sunny, and almost certainly less exotic! Perhaps it would be a railway embankment in Leeds, or at the tree at the bottom of my garden, or how about the toilets at Stonehenge. I chuckled – *James Redfield, Dan Brown, eat your heart out!* Well, at least I was sure that hired assassins were not in hot pursuit. But I toyed with the idea of imaginary headlines:

MAN GUNNED DOWN IN STONEHENGE PORT-A-LOO.

I smiled to myself, only to realise that by chance I was looking into the eyes of a rather buxom local lass, who was returning my smile with one of her own. Her huge tattooed boyfriend had seen the eye contact and was eyeing me up menacingly. *Whoops!* I shuffled away to my left in an attempt to melt into the crowd.

But the thoughts of would-be assassins had brought me back to thinking about the warning of Bel, and my encounter with the *Ramblers For Jesus* at Men-an-Tol. A shiver once again ran up my spine. How would the knowledge I was relaying be greeted by the world? On one hand I was sure that the book may appeal to the 'converted', you know, genuine seekers, Pagans, New-Ager's, aged hippies, woolly-hatted travellers, UFO space cadets, crop circle insomniacs, workshop junkies, etc, etc. But did the knowledge I was to unleash onto the world threaten anyone? In particular, did anyone stand to lose from the publication of the book? *Organised religions* popped into my head for starters. In particular the fundamentalist elements of religions, which had caused untold suffering throughout history, as indeed they still were, due to their intolerance of the beliefs of others.

I felt uneasy at the thought of being embroiled with the uneasy bedfellows of politics and religion, who had been having a combustible affair for many centuries. I did not want to be thought of or treated as another radical like Salman Rushdie, Martin Luther

King, or even Dan Brown for that matter. Once again I had to tell myself to get a grip and get real. I would be comparing myself to Jesus next! He too preached a radical message of love, eternal life and Truth, and look what happened to him. Perhaps I would be martyred. *Hmm. Now what would they call me and would a new religion be founded after me? And what would those misguided souls be compelled to call themselves - the 13 Moonies? Enough! Snap out of it - Jesus Christ! Hang on, that's been done!*

Thoughts of Monty Python's *Life of Brian* brought a smile to my face and with it a chuckle, which was fortunately swallowed up by the music and the clatter of colliding wooden sticks. Perhaps the glass I was drinking from would one day be regarded as the new Holy Grail. And perhaps there would be a blue plaque bearing my name on the outside of that port-a-loo at Stonehenge. I could see endless streams of New Age pilgrims piling off coaches to view my statue, mounted on a granite block under spotlights, whilst dolphin music played in the background. *No, not dolphin music, please!* But these thoughts did have a more sombre side. For that sort of zealous behaviour was exactly what Bel had warned me of. Religious beliefs often consume people to the extent that they feel they have to defend their holy scriptures, attacking anyone they see as a threat to their ideology. *But surely not me, not little ol' me.* I then feared that I might not even get a publisher to take the book on, not because the book wasn't sensationalist, but simply because it was unbelievable, or perhaps badly written. I panicked a bit. I knew it was fear that was talking, but I hoped the headaches would be worth it in the end.

So the Morris Dancers eventually clogged their last stomp and retired into the pub, and although the beer still flowed, the Neanderthal and his buxom girlfriend collapsed into a waiting taxi. The glass I had been drinking from was unceremoniously washed and racked with the others, and a good time was had by all on that lovely Beltaine evening. But where the hell was I going on the forthcoming Full Moon, not a week away? Well, it called for another shot of good old synchronicity. Somewhere, someone or something held the answer.

Come Watson, its Elemental really.

OK, Holmes, you lead the way.

So I re-entered the pub just after 10.30pm, but this time for a fruit juice, to keep me under the drink-drive limit. A stool at the one end of the bar was free so I sat down, sipped my cold drink, and people-watched. It was a strange mixture of folk, from farmers to

Morris Men, from regular punters to tourists and ramblers. As I scanned the room I picked up on various conversations, or one side of them at least, as the focus of my ears followed my eyes. Two older guys, who I took to be farmers, were conversing about the whys and wherefores of muckspreading, which all seemed like a load of crap to me! It did make me wonder, however, if I would one day be accused of such a practice, metaphorically speaking of course. Two couples were exchanging jokes in the far corner, and next to them sat two women who I could see were holding hands and rubbing knees under the table.

Over the next hour the merry band of Morris Men took turns singing old songs, woven between intermittent recitals on guitar, drum, accordion and harmonica. At times the whole troupe belted out folk songs, which pulled at the roots of my consciousness, as if I had heard them before, perhaps in another life. The air literally shimmered with atmosphere as onlookers periodically joined in verses they recognised – in fact at times the whole pub resembled an 18th Century tavern. And I was part of it all, for I knew that those guys were tapping into something that had almost been lost, songs that were sung when people still lived and worked close to the Land, songs of sowing and harvesting crops, of courting couples, and of sailors missing their sweethearts.

The magnificent distraction died down a little as a few of the ensemble prepared to leave. *So where is the synchronicity here, Mr Jung? I have come here looking for an answer – so where is it?* No sooner had those enquiring thoughts gone out to the Cosmic Kitchen than there was a loud bang on the table around which the Morris Men were gathered. A spokesman for the company, a man of around sixty with a long grey beard, rose to his feet. In one hand he held a metal tankard, in the other a clay pipe.

'All right, lads… and, er, ladies. Settle down now. Just a quick reminder about our next event. We will be dancing outside the pub at Avebury this Sunday morning, for the May Full Moon. Eleven o'clock and don't you be late, mind. Free food laid on afterwards… but not the beer!'

The room acknowledged his announcement with a mixture of fabricated groans and genuine laughter as he sat down and the rim of his glass disappeared into his thick grey moustache.

No one heard my whispered exclamation of gratitude.

Avebury! Thanks M' Lady.

5. Third Moon – May: Avebury, Wiltshire Lesson – Connecting With the Land and Self

© P Knight

The Sun does rise, and make happy the skies;
The merry bells ring, to welcome the Spring.
(William Blake)

So there I was on the afternoon of the Full Moon, standing in a field at Avebury, Wiltshire. And I was again talking to myself.

'My word, that was big. A 20ft phallus? Seriously big!'

My guidebook, *The Wessex Astrum,* informed me that the large concrete pillar in front of me marked the spot where the 18th Century antiquarian William Stukeley had noted a huge phallic-shaped megalith called the Obelisk, prior to its destruction. Quite recently, it went on, Terence Meaden had noted that the shadow cast by the rising sun at Beltaine would have thrown a phallus-shaped shadow behind said stone, reaching another megalith some yards away, which displayed a large, vulva-like crevice. He proclaimed it as the *Sacred Consummation of the Gods.* I walked across to stone 106 and there it was, a metre long gash that was accompanied, immediately above it, by the semblance of a clitoris - I kid you not! In the north circle, Meaden had also surmised how another stone cast a shadow into the Cove, more imitation of the sexual acts of the Gods, it would seem. Well, all this sex talk was making me a little hot under the collar, I must admit, especially wandering around in the warm May sunshine in fields rife with well-tanned, half-naked traveller/hippy chicks!

At Avebury, the Michael and Mary energy currents of the St Michael Line *come* together (perhaps in light of the above sexual symbolism, I ought to say *merged!*). I wandered around the mighty henge following the flows and I could feel some tingling in my fingers when I placed my hands on stones that stood on the currents. My dowsing rods twitched on occasions, even though my abilities in the dowsing direction were still limited. (I'd only had my dowsing rods a couple of weeks and was still reeling with wonderment every time they moved, seemingly of their own accord.) Avebury was huge too, no, I mean mega! A henge, an outer circle of stones, then two more circles within, and even more stones within these. And all these were erected (no pun intended!) in the Neolithic, some 4,000 years ago. Although well over half the original number had now gone, walking around the monument was still a profound experience. The warm afternoon sun beat down and I frequently sheltered in the shadows cast by the ancestral monoliths. Here and there I could make out faces and creatures in the rocks. I stood in front of one such stone (No. 206) that displayed a spiralling horn branching out of the top of a profiled head. *Wow!* I was impressed, and my guidebooks assured me that these strange simulacra were not the result of weathering or vandalism, but were integral elements of the stones that had been selected. Easter Island had nothing on these guys, who were many centuries older of their Oceanic brothers.

Well, my Goddess, they certainly went to town revering you here. You must have been well pleased.

'I was.'

'I wish you wouldn't do that!' I called out aloud, once again feeling ambushed.

'I am sorry. But as you approached, did you not see my pregnant tummy – otherwise known as Silbury Hill? Did you not feel me close? Did you not experience my pulse in the stones you touched and feel my spirit move your dowsing rods? Have you not seen my face in the stones?'

I looked around, but as usual I was alone, so to speak.

'Yes, but these stone faces are just expressions of aspects of you, selected from someone's imagination, aren't they?'

'But wherever my image is perceived, there I am. I am present every time you see a face in a tree, a cloud, a beach pebble or, as here, in a standing stone. Wherever I am perceived, there am I. Do not denigrate imagination, for it can be a bridge across which you may reach me, a gate to connect you to forgotten regions of your human experience. Nature is imagination.'

'That may be, but I still sure wish I could see you.'

'But you do see me - every time you open your eyes. As I told you, I am everything.'

'Yes, you told me that, and I am daring to believe it. But those who built Avebury selected stones with faces, like this horned guy, to give them something to focus on, some image, some icon to help them connect with you, didn't they?'

'Yes they surely did, my son, in much the same way that Christians have the cross and images of Mary, Muslims have the crescent, Pagans the pentagram, Buddhists venerate statues of Buddha, and how Jewish households contain the Menorah. People seem to need mandalas, symbols, emblems, holy relics and so forth on which to focus and help keep their faith. For they need reminders, through man-made objects, of their religious myths and the lessons held therein. But I bring you a message that will relieve you of such burdens. And it is a simple truth.'

'What is it, My Lady. Please tell me.'

'It is this. The primary object you need to venerate is the Land, and the only concept you need to hold dear to your heart is Life itself.'

'The Land? Life? Is that it? But what… what do I have that I can focus on?'

'The Land.'

'Yes, you've said that, but what do I connect to, what do I revere?'

'The Land.'

'But what will be our sacred object, holy book or messenger?'

'The Land.'

'This could go on all day. Will you please show me.'

'I thought you'd never ask! Come, for it is almost the moment of Full Moon. Let us go for a walk and I will show you. Please walk straight ahead, climb the bank of the henge and be seated on the top.'

I walked across the field, past stone No. 68, and descended the ditch that lay beyond. The climb out of it and up to the top of the steep, ancient bank was quite an effort under the warm sun and I sat down at the top somewhat short of breath. I surveyed the countryside to the east, from the rolling fields spread before me up to the skyline a mile or so distant, along which I knew ran an ancient ridgeway path. The very last paragraph of *The Da Vinci Code* flooded into my consciousness:

For a moment, he thought he heard a woman's voice... the wisdom of ages... whispering up from the chasms of the earth.

The words seemed so apt as I sat there, awaiting more wisdom from my teacher.

'Dan Brown could have been referring to you, couldn't he?'

'Indeed, he could, and in a sense he was. Mr Brown has done a service to Mankind in persuading many to sit up and question their world, and what they had been led to believe was historical fact. People are no longer content to be led without question. Those days are rapidly coming to an end. But look now at the Land, the landscape before you. Everything you see is alive with life-force, for I breathed it into existence. I gave birth to all you see.'

'And in the beginning was God, or the Goddess, so to speak.'

'Yes, I am the Creator and the Creatrix that tribal cultures and religions have spoken of for millennia. But whilst people worship only aspects of divinity, such as manmade icons, and even these standing stones, they cannot fully touch the whole of me. True, these can help you focus and may lead you some way towards me, but they are not wholly me – only the Land, only Nature is this. By following a spirituality that connects you with the Land, as ancient cultures once did, you have the potential to open up a two-way communication. You are coming home to your mother and, ironically, to yourself.'

'Sounds very cosy and simple, but were my ancestors really in touch with the Spirit of the Land, or is it all New Age fantasy?'

'To ancient peoples, like the shaman designers and builders of Avebury, the landscape was full of meaning, telltale signs of Spirit. This natural symbolism confirmed to them that the Land was an energetic and living entity. It was into Nature itself that tribal myths were woven. The landscape

is quite literally an open book onto which legends are inscribed, the Land itself a repository of sacred images. Strangely shaped rocks, the outlines of faces and breasts in hills, or a simple holed stone found on a beach, can reveal ancient timeless stories.'

'So ancient myths are, in a sense, passed onto us by the Land.'

'Indeed, excellent! It was not the people that possessed the legends, but the landscape itself – for I dreamed the myths. Wiser people perceived what was being offered to them, the messages I was communicating. In this way many knew they had a bond to the Land that was not merely geographical, but also spiritual. In ancient times, wise ones saw much in this way, but later came those with more closed minds, who saw nothing but rocks, fire, water, life and death, and as a result birthed fear, as people still do.'

'So are you telling me that ancient myths and folklore speaking of fairies, giants, gods, goddesses and such were not so much invented by us to explain the world around us, but were given to us by you, by the Land?'

'But of course. I have been speaking to people before they could verbally communicate with each other. I have been reaching out to you, my children, since before the beginning of what you call time. Hills that resemble the tummy of a pregnant woman, or the peaks on a skyline that mimic a head, or the wizened face in a craggy tor, were all formed from and by my spirit, not by humankind. They are expressions of my holiness, my divinity and my evolution. They are made of my own body, partly as expressions of who I am, but also as a means for you to recognise processes that are going on beneath the surface appearance of the physical world; THE LAND IS ALIVE!'

'Some will say that tree trunks resembling faces, or rocks that look like heads, just happen to resemble things by chance.'

'And what would be the point of me creating forms you would not recognise? I have always reached out to Mankind for recognition. But I could equally say that I have been talking to myself, for you and I are one and the same.'

'But what about the scene before me now? Let's see - some fields, a few scattered clumps of trees, some grazing cows and sheep, and birds overhead. Where is the symbolism and where are the messages here? Where is myth?'

'Where is it not? There are messages all around if you have but eyes to see, and an open heart. At our next meeting, in fact, we will look closely at the Web of Life, and how the threads of Wyrd tremble with every action that manifests in the cosmos. You will come to marvel at how everything that exists plays its part on the Earth, how you yourself send ripples out across the Universe.'

'And the only way this could be is if you and I are one, right?'

'Right. But for now I want you to perceive that the Land truly is alive, and not just in some abstract, Pagan, romantic or poetical way. Spirit is present in every single atom that exists in physical form, be it those trees, the cows, or the sheep you see, or indeed the whole galaxy. Deep down you know this. Deep within your subconscious you yearn to remember, you seek to re-discover that which you have lost. You have separated yourselves as a species from the Spirit of the Land as part of the human experience. The Land is an element of you all, and every person is an element of the Land. What affects one will inevitably affect the other. Just as you are consciousness, Nature too exists as a state of consciousness. But remember that the physical landscape is but one expression of this consciousness, and that many more levels exist. Physicality is an outer manifestation of my being, but there are more realms hidden from your eyes. In between your physical lifetimes, much of this will become apparent to you, but not everything. Planet Earth is truly a blessed school, where you can learn and experience things you cannot in the Otherworld.'

'But what can I do? How can I move forward to see such a living landscape? I'm no Druid or shaman.'

'You don't need to be. Everyone has the ability, potential, and indeed the birthright, to perceive geography as sacred, to see myth in topography, to feel the power of my breath as it caresses your body, to see that which is normally hidden. Come. Relax. Look again at the landscape before you.'

I once again surveyed the rolling chalk hills. It still looked the same as it did when I'd sat down.

'Now close your eyes... relax... be still... open up to all of your senses – touch, sight, hearing, taste and smell. You are part of the Land; indeed the Land would not be complete without you. It speaks to you. It touches you. I speak to you. I touch you. Be still... listen... SEE!'

'OK, My Lady.'

Be still. I can do still. Listen? OK. Relax - how? I am sitting here on a Neolithic earthen bank conversing with the Divine! OK, I'll do my best. Here we go. May the Force be with me!

'I always am.'

I don't know how long I sat there, eyes closed, under the warm May sun on that ancient bank. Time seemed to stand still. But I gradually became aware that the sounds of the Land, the birds, mooing cows, bleating sheep, even people talking in the distance, all seemed more acute - the sounds were sharp and crisp. I also became aware that my fingers, which were resting beside me on the grass, were tingling. They seemed to merge with the earth and I could feel my pulse racing through my body more strongly than ever before, and that this pulsing was being matched by a similar rhythm coming from beneath. I felt as if I was melting into the ground, being swallowed up by chalk and earth as I fused as one with it. Energy shot up my arms and surged through my entire body, and I knew what She meant about being one with everything. It was sheer bliss. My heart exploded with ecstasy and my mind was purged of all doubts. Colours flashed before my mind's eye, and lines of rainbows shot off across the Land. In the field in front of me, energy flows spiralled and danced, and made what looked like a spectral crop formation, which shimmered for a few seconds before fading.

'Now open your eyes.'

'But I don't want to. It's too wonderful, too divine.'

'You are correct, it IS divine, all of it. But please open your eyes.'

With some reservation, I did as requested. What greeted me would live in my mind forever. I can only describe it as my Neo moment. The field, the cows, the sky, the birds, everything around me was now composed of beautiful iridescent rainbow colours, and the whole scene shimmered with waves of swirling energy. In fact, everything **was** energy, everything was connected, and nothing was separate. The iridescent trees merged with the Land, and the sky melted into the Land at the skyline like a watercolour painting that had been left out in the rain; there was no longer any clear-cut division between air and earth, organic and inorganic. Swirling spirals of rainbows passed from one object to another, portraying the very dance of life She had spoken of. I also saw the tracks of rainbows criss-crossing the fields and knew they were the lines of force dowsers detect. They danced like courting serpents, occasionally merging like mating lovers.

In a couple of places, energy seemed to be spiralling out of the ground and flowing straight upwards, disappearing into rainbow skies above. I could no longer doubt what She had told me - geography was alive, everything was. I looked down at a small chalk pebble that had weathered out of the grass-covered bank close by. It too pulsated with light and energy. I reached out and picked it up, and light passed from the pebble through my fingers and up my arms. My own pulse was amplified and I could see similar waves of energy pass from my fingertips into the pebble. Energetically, there really was no barrier between us, as the pebble and I merged into oneness.

Is apparent separateness all down to relative density?

'... And relative vibration, which is determined by the level of consciousness that imbues any physical object. Everything vibrates to the rhythm of life; it is all a matter of relativity whether you see yourself as harder or softer, alive or inanimate. All is consciousness, I am all, and you are all. How can you separate yourself from all other physical things when no separateness exists – it is all illusion. Mystics have been saying this for centuries, but few had ears to listen, hearts to feel, or minds to accept. The physical illusion is rampant and very persuasive – it has to be. You have not been seeing the world the way it really is, but rather the way you are. But your eyes are now open to what is really happening, which is an unfoldment of beauty and pure love. When you look at Nature in this way, you look into your own soul. You come alive!'

'Can anyone else here see what I am seeing?'

'They could, but they aren't. Many come to Avebury with good intentions, with Truth, ecology, the environment and Paganism close to their hearts. This is good, this is very good, but most do not appreciate that this and other sacred sites were not built ON the Land, but WITHIN it. Sacred sites are part of the Land, not separate from it. They co-exist in the dance of Life. But even open-hearted souls who appreciate this much still see themselves as separate from the Land, from sacred sites, separate from each other, and from me. To get interested in ecology, sacred places, shamanism, ancient myths and such is exemplary, and these may take people on their first steps back to me. However, all too often people

then get bogged down with the complications of trying to explain what they find, and how to go about knowing me. They need everything explained and rationalised...'

'Tell me about it, I'm a male Virgo!'

'... and they end up going around in ever-decreasing circles: how straight should a ley line be? Is that crop circle real or hoax? How can I cast a Wiccan circle? Which group of Druids should I join? What is the correct way to dowse? Should I as a Pagan go into churches considering what was done to the wisewomen? Should Pagans eat meat? Questions, questions, questions.'

'Yeah, been there, done that, got the t-shirt with the crop circle on!'

'An enquiring mind is all well and good, for in a sense you are trying to find things out for me. But I have already asked all these questions thousands of times before, and I have come to this conclusion - simple is best. I am here this time to simplify! When you complicate, you lose purity. When you try to explain, you slip further from Truth. Someone once said, 'The wise man knows that he does not know.' Whenever people say to you that they know all the answers about crop circles, stone sites, UFO's, ley lines, earth energies, conspiracies, God, the meaning of life, whatever, just smile politely and walk away. They do not know the answers to these issues, for I myself do not know where this is heading, so how can they? Believe me, when I know all the answers you will be the first to know.'

'Simple is best? What do you mean?'

'Take yourself. Over many years you have chanted, fasted and meditated. You've also chanted, out-loud in your shower, many positive affirmations. You've spent enlightenment weekends at large country houses, hugging groups of people you'd never met before. You paid large sums of money to have just the right crystal. You dipped your toe in every spiritual pond you could find. Did you not do all these and more?'

'You know I did - your point being?'

'These are all very well and good, and can be tools to point you in my direction. But they can also be distractions, and can in fact deprive you of that which you seek, which is love, which is I. People get bogged down by rituals, props, theatre and icons. They feel they have freed their minds, but have in

fact imprisoned themselves with just another set of rules and theologies. The meaning of Life is really very simple – live it! Experience it fully. Experience it in the Now. Experience your humanness, your body, your mind and your heart. But most of all, above all else, experience the Land, experience Nature in all my glory. When you do that, you experience Divinity.'

'Oh I intend to, my Mother.' The technicolour show continued before my mesmerised eyes.

'Planet Earth is a blessed place and everything on it is therefore blessed. It really is the Only Planet of Choice, my son. The physical Planet Earth began with a thought. And that thought was that the physical and spiritual Earth planes would have total freedom of choice. This is Earth's part in the evolution of the Universe. The question was this: what happens when a Planet is given total freedom to evolve how it wishes? So do not waste too much time on trying to discover how it all works, for you will never find all the answers using the processes of the mind. Many have tried. Realise that your only limitation is the refusal to believe that total choice really exists.'

'Yes, I see what you mean, but this is heavy stuff!'

'That is because you are trying to rationalise what I have said. To connect to me is a voyage of discovery for your Soul and your heart, not your mind. Use mental processes and reasoning to kick start your quest to find out why you are here and what life means. But do not let your mind imprison you, for it surely will in its effort to keep you safe and sane. Your inner wisdom will soon tell you that you cannot know the answers to Life's puzzles, for that is not why you are here. But do not get despondent at this point, as many do. Use this realisation as a springboard to experiencing both life and love on this planet, rather than trying to get off it, like many have. 'Dropping-out' is no longer an option, not now, for it is time for truth-seekers to be pro-active, to take responsibility. If you were not meant to be on Earth you would not be, in fact, could not be. I send out this message, to every single member of Mankind, to everyone who is in physicality at this moment:

Will you all please grasp that the most important thing on this planet right now is YOU – all of you!'

'Cool. But are you saying an enquiring mind is a bad thing? Surely this is not so.'

'I did not say that. But your mind wants familiarity. It wants logic and the explainable and the repeatable. Your mind says 'don't go too near the edge', whereas your heart yearns to leap off. And this struggle may last your whole life and never be resolved. But if you do eventually close your eyes and step off the edge, not knowing whether or not your next metaphorical step will be on solid ground, that is where you will find me. When you say to yourself 'I haven't got a clue where I am going but I am going there anyway', that is where you will find me. When you go out into the Land and experience it utterly in the now, without any effort to rationalise, quantify, measure, alter or manipulate, then you will find me waiting for you.'

'You make it all sound so easy.'

'It can be. But to most it will not be. And it will take much time and effort for you too, my son, to connect with the Land to your true potential. Fortunately, most of that 'effort' is not about any kind of strict discipline regime, or cramming your mind with new knowledge. Quite the opposite in fact, for it is about emptying your head of much of the conditioning and beliefs you have formulated about your world. You must reprogram your thinking mind to also spend time not thinking, instead feeling, without rationalisation. To see life without judgement, to observe life's longing for itself, its beautiful dance, without the urge to explain, is the key. The adage that too much information is a bad thing is so, so true in this case. All you have to do is experience both your humanness and the Land to your full potential. Connecting with the Spirit of Planet Earth is not really about the acquisition of knowledge at all - it is about attaining love. It is about feeling, experiencing, appreciating, becoming intoxicated with the sheer joy of life.'

'Some people are gonna say you're implying that you can be as thick as two short planks and be connected to the Land. And there will be others who've got all the 'right' books on their shelves, have been to the 'right' gurus, spent thousands on workshops to move in certain spiritual circles, who will cry that you are saying knowledge is bad.'

'Then perhaps we need to make the distinction between knowledge and wisdom, for they are not necessarily the same. To be well read, to be under a trendy workshop leader, or to fill your head with the latest New Age speak, no matter

how well intentioned, does not make you wise. Some of the wisest people who have walked this Earth have been impoverished, humble souls. But they were rich in understanding, for they knew that wisdom cannot be learnt from books alone, that it is a quality and an integrity that comes from reading your own soul, your heart and from constantly questioning your motives. The Land is your biggest teacher here, for it only does that which is honest and necessary, and does so without judgement. Why would I judge myself? HOW can I judge myself?'

The swirling technicolour display of energies gradually faded from my awestruck eyes, initiated I think by a small yapping dog somewhere behind me. Soon, the images had gone and all was back to how it had been.

'It's gone, it's all as it was before.'

'You think so? All is as it was, is it? You have seen what the Land is really like and the spirit it possesses, and this perception means you may never see things as you did before. Over the coming moons, you will come to interact with the energy flows associated with sacred sites and leys, you will meet your totem guides, you will connect with tree spirits and even witness ancestral spirits. Are you up for all this and more?'

'You bet ya! Scottie, take a hike for a few months, I won't be beaming up just yet.'

'That is good. But there may be times you'll consider changing you mind, and wish the Enterprise were still in orbit. Initiation into a new state of being is often traumatic, as your old beliefs go out the window. But I promised that no harm would come to you. When you feel fear, acknowledge it, thank it, but then let it go. Say to it, 'I hear you fear, but this time I choose love.' That way you choose me.'

'Hang on a minute. Time out! What do you mean traumatic, and what will I fear?'

'Is that love asking the question, or fear?'

'OK. OK. But fear is my brain trying to keep me safe, right?'

'It is. But 'safe' will not bring you to me, and will not bring you to experiencing the power within yourself. Out on a limb is where you and I are heading. I am so excited.'

'Hang on. You have never showed emotion before. *Excited?* Where did that come from?'

'Why don't you tell me?'

'Can I phone a friend?'

'No. Tell me. Where did my excitement come from?'

'Well, it cannot have come from fear, can it now. From love then, yes, it came from love.'

'Correct! And I have showed my emotions before. Is not the whole of creation an expression of my love?'

'Yes, but by that reckoning the love you have for me, for humanity, and for the whole planet, is really self-love.'

'Right again. And this is exactly why loving the Land is Man's surest way to self-love. Do you get it?'

'Yes, I dig it, as the archaeologist said. I just haven't taken it fully on board yet. But it sounds so simple and beautiful and all-encompassing and profound.'

'Yes, it is all those and more. I did say that I am bringing a message of simplicity this time. Why do people think things have to be complicated to be profound? Now tell me, my son, is your passport still valid?'

'Wow! You mean we are going to Macchu Picchu after all! You said I create my own reality... can you throw in a sandy, sun-soaked beach too?'

'Well now, there are beaches in Ireland, but I cannot promise sunshine – it all depends on how I am feeling.'

'Ireland? Oh well, not quite Giza or Table Mountain, but I guess Ireland is cool. They have lots of ancient tombs there, don't they?'

'Yes, and you and I will meet in one of them. Go to the Mound of Spirals. But do not forget that you and I are never apart. You only think we are, but it is mere illusion, a trick of the light. Until we speak again, I want you to think about and indeed follow the passage of the days, of day into night, and the phases of the moon as She shrinks and grows to full. See the ebb and flow of the landscape, from the daily tides to whole seasons, as I constantly change and evolve.'

'I will, I will. The Land is becoming so magical to me. I'm so excited too!'

'And be aware that natural changes and cycles reflect your own inner changes and outer physical evolution, for you are part of Nature, not separate. The processes you see without are also within you. Learn from Nature, for She can teach you important lessons that could enhance your life. Patience, for instance. As I said before, everything in and on the Land happens at exactly the right moment it is meant to, not a

second too soon or too late. And so it is too with your own life, even though at times it may not seem so.'

'Tell me about it!'

'... And balance. I only do balance. The Earth only does balance. Man's activities upset things temporarily, but I have ways of dealing with this, so do not fear, even though it may be unpleasant for some. These are not acts of retribution, just means to restoring equilibrium. Balance will always be maintained, even if it may sometimes appear not to be the case. And I want you to mark the turning cycles of the year by honouring its festivals, by focusing on how they represent my changing seasons, expressions of my ever-changing moods. Observe how Nature is never still, never dormant. Forget not the insects and bees in winter, though they sleep, for winter is huge as I hold summer in my womb.'

'That was beautiful.'

'I will be quiet for now, for two people are waiting to meet you, although they do not know it.'

'May the Force be with you, my Mother. And thank you.'

'It always has been, for I am the Force. And so are you, my son, so are you. Fairwell.'

I knew I was alone once more, yet not alone. For I knew that whatever I said, or did, or thought, the Goddess was also experiencing it all.

I trekked back across the fields, past tall monoliths, towards the Red Lion pub. *Two people, eh? Now I wonder who they are?* As I approached the pub car park, I became aware that a small fracas was ensuing; gesticulating protestors were waving aloft some banners. About twenty people, most of whom looked like your stereotype Pagan-come-hippy, plus a guy with a white beard in a Druidy-type cloak, were facing up to two men in green jumpers, whom I soon identified as National Trust staff. I stopped just short of the impassioned debate, which was in full swing and getting increasingly heated.

'Yes, but the site is for everyone, it doesn't belong to the National bloody Trust, or English frigging Heritage, it belongs to the people!' shouted one protagonist.

'Yes, that's all very well and good,' replied one of the officials, 'But what state would Stonehenge be in now if we did not protect it by limiting access. It would be a shambles and would not be there for our children's children.'

This was met with a torrent of abuse, with cries such as, 'It *is* a shambles, mate', 'Nobody owns the Land', 'Its been there for thousands of bloody years without your help,' and, 'It's just a big capitalist money-spinner – why should we pay to go into our sacred place - we're not bloody tourists!'

I was aware of plans to possibly close off the Avebury stones and parts of the village because locals had complained that at certain times of the year, such as around the solstices, the place had allegedly been 'overrun with Pagans and travellers', and that 'disturbances' had taken place. National Trust owns the land on which the stones and the village stood, so they potentially have the right to restrict access, as at Stonehenge. As the debate raged further, I saw both sides of the argument and in fact appreciated that the two sides were actually fighting for the same thing, the stones, but that each had become too firmly entrenched in their own camps.

I was suddenly and unexpectedly approached by two tattoo-covered, dread-locked protestors, a guy and a girl, both in their late twenties and very sun-tanned. They could see I was an independent onlooker and were perhaps eager to know where I stood, with the view of converting me to their point of view. And I'd just sent Scottie on vacation!

'Well, mate? Where d'you stand then? Don't you fink the stones should be open so we can come an' visit 'em, just as people 'ave been doin' for fousands of years?'

Good question. What *did* I think? *Oh well, here goes!*

'I think that access to the stones should continue, but only as long as visitors respect the sanctity of the place, and treat it as sacred, and not just as a place to get pissed and party at, or use as a political pawn, or come here because it is fashionable to do so. To disrespect this sacred place is to disrespect Planet Earth.'

I think I took them aback slightly. I surprised myself actually, with the conviction of my words, which came from the heart.

'Yeah, cool man', one of them replied, 'Yeah, that's jus' what we fink. But it's about respect and freedom of speech too, innit?'

'Yes, of course,' I continued, 'but not for the sake of it, surely. We must not lose touch with why this site is here, and what its purpose was. It was for connecting with the Cosmos, with the Goddess, with the Land. And it *is* for connecting with ourselves.'

I could see they were impressed and now saw me as being at least a little sympathetic to their cause.

'So who the 'ell does Avebury belong to then,' my impassioned brother enquired, '... and Stone 'enge for tha' matter?'

I pondered my reply for a few moments. But there was only way I could put it.

'Avebury, Stonehenge, and all other ancient sacred sites, belong to the Land. But they also belong to the Earth... and to you and I and all creatures that are of the Land... they belong to our ancestors, yet belong to today's people ... they belong to all of Mankind, yet also to the Goddess and the Gods... they belong to Life itself... they belong to the past, the present and the future... they belong to no one and yet belong to everyone. Need I say more?'

They simply nodded back, open-mouthed and speechless before me, as if Deep Thought had just given them the answer to life, the Universe and everything! I turned away with a nod and a departing smile and proceeded into the pub for sustenance, leaving the dispute behind me just as a police car arrived. It was a close encounter of the thirst kind that I needed now. *Well, at least two people are thinking rather than shouting their heads off.* I was smiling from ear to ear - did I really say all that? Where did that come from? I knew the answer, of course. It had come from my place of inner wisdom. It had come from her.

I sat down with my pint to ponder. *So I'm off to Ireland, hey?* Ireland - the land of Guinness, leprechauns, rain, green fields, shamrocks, more rain, and home to a people who had been the butt of a thousand jokes. The land of music too, giving the world Sinead O'Connor, The Pogues, Thin Lizzy, Bob Geldof, U2, and er, The Nolans (oh well, five out of six isn't bad!). But my destiny lay there in June - month of the Summer Solstice.

'Go to the Mound of Spirals.' Hmm. She had also mentioned something about Wyrd, and the Web of Life. At that moment in time I truly felt a deep connection with life, the Land, and everything. I hoped the feeling would last, I really did. She had said that I would always see the world differently now, and She should know. And I knew it too.

Ireland, to be sure! I hope it doesn't rain too much!

6. Newgrange and a Meeting with Einstein

© P Knight

The most beautiful thing we can experience is the mysterious.
It is the source of all true art and all science.
(Albert Einstein)

It really wasn't Exeter's fault. Airports all over the world were pretty much the same; rubbish on the floor, announcements you can't comprehend, toilets with no soap, delays, bored young children, more delays, and the guilt. You know, the guilt: although you've got nothing to hide (well, most times anyway!) you still feel and act as guilty as hell as you walk through customs. Perhaps this is how they tell, for the hardened smuggler or terrorist would probably be the coolest person in the queue, whilst people like me sweat buckets over that small bottle of cheap perfume I've got my mother. And I could never get the hang of what I could or could not bring back. Just how many packets of roasted peanuts could I cram into my rucksack before I was whisked off to some cold backroom for an anal search? And were my dowsing rods going to set off the alarms, resulting in me being confronted by armed police? Oh well, if push came to shove, I could offer to do a Feng Shui profile of the police station! A potted aloe vera plant and a wind chime in the correct position would surely be beneficial to the flow of the Chi in my cell.

So there I sat, not waiting for a plane to jet me off to some hot, foreign clime for a sun-soaked adventure, but instead waiting patiently for the daily flight to the fair city of Dublin. I'd never been there before, so I was really looking forward to it. It was still the day before Full Moon, but I intended to make sure I was where I was meant to be, and on time, as well as to take in some of the sights. As I waited in the departure lounge, I noticed that some of the other passengers were priests and nuns, reflecting Ireland's bedrock of Catholic faith. I swear one of the priests was chatting up one of the younger, prettier nuns. I wondered how my book would up shake that lot, if at all. Would priests soon be damning me from the pulpit, or offering prayers for the salvation of a mortal sinner? Would they even notice? Would the world take notice? *Why do I doubt? OK - fear. She said fear would raise its ugly head. No, I choose love.* Fear was in my head, but my heart knew that what was unfolding was right. The world *would* take notice – the Goddess knew what She was doing, surely.

I wonder if She ever has doubts. I doubt it!

The plane touched down in Dublin on a rather fine, pleasantly warm June afternoon. *No rain yet then - good!* It's one thing not being despatched to the Pyramids or Uluru, but quite another to have it rain all the time! The Goddess said the weather depended on how She was feeling.

I hope She's in a good mood.

I picked up the keys of my hire car at the airport desk and was soon on my way. My B & B accommodation was in Julianstown, a small village about thirty minutes drive up the M1. My host showed me to a pleasant room, complete with shower and TV – what more could I want? A conversation with the Goddess, that's what. It was in fact Full Moon just *after* midnight, 12.02am to be precise, so I wondered whether contact was to be tonight or tomorrow. And I still didn't know where it was to be. But I had what I thought was a fair idea. **'Go to the Mound of Spirals.'** In my mind that could only be one place - Newgrange!

This Neolithic chambered mound was celebrated across the archaeological world for the truly superb examples of prehistoric architecture and art. Its carved stones displaying spirals and other designs had few equal. The passageway famously aligned with the winter solstice sunrise, the rays of which were channelled into the main chamber. Yes, it had to be Newgrange. It also seemed to fit in with my B & B hotel at Julianstown, which was only twenty minutes drive from the Boyne Valley Visitor Centre, where tours of Newgrange and nearby Knowth were arranged; I obtained the lodgings at the last minute due to a cancellation, a nice bit of synchronicity I thought.

By 2.30pm I was pulling up in the car park of the Visitor Centre. I had half an hour to wait until the next available tour, so I had a look around. The building was impressive, with huge plate glass windows that afforded a refreshing air of space and light, complementing imposing massive blocks of stone, which decorated spacious corridors. The exhibition area was equally imposing and informative. Fine images of stones bearing spirals and other ancient motifs covered the walls. I was getting excited, for the Goddess had chosen one of the most spectacular Neolithic monuments in the world, one that had been sacrosanct for thousands of years.

My time to embark onto one of the small shuttle buses duly arrived and I was herded, be it politely, on board. I was accompanied by a selection of Italian, French, German and Spanish tourists and I appeared to be the only Brit on the bus, which I thought strange. I thought that I would be sharing the trip with assorted travellers, hippies and dowsers, etc. Was I the only one there who had come as a true pilgrim, seeking answers to deeper questions?

After about ten minutes of winding country lanes, we arrived at Newgrange. As I approached on foot, the sheer scale of the monument swamped me. *Wow!* There were huge standing stones, kerb stones covered in ancient symbols, and walls of gleaming quartz – talk about first impressions! The entrance was guarded by the well-photographed prone kerbstone, which bore spirals and other enigmatic carvings, and next to it stood our guide. His name was Paddy. It had to be, didn't it! After explaining some of the basic archaeology, we were led into the heart of the structure. We crept warily along a dark, narrow passageway until we were able to stretch out in the main chamber. Paddy explained how, even today, the rays of the winter solstice sunrise streamed down the narrow passage into the chamber. The stones were decorated with all manner of sacred embellishments, and there, at the very back, was the famous triple spiral. As Paddy shared his wisdom with the group, I lent over and gently stroked the sacred etching. A feeling of total peace swept over me, as I connected with the artist who had carved the spirals all those millennia ago.

So where are you, my Goddess?

Paddy retired to the outside of the tomb, leaving us mere mortals to spend time inside. After about ten minutes, the last of my fellow tourists had also wandered back outside, and I was alone in the main chamber. The feeling of mystery and sanctity was palpable and I felt I was going to burst with awe and wonderment for the images around me. My fingers tingled on contact with some of the stones, just as they had at Avebury.

'So where are you, My Lady?' I whispered, '… is this the place and the time?'

I waited… and waited… and waited.

Just as I was drifting off somewhere else I was shaken back to reality.

'Time to go now', called Paddy from the outside, '… sorry, but the next bus is here.'

I was disappointed. *Where are you, My Lady? Have I got it wrong?* I had been told to, **'Go to the Mound of Spirals.'** Then it dawned on me. Perhaps I had been meant to go to another mound. Then I remembered Knowth, the neighbouring complex of cairns close to Newgrange, a site also rich with spiral carvings. The next part of the excursion included Knowth.

Keep faith, man, keep it together. OK. Knowth it is then.

As the bus approached Knowth, I was full of anticipation. All the effort spent to get here, the car journeys, the flight, the B&B, the time expended, was soon to come to fruition. Knowth was impressive by any comparison, a huge central chambered mound, five and a half thousand years old, surrounded by several smaller ones. The carvings displayed there were as impressive as at Newgrange, both inside the passage grave and on the external circle of kerbstones.

'Well, Knowth, here I am', I said under my breath as I crossed the lane from the bus.

But this time, we were met with a cold wind and lashing rain. Our new guide, Patrick, did his best to cheer us up with a barrage of interesting facts, interspersed with large helpings of Irish wit. The kerbstone carvings were indeed stunning, and the sanctity of the place could be felt. He showed us several of the external stones, which were inscribed with all manner of mystical carvings – spirals, serpents, concentric circles, lozenges and a variety of other geometrical designs.

Yet despite the impressive carvings, after ten minutes of driving rain and wind we were only too glad to be led as one huddled, dripping ensemble into the dry, calm interior of the main cairn. But inside there was more disillusionment and frustration. There was no access at all to the passages or chambers, only into a small, artificial anteroom. It had plaster of Paris walls and a few photographs of the ancient artwork that we would not be permitted to see for ourselves. I was gutted. I stood hemmed in by fellow tourists, raindrops still dripping from our noses, clothes and umbrellas. *Where are you, Goddess? Where are you?* After Patrick's piece was said, he announced that we had to be back on the bus in five minutes. *Five bloody minutes! Hey, I am here for an audience with the Earth Mother, you know!* My frustration was beginning to boil up like the stirrings of Vesuvius.

Keep it together, man. She knows what's going down.

By the time the bus had dropped yours truly, windswept and wet, back at the Visitor Centre, I was feeling as low as a turkey the week before Christmas. I stood in reception, still dripping, surveying the map of the Boyne Valley sites on a nearby wall. *There's Newgrange, and Knowth and, hang on a minute, what's that other monument on the map? – Dowth!* This was once the third major tomb in the Boyne Valley, but the tour buses did not visit it because it was less well preserved. Was I meant to be at Dowth instead? I rushed outside and found my car midst the hustle and bustle of an almost bursting car park. All these people milling around like ants - I didn't want any of it! Following my guidebook and map I arrived at the roadside next to Dowth about fifteen minutes later and, fortunately, the rain had subsided.

Surely this has to be it.

I entered the field which contained the ancient Neolithic mound and was pleasantly surprised to see that no one else was around, a complete contrast to the tourist magnets of Newgrange and Knowth. The mound was impressive; I would guess about 25ft high. But on walking around the base of it I soon came to a spot where I could see that a gaping crater now occupied the space where the centre of the mound had once been. The 1840's excavations had ripped the heart of the monument. A rush of great sadness swept through me, as I stood witness to the folly and arrogance of so-called knowledgeable academics. It was as if the womb of the Earth Mother had been subjected to some sort of hideous hysterectomy.

Continuing further round, I found the entrances to the two passage graves, but both were barred by metal grilles and I could make out little detail of the dark interiors. One aligned with the winter solstice sunset, and in that direction an accompanying outlier stood in the next field. The desperate energy of the place must have been gradually seeping into my being for I now felt drained and utterly depressed.

In a vain attempt to cheer myself up I recalled the joke about the archaeologist who was disillusioned because his career was in ruins. But it was no use; feelings of sadness and despair overwhelmed me. I felt negative vibes, completely the opposite to the positive energies of Newgrange and Knowth. When they ripped out the heart of the sacred monument they had taken out its very soul. How could people have done this, all for the sake of cheaply available building materials, or to fill private collections? I stood there looking at the gaping chasm that had once been the nucleus of the mound and cried to the heavens.

'Where are you, My Lady? Why did you allow this to happen? Why are men such idiots? I am here – where are you?'

But my words went unheeded, save for a hare I had disturbed in a nearby thicket. He came closer to watch me knowingly for a minute before scampering away into the distance, taking my confidence and self-esteem with him.

It was now 5.00pm. I was now feeling even lower than that turkey before Christmas, and as rejected as a ham sandwich at a Bar Mitzvah. I thought I would return to the Visitor Centre in search of inspiration as it was open until 6.00pm, and it had a good restaurant. Perhaps a cup of tea and the biggest cream cake I could find would help - it had in the past!

Back at the Centre the hoards of visitors had mercifully subsided, and I easily found a vacant table by the colossal windows. Images of flying swallows were etched onto the glass and, as the rain lashed down, I wished I could have flown off with them to some Mediterranean destination. She said the weather would depend on what mood She was in. I wondered if it was something I had said or done. I stared outside as the tears of the Goddess rained down. The tea was good but after a few mouthfuls of my very sticky cake I could eat no more. I was fractious as hell, and my stomach churned with frustration, as doubts resounded around my confused head. *Have I got it all wrong?* Had the 'signs' along the way been nothing of the sort? She said the meeting was to be about Wyrd; well it sure was turning out like that – weird that is! Above all, I was angry. I had thought that the signs I had followed had been *prophetic,* but at that moment in time I felt *pathetic.* I could feel it gradually, but inextricably, consuming me.

Help!

No sooner had my impassioned plea gone out to the Universe, I noticed I was being eyeballed by a man seated a few tables away. Although he was staring straight at me, his eyes were not threatening, but were instead full of warmth. He was around his late 50s or early 60s and looked a lot like Albert Einstein, sporting a grey moustache and wild silver grey hair. The design on his T-shirt caught my attention. It was a print of a photo of Einstein. Really, I kid you not! *Yes folks, Einstein is in the building!* I was unclear as to whether this guy was making light of his resemblance to the great mathematician, or whether he had a fetish for him. Perhaps it was the great man himself. Yes, perhaps it *was* Einstein, and he had managed to manipulate time, and had come forward to the present day to see what Ireland was like on a dismally wet afternoon. Perhaps he could even tell me what the hell E=MC² meant. Come on, don't tell me you know! And the questions I had to ask him – where would I start? *Is 42 really the answer to life, the Universe and everything? Do you know Dr. Who? OK, that's stupid.* Perhaps Scottie had beamed him down. I was being flippant, of course, but humour had always been my way of coping, and at that moment in time I needed something to get me through.

Well, I had asked for help, and it seemed I was going to get it, for 'Einstein' suddenly stood up and was heading straight for me, his resplendent grey locks trailing behind him, blown by over-zealous air conditioning.

OK, Albert, what you got?

'May I join you?' His voice was gentle yet powerful.

'Yes, please do.' He sat down opposite me and we introduced ourselves. His name was Ken, '… a humble Druid from Somerset, yet now residing in London. But you can call me Al!'

He smiled, pointing at the image on his shirt.

Hey, this guy has a sense of humour. Good start.

'Hi Ken, pleased to meet you.'

'Likewise, I'm sure. You must excuse me, but I have been watching you for sometime prior to you noticing me. And although I have been watching you for the last ten minutes, I have been waiting for you for the past two hours. You see, I felt compelled to come here today, presumably to meet someone, although I knew not who. But, of course I do now. It is you, my friend, it is you! Tell me, how are you?'

Although we had only just met, there was something about him that made me trust him totally – he gave off an aura akin to that of Santa Claus himself! His eyes were honest and his voice and manner had already relaxed me. He had a sense of humour, so might be able to cheer me up. *OK, let's go with the flow.*

'Well, Ken…' I replied, staring into my half-empty cup, '… I've had quite a day, but not in the way I thought I would. You see, I too was meant to meet someone here, but She didn't show. And my disappointment has turned to anger. But I don't actually know what is pissing me off more. Am I angry with myself? At her? I feel so rejected.'

'Ah, anger and rejection…' he replied, '… two bummers, aren't they?' He half-smiled, which relieved my troubled mind.

'But you know…' he continued, '… we are never upset for the reason we think we are - never. There is always something else going on deep within our subconscious that is causing us to react the way we do. The obvious up-front annoyances are simply the triggers for deeper stuff. Tell me, my friend, has rejection been an issue in your life before?'

I thought briefly before replying. 'Well, yes, I did some releasing a few years ago to do with my father's alcoholism and how I felt it had affected my childhood. But I'm not sure I have any rejection issues now.'

'Think, my friend,' he went on, 'I feel you should look more recently.'

I felt like a patient on a therapist's couch. Then it struck me like a thunderbolt.

'My father passed away suddenly in January. And that same month I was dumped by my ex, whom I had had a three-year relationship with, which also hit me hard. I thought I had got over both issues but, my God, that's it. I still feel the pain of both my father and my ex abandoning me. Even my father?'

Ken offered comforting words: 'Past hurts go deep, and often linger in our subconscious, insidiously hiding until we awaken them with something that reminds us of a former painful experience. Then all the past pain surfaces as anger. But now you can release the pain and move on. Tell me, my friend, who has let you down today? Was it a young lady, a potential lover perhaps?' He gazed at me with a twinkle in his eye, as if he knew more than he was letting on.

'You may think I'm nuts, Ken, but today I have been let down by … by… the Goddess.'

'Ah-ha! I knew it! I knew it!' he exclaimed loudly and exuberantly, simultaneously clapping his hands three times.

'…I knew there was something magical going down. Fantastic, my dear friend, fantastic!'

'Fantastic that She has let me down?' I replied confusedly.

'No! Fantastic because the time is finally upon us. The time many have predicted for years. Tell me, the Sacred Mother has contacted you already, has She not?' His eyes beamed with anticipation.

'Yes, She has, and is narrating her wisdom that I may put it down in a book. You are the first person I have told of this. But I expected to find her here today and She has not contacted me. I feel I have upset her, or I worked it out all wrong. It's all my doing – Mea Culpa.'

'Bollocks!' was Ken's immediate response. He banged his fist on the table and my teaspoon was catapulted onto the floor just in front of the next table, at which sat two Japanese tourists. After their initial surprise, they nervously smiled across at us and one of them returned the spoon, accompanied by a small bow.

'Now, listen here, my brother, and listen good,' Ken continued in an intense and reprimanding voice. 'The Goddess will not reject you. She will never abandon you. She will guide you through to the fruition of this great adventure, this quest of yours. It is you who doubt, my friend, not her. I bet you came here because it is Ireland's most sacred Neolithic site, with all the spirals, big stones and whatnot. But I'll wager that She did not actually say it was to be here, did She? The answer is *no* to that one, isn't it?'

I nodded. I felt I was being given a lesson, but was prepared to accept anything that would get me back on track.

'Exactly', continued Ken, '… and seeing as it is approaching Full Moon, I suppose this is part of the deal, hey? You are contacted every Full Moon, right?'

I nodded again. Ken ran his wizened fingers through his grey beard.

'Hmm. Right. Well, for a start off, our Heavenly Lady is not fully ripe until just *after* midnight tonight, is she not? You see, it was a mixture of doubt and impatience that brought you here **a day early**. But this is the wonder of the Web of Wyrd, because for all that, synchronicity and the wheels of life have led you here today so that we could meet. Do you see? There are no mistakes in the Universe. Our Lady knows exactly what She is doing, even if you don't, or worse still, if you doubt her. You see, my friend, She has not rejected you, far from it. She has given you the opportunity to recognise the presence of, and release, that old pent-up anger, and also set up the arena for your lesson. I bet it is something to do with synchronicity, meaningful coincidences, the Play of Wyrd no less. Correct?'

'She said it would be, yes.'

'Oh, how wonderful. You know, She does have a divine sense of humour. I love it. The lesson has already begun my friend; you just did not grasp the fact. Now, let me think. I wonder where you really are meant to be tomorrow, for the Full Moon. What exactly did She say to you?'

'She said we would talk next at the *Mound of Spirals*, so naturally I thought it was to be at either Newgrange or Knowth.'

He was silent for but a few moments, before his face lit up with a beaming smile that levitated his bushy, grey moustache.

'But, of course. That's it!'

'That's what?' I enquired, leaning over the table in anticipation.

'It's where I was drawn to go earlier today. A fine area, full of ancient cairns and standing stones, all on hill tops with stunning views. Carvings too, and it's considerably quieter than this cattle market. And there are mounds, my friend, lots of mounds containing oodles of spirals.'

'Yes, Ken, but where?'

'Loughcrew. Yes, that's it, it has to be Loughcrew. It's quiet, relatively isolated, not like here, and still comparatively pure and sacred.'

I sat back in my chair, consumed by a mixture of utter relief and joy. *Loughcrew.*

Ken reached across the table and held my hands within the strength of his own. Our eyes met in a moment of pure bliss and I knew then that this man, whom I had just met in an Irish café, would become a trusted friend.

'Come,' he said, pulling me to my feet, 'Let's look around the bookshop here for a guide to that area.'

We soon found one, which I purchased, and we sat down on a nearby bench and flicked through it. He pointed out where he had been that morning and which cairns displayed the finest carvings. He also showed me the ones that were manned by guides and those that were more isolated. We sat for over half an hour talking about events that had transpired to get us to meet, until a '*closing in 5 minutes*' announcement came over the public address system. As Ken walked me to my car I felt a close bond with this gentle, wise and yet powerful man.

'Come with me, Ken. Sometimes I feel this is all too much for me, that I'll cock it all up.'

'My friend', he said, as he held me by the shoulders in a show of deep affection, 'I wish I was coming with you, but I cannot. It is for you and you only, this journey with Our Lady. She has chosen you, not I. And for what it's worth, I think She has chosen wisely. You'll be up to it, just keep faith, be true to yourself, be strong, doubt not the innate wisdom within you, and fear nothing, for She will guide you. OK?'

'OK, I guess. But I want us to get in touch again, please, for I feel we will have so much to share.'

'It's a deal, my friend', and we duly exchanged emails, addresses and phone numbers. I opened the car door, and we exchanged a final hug. So much positive energy passed between us that I wanted the embrace to last forever.

'You will not fail us, my brother, you cannot. I will spread the word amongst the Elders, the Wise Ones and Guardians, for they too will be comforted that help is at hand for the Earth and Mankind. Now go, and make sure you get an early night's sleep, for tomorrow you have an important appointment with a very important lady. Skidaddle!'

As I drove away from the car park, I knew that once again all was as it should have been. I also recognized that it had been all along, if only I had comprehended it. I saw the Full Moon rise just before I retired, and thanked it for blessing the Earth and me with its healing light. I slept like a log that night, safe in the knowledge that Loughcrew would hold blessings a plenty.

7. Fourth Moon – June: Loughcrew, Ireland
Lesson – The Play of Wyrd

© P Knight

The fountains mingle with the river
And the rivers with the ocean,
The winds of heaven mix forever
With sweet emotion;
Nothing in the world is single,
All things by a law divine
In one another's being mingle.
(From *Love's Philosophy,* Percy Shelly)

I spent much of the morning resting and entering the details of the previous day's events into my laptop. After lunch at a local alehouse, I set off for Loughcrew. After a drive of around thirty minutes, along refreshingly empty Irish roads, I arrived at the car park. It was a far cry from the Boyne Valley – no buses brimming with tourists or visitor centre here. It was a warm June afternoon and all around me birds were singing. The sun seemed incredibly high in the sky, casting but short shadows, and I felt good to be alive. I stood with guidebook in hand, comparing its contents to that of a plaque that had been erected at the edge of the tarmac, displaying a map and various wildlife images. Next to it, sitting on a bench, was a grey-haired man, around 65-70 years of age, sporting a tweed jacket and puffing away at the contents of a long clay pipe. He looked as if the Irish Tourist Board had planted him, as an example of an archetypal rural Irish fellow!

What next, leprechauns?

'Good morning to you, sir', he exclaimed in a broad, beautifully rich Irish tongue.

'And a good morning to you, too.'

'Now, if it is the cairns you'll be after, then there is surely a guide up at the main one. She'll be up there until about one o'clock, when she has a mind to come down for her lunch. It's straight up that path there. But mind the steep climb, too steep for these old legs now, I fear. But it's worth the climb, to look out from top of the *Slieve na Calliagh.*'

The confusion on my face was obviously plain to see.

'Oh, sorry sir,' he explained, '… that means the *Witch's or Hag's Mountain.*'

'Thanks very much. Have a good day.'

'I will to be sure, sir, make no mistake. And you too.'

Mountain of Witches, hey? Might just be the right place, then!

As I started my ascent I looked ahead and could see that the climb was indeed a steep one. So I enjoyed the views and even composed my own version of an Irish joke that I had heard years before. My version goes like this: An Englishman visits a stone circle, and sees a rustic looking chap leaning against a fence. The Englishman goes over to him. 'Excuse me', he enquires, 'How old is the stone circle?' 'Well now, let me see,' replies the local, '… it must be 3,005 years old, to be sure.' 'That's very precise,' replies the Englishman. 'Well, sir,' continued the Irishman, 'it is, but you see it's no mystery really. When I moved into the area I was told the stones were 3000 yrs old and I've lived here for five years.'

The climb up to the top of the hill was steep and arduous in the June sunshine. Cairn T was the biggest of the Neolithic cairns in the Loughcrew area, and the most frequented because it was still complete and contained many ancient carvings, some of which were illustrated in my guidebook. At the top I was greeted by a local lady who showed me, along with four other pilgrims, the markings in the interior of this magnificent passage grave. The images spoke to me across the eons of time, and although I did not understand their meaning, their power entered my being. She told us how the carvings on the back stone were still illuminated by the sun as it rises at the Equinoxes. It made me think about who had lovingly carved them, thousands of years ago, and who had sat there awaiting the rising of the Sun God. As the others departed the chamber for the bright sun, I lingered inside. I sat down, very still, in one corner of the ancient chamber. I felt safe and secure in the darkness, as if nurtured within the very womb of the Earth Mother.

'Are you here, My Lady? Is this it?'

But, as before, there was no reply.

After about two or three minutes the guide requested that I return outside, as there were more visitors waiting to come in. *OK, not this place, but I know it is somewhere around here.* Coming out into the bright light of day felt a bit like being reborn. From the darkness of the tomb I had to stoop along a narrow passageway and could only stand upright when back in the outside world. It reminded me of birth; after being in the foetal position in the moist darkness of the womb, the newborn infant emerges, to be confronted by the light of the outside world. Was this one of the functions of this place? Perhaps they were more than mounds of the dead, but were also places for the living, for initiation, rites of passage and spiritual rebirthing.

OK. It worked before: Help me, my Mother. Where do I go?

I walked around the exterior of the mound until I came to a huge strangely cut rock that looked as if it had been carved into the shape of an altar or, more likely, a huge chair. I scrambled onto the top of it, and dangled my legs over the edge, staring across the endless Irish landscape below. My guidebook said it was the *Hag's Chair*, where tradition says *Callaigh Waura* sat, and it narrated an ancient rhyme about her:

I'm the Callaigh Waura, I have many changes seen,
I saw old Cairne Bawn a lake, but now it's a mountain green.

It was as good a place as any to focus.

'Well, Callaigh Waura, Hag of the Mountain, where do I go?'

My eyes scanned the valleys below and over to an adjacent hill to the west. My attention was drawn to the summit, on which sat several large bumps. My book revealed that this hill was Carnbane West, and that it was littered with further Neolithic passage graves and megaliths, some of which had *spiral carvings*! I could not take my eyes off the mounds, and felt a magnetic pull from them. The words of the Goddess echoed around my head: **'Go to the Mound of Spirals.'**

'OK. OK. I hear you calling. I'm a-coming!'

Back down at the car park, I scanned around briefly for the old man, but he had gone. My map showed that access to the mounds was via a field a short walk up a lane, which I followed, my pace quickening with every stride. I arrived at a gate where my map showed access should have been, but it was locked and bore a bright yellow notice, bearing letters in large black print:

NOTICE
IF YOU PASS BEYOND THIS
SIGN YOU ARE ON A FARM
TAKE NOTICE THAT THE OWNER EXCLUDES THE
DUTY OF CARE TOWARDS VISITORS
UNAUTHORISED ENTRY IS PROHIBITED

'Say, what?'

Hang on a minute. This is the only way to get up to the cairns where I have an appointment with the Earth Mother and you are telling me to back off!

'I don't think so!'

I lent on the gate, looking up the hillside to the summit of the hill. A single large mound on the skyline tantalisingly beckoned. I looked all around the immediate vista. Where was the farm then? And should I even bother to ask permission? What if they say, 'clear off, you English weirdo'? I had never trespassed before, well hardly ever, in the pursuit of visiting ancient sites. Perhaps this was a test of my faith. But how? Was I meant to ask permission from the farmer, and have faith he would say 'OK, sunshine, only too glad for you trample across my land to meet the Earth Goddess', or was I to have faith that no harm would come to me if I legged it over the fence and sauntered up the hill? It certainly looked isolated, and I could see no movement or signs of life in the field except several sheep, which munched away at the lush Irish grass, unaware of my dilemma.

I had stood there deliberating for about five minutes, when something caught my eye high up in the blue skies above. It was a large buzzard! I instantly thought of the one that had hovered over me at Men-an-Tol. I was mesmerised as the bird effortlessly rode the thermals, the epitome of grace and freedom, until, without warning, he veered off in the direction the hill. The bird got smaller and smaller until I was straining to see it. He disappeared out of sight over the very mound I had been looking at, the object of my desire.

'Thanks for the sign, my friend. Right, M' Lady, here I come!'

I was over the gate like an Olympic hurdler and hotfooting it across the field to begin my ascent. I passed a standing stone to my right, but my focus was divided between keeping sight of the mound above me, and avoiding cowpats. The climb became arduous as the sun approached its zenith, and I stopped a few times to slurp from my water bottle. Within ten minutes I was at the crest of the slope.

And what a sight greeted me. From down below, only one ancient mound had been visible, but I could now make out at least a dozen, spread across an expansive, grassed-covered plateau. I took time to survey the ancient cemetery, noting that whilst some of the tombs were complete, with roof and all, others were open to the elements, displaying the classic cruciform plan of Irish passage graves. Access to the two intact mounds was unfortunately restricted by iron railings, as at Dowth. Although I was frustrated by this, at least they had not been destroyed, as at Dowth and elsewhere, where mounds had been pillaged. As I wandered around the primeval assembly I found stones carved with spirals and concentric circles, and my fingers tingled whenever I paused to gently stroke them.

My guidebook told me that the Carnbane West cemetery comprised about a dozen cairns, all over 3,000 years old. Several of the passages were aligned with astronomical events, such as solstice sunrises, and the summit offered a magnificent 360° panorama of the Irish countryside below. My prehistoric ancestors must have felt truly elevated, halfway to the Gods.

I sensed that one passage grave was calling me more than the rest - Cairn H. Although the passage and chambers were open to the elements, I nevertheless had to stoop under a solitary remaining lintel near the entrance of the passage, an act that ensured deference to the spirits of the ancestors. The main chamber lay ahead, flanked by two smaller ones. On one elongated prone stone, low down to my right, were carved two concentric circles and a spiral, similar to those I had seen at Newgrange and Knowth. I sat down in the end chamber, whose walls offered respite from the high sun, and gazed back along the passageway. It was aligned with the hill I had been to earlier, and the massive mound of Cairn T stood prominent on the summit, an alignment that was surely intentional.

I settled down, nestling on my rolled-up rainwear, which acted as a welcome cushion against the cold stone floor.

'Well, My Lady, are you here this time?'

'But have I not been with you always?'

'I have found you, thank goodness,' I cried out.

'You can indeed thank goodness. But be thankful only that we are again speaking with each other, for surely you know I have been with you since you stepped off the plane at Dublin, and before that. We just needed to decide where we were to communicate.'

'But I thought it had been you who had been elusive, that you were testing me to see if I could find the right place.'

'Well now, seeing as you and I are one, as you may remember, then I suppose we are both accomplices in what has transpired. We both felt that the hustle and bustle of the tourist places yesterday was not right. The threads of synchronicity that we both created and followed were an important part of the journey too. I think we did very well to get here for it was you and I equally that determined the outcome. And on the journey you met a wise man who may well become a close friend to you, a man of great integrity and wisdom, whom you would do well to consult in the months ahead.'

'Ah yes, Ken aka Albert Einstein. Yes, he *is* a fine man. I felt a great affinity with him.'

'And so you ought, for he has been both male Druid and female wisewoman in past lives. You will learn much from him.'

'It's *so* good to hear from you again', I exclaimed to the heavens. 'Oh, My Lady. I have doubted so much this time. I feel I have let the side down somewhat. I could have been here yesterday.'

'But yesterday wasn't the right time.'

'How come? I've wasted so much time.'

'Oh, don't worry about time. Why worry about a figment of your imagination? See time as but a flowing stream you go fishing in. Anyway, if yesterday were the right time you would have been here. Do not doubt the exquisite interconnectedness of all things. Everything happens at the moment it is meant to, and not a millisecond too soon or too late. This is the manner of Wyrd.'

'Ah yes, Wyrd. That's what you said this lesson would be about. So what's this Wyrd then – something weird no doubt?'

'Ha-ha! Very good. In fact, the word 'weird' does derive from the ancient Wyrd, meaning something that was unexplainable. Well, it's very simple really, as natural laws are when you learn to live in harmony with them. Many wise people have sought to explain the processes of Life as being a web, like that of a spider. This analogy is very good and still adequate for these times. It is an error of judgement to assume that events far apart are in no way connected. Everything is linked to everything else in the Web of Life, and the smallest event anywhere influences the whole, be it on an obvious level or else on dimensions not so apparent. However, any movement or thought will always have an effect on energetic planes. The smallest movement anywhere on the web can be felt everywhere if one is attuned. You could also see your world as a woven fabric, where nothing happens that is not connected to everything else. Coincidences, or acts of synchronicity as psychologists would have it, envelop you every second of the day and to read them is a sign of being at one with natural forces. The web connects all things and you can read the signs because you are immersed within it, not some detached onlooker.'

'And what is at the centre of the web?'

'Why you are, of course, and every other living being. The Greek philosopher Empedoclies had grasped this reality way back in 430 BC, when he wrote: 'The Nature of God is a circle of which the centre is everywhere and the circumference is nowhere.' No matter where you are, you are at the centre. You really are the centre of the Universe.'

'Heavy! So Wyrd makes everything happen, makes the Universe turn.'

'You are almost there. But try to understand that Wyrd does not MAKE things happen, but rather Wyrd IS the event, Wyrd IS the manifestation. Wyrd is not fate or some destiny you are bound up in, from which you are destined never to escape. Rather it is the flow of the forces of life, the intelligence that underpins all things, and the stream in which you are all immersed. In eastern philosophy, for instance, it is the motion of the Great Tao, the flow of Chi. And because you are an innate element of life, you can affect the whole. This is the power of your free will. You really can make a difference

81

to this planet. Your smallest act reverberates around the globe. I, the Earth Mother, feel everything and act on all thoughts, actions and choices made. Thought always precedes manifestation.'

'So we are not all victims of our birth, or our birth chart, or even of some Matrix-like conspiracy to control us.'

'Goodness, no! Conspiracies are mere distractions from your true path. They all run out of steam sooner or later. The human mind is incredibly inventive and imaginative, but also very fearful. It has sacrificed pure light and love in order to fully enter the human experience, and fear simply reflects this longing to return to Oneness, to reunite with me. Whilst you are concentrating on conspiracies you cannot be focusing on love. As regards the Matrix and similar works of fiction, try to appreciate that the Universe is not so much the product of a great machine, but rather a great contemplation. Perhaps you could imagine that the physical Universe you know is taking place inside a gigantic, infinitely large mind. You are somewhere inside and from your internal position cannot possibly realise you are part of a huge mind. You may be tiny in comparison to the whole organism, but if you were to be surgically removed, the mind could not function as before, for it would no longer be whole.'

'Reminds me a bit of the movie *The Truman Show,* about a guy whose whole life was a TV reality show, right from his birth. He had no idea that he was living in a gigantic studio set.'

'There is relevance in what you say, for likewise the Universe is too vast to take in, and you yourselves cannot step outside to observe it. But the reality of the Universe is that it is actually happening, it is not fiction, not the product of a scriptwriter. It is the product of the Universal Mind, rather than Universal Studios. And most important to realise, it is the product of YOU.'

'That's cool, I think. You know this is mind-blowing stuff. Well, of course, you know. I find the concept of everything affecting everything else, and meaningful coincidences, fascinating. So Carl Jung was on the right track with his theory of synchronicity.'

'Yes, spot on. Mr Jung studied the mind from a spiritual prospective and concluded that if all living things have consciousness and are part of a collective unconscious, then all things must potentially have an effect on everything else. It may not surprise you to learn that he was a shaman in a

former life. His books have been misinterpreted and remain unread by most people because they are not accessible and can be technical, often labelled as psychology. It is time to simplify, remember? Hence you, my friend, who will take centre stage, for you are not so learnéd...'

'Thanks very much!'

'... so you will present the book and yourself to a wider audience. You will be able to tell people that through the processes of Wyrd they can control their destiny, foretell possible futures that may come to pass, work with these or indeed change them, read the signs in nature that foretell both potential disasters and successes, and learn how to be positively proactive with the planet, especially in a more spiritual way. Everything is connected to everything elsewhere along the web. How can it be otherwise? I have not detached or amputated chunks of myself and cast them out. I, the Goddess, am whole and complete and I sense all and act on all. This can be your point of power, or it can be your place of helplessness. Love or fear, remember? You choose, as does everyone.'

'You say we can foretell events that may come to pass. How is this possible, for you once told me that you haven't got a clue what's going to happen in the future.'

'This is true. Nothing, absolutely nothing, is predestined. Anyone who says otherwise is in error. I have not decided how anyone's life will turn out, never have done and never will. You are in control of your beliefs, hopes, fears, and your entire destiny. By following signs and portents you can, however, get indicators of POSSIBLE futures based on the present flow of Wyrd in your life. And there is your power to enhance your future, for you create it! We are a magical partnership, you and I. What you believe will manifest. All things come to pass because you and I are one, and together we manifest your beliefs - because they are also mine.'

'This is great news. But although on one hand I feel empowered, on the other I feel daunted. Why?'

'It was your wise sage Nelson Mandela who once told his people that they should not be afraid because they were weak, but because they were powerful. He understood the responsibility and influence that comes with suddenly finding that you are in the driving seat, which is in fact a good analogy. You have been taking your 'driving test', so to

83

speak, since you were born, but most people do not 'pass' in one lifetime. Others 'qualify' with ease because they have done so a hundred times before. Sometimes people glimpse the power and freedom that this knowledge brings but are unable to change their lives, because they are stuck – it is fear again saying 'don't change, it's too risky, better the Devil you know!' But I urge you all to use fear as a conduit for change and growth. To go beyond fear is to live. Beyond fear is where I wait for you with open arms. You create your own reality whether you believe it or not, so you may as well do it consciously.'

'Fear is a real bitch sometimes. But one thing occurs to me. If I create my own reality and think positively, why can't I leave my door unlocked when I go out, or drive my car without my seatbelt fastened, and know that I will be safe?'

'You make a good point. But we could make the distinction between self-loving and that of challenging the physical laws of your world, laws your soul has agreed to abide by. If you walk in the rain without an umbrella, you will get wet, and if you go without food, your physical body will perish. Acknowledging your divinity and Oneness in fact releases you to be MORE in tune with your physical world. To use an umbrella, a seat belt or a lock on your door is to honour your world and the Divinity it is, but without fearing it. How can you say you truly love yourself if you do not lock your doors in an area of high crime? Are you honouring your body and your sacredness by stepping out into a road without looking to see what is coming? Of course not.'

'OK. I am cool with that and will try to think in the way you suggest.'

'Good. But let's get back to creating your own reality and the processes of Wyrd. We have touched upon the spider's web analogy. In Cornwall I also spoke about the Cosmic Kitchen, whereby every thought and belief will eventually come back to you as physical manifestation, unless you counteract it with another of more conviction. There are no chance happenings – there is no anarchy in the physical Universe. The way this works is through the progression of Wyrd, which some cultures call karma. Your thoughts go out across the Universe, reverberating along the fibres of the web, and interactions happen with other energies to manifest your physical reality. This is why it is so important to be

84

positive and, equally imperative, for you not to be negative. Try to realise that it is not so much a necessity to see yourself as good, but rather to stop seeing yourself as bad, or a sinner, a loser or a failure. Previous mindsets will have lured you into that state, and your present negative thoughts keep you there. I create what you order. But the power is in both our hands, equally. What a team!'

'So if things are not predestined, how can we alter future events that would otherwise have come to pass, and how can we predict things, through runes, tarot or astrology for example, if nothing is set in stone?'

'Another excellent question. Divination practices, such as using the runes, the tarot, tea leaves, astrology and any of the other disciplines you have devised, cannot possibly predict the future, as you rightly deduce, because the future has not been decided upon. Rather they give POSSIBILITIES of what the future may hold, based on the way the web is currently reverberating - but these possibilities are almost endless. Possible futures can be regarded in much the same way as a fisherman heeds the wind and tides, for by observing them he can cast his nets accordingly. Divination tools can help you live in harmony with Nature, rather than going against the flow. It is important to realise, however, that if you change the way you think, or replace some projected thought with a new one, then that too will go down the web and set in motion new potential futures. This is your creative power – you create your life.'

'So we are all fishers of men!'

'Indeed. So by watching the signs, heeding the lessons, observing portents, reading the stars, the changing seasons, the phases of the moon, and taking note of meaningful coincidences, you can control your destiny to a much greater degree than you would ever have thought possible. Using the fisherman analogy again, it is as if you exchange a sail for an engine. With the sail you were, to a certain extent, in control of your destiny, but were always at the mercy of the winds, and could even be becalmed through lack of a breeze. Upgrading to an engine gives you power over when and where you travel across the seas of your existence. And self-belief in your personal power is the fuel.'

'Sometimes I feel I never even got my sail up, and even if I had it would have been moth-eaten!'

'This is how many people think today, especially in the West. But everyone's boat can come in, if you will excuse the pun, if you realise that you are not galley slaves, aimlessly rowing to the beat of someone else's drum, but are all captains of your own destiny. We are all dancing to the rhythm of the same drum. Julius Caesar said, 'Carpe diem' - seize the day. I would go one further and say to you, Carpe vita – seize your life!'

I looked up at the sky, which was filled with puffy white clouds that gently jostled for position in the blue firmament. I watched a flock of geese pass by, honking on their way, and even higher up I saw a buzzard, perhaps *the* buzzard, circling around, out of sight at times due to its high altitude. I felt part of it all, and longed to understand more of synchronicity, from the passing of a buzzard overhead, to colliding with a stranger as you go around a corner. Everything meant something. All was connected. All was moving to one drumbeat, that of the Goddess. I looked around at the ancient megaliths that enclosed me, and knew that in ancient times someone had sat just where I was, someone who perhaps was also looking at *their* Universe with new eyes.

'Happy Full Moon.'

'Happy Full Moon, my Mother.'

I closed my eyes and could sense the alignment of sun, earth and moon.

I am at the centre - aligned with the cosmos.

'Indeed, the alignment you now feel is a wonderful example of the Divine sacred geometry that imbues the Universe. Although I have spoken of a Universal Mind, there are nevertheless laws that drive the Cosmos. In fact, this regular and geometrical perfection enables your thoughts, desires and fears to come into physical manifestation. The whole of Nature is ordered to perfection and is beautifully geometrical. It is this that I will speak of when the Lady of the Night next ripens.'

'I hated geometry at school. How am I going to get my head around sacred geometry?'

'Do not worry, because your head, indeed your whole body, is a manifestation of sacred geometry. It is beautifully simple, as is the whole Universe if you stop trying to analyse it, and just experience and appreciate. Next time we shall talk at a temporary holy place next to the red beast. Farewell for now, my son.'

'Goodbye, my Mother. And thank you.'

It must have been half an hour before I moved from that hallowed spot. I drifted in and out of meditation and felt tingling in my hands and feet on several occasions as the life-force of the Goddess flowed through the ancient chamber. I spent the early evening exploring the other mounds on the summit, walking quite literally in the footsteps of my ancestors. Being June, it was well after nine o'clock before sunset came, and I stood on a nearby ancient cairn to see the glorious orange orb sink into the body of the Mother. In the opposite direction the moon was rising out of distant hills in the southeast. She would remain low in the firmament that night, as if too timid to venture higher, for she was riding Capricorn the Goat, whose stars are always low in the sky from these latitudes.

As I drove back to Julianstown, the moon continued her ascent in front of me, guiding me back to my bed. As skies turned to purple and eventually deep blue, clouds scudded across the face of the Full Lady, and the first stars twinkled. My concentration was fully on the road ahead, for I knew that I would have total recall of all the events of the day. The car roof was open and the warm mid-summer air blew in and with it the invigorating aromas of the Irish countryside.

Back at my lodgings, I entered the day's events into my laptop, taking care, as I always did, to back up on my memory stick. As I pressed the keys and gazed at the letters that materialised on the screen, I felt that the Goddess was looking over my shoulder. If I had turned around, no one would have been physically there, but She was there all the same. Yet it was more than this – She was looking through my eyes. Every time I made a mistake, or nearly missed something out, it was She who did the correcting, like a schoolmistress looking over the shoulder of an eager student. But this was exactly how it was, of course. Earth Mother, the Land, is our tutor, and we are all her students.

8. Chasing Rainbows – Fourknocks, Tara and Castleruddery

© P Knight

The soul would have no rainbows
If the eyes had no tears.
(American Indian proverb)

I arose next morning in buoyant mood. After a good breakfast I settled my account and bid my hosts farewell. If they only knew the adventure they had unwittingly been a part of. I had seven hours to kill before my mid-afternoon flight from Dublin, and I was going to fill them with something meaningful. A little research the night before had revealed three sacred places I had to visit.

North of Dublin, set amongst rolling hills and quaint backwater villages, was the Neolithic passage mound of Fourknocks. A lady at the village post office told me I had to obtain a key to the monument from a house at Davidstown, the nearest village. A knock at the door produced a middle-aged, typically polite Irish gentleman, with a broad accent. A deposit of ten Euros secured me possession of a large iron key and ten minutes later, after a few wrong turns at unsignposted junctions, I parked by a sign proclaiming that the ancient mound was somewhere across the road.

A long, sloping, uphill path skirted an open field and as I ascended, the landscape opened up with glorious vistas to the south and west. The grass-covered mound itself was imposing, perched on a commanding position on the crest of the hill. There were more magnificent views to the north, which was, unusually, the direction to which the entrance faced. As at Loughcrew, there was a welcoming contrast between here and the mêlée that had been Newgrange. I paused at the door and, after composing myself, I assured the ancestors of the place that my intentions were honourable.

I unlocked the heavy, black metal door, which opened with a loud creak. At first I could see nothing inside; the day was bright and the interior dark and mysterious. In fact such was the serenity of the place that I felt obliged to first ask permission before entering. I sensed no adverse feelings, so knew it was OK. I entered and after treading a short passage found myself within the belly of a large chamber, which was in fact bigger than those of Newgrange or Knowth. Daylight streamed through the door, as well as through some modern vents above my head. As my eyes got accustomed to the dark, I made out the grandeur of the stonework. Three alcoves were set into the sides of the chamber, two of which were capped with large lintel stones bearing ancient carvings of zigzags and wavy lines. Two other stones were embellished with further enigmatic designs, including circles and one that vaguely resembled a humanoid figure. They were quite spectacular and I took time to pause at each, running my fingers delicately and respectfully over each archaic wonder.

I clambered into one of the alcoves, which measured about 4ft wide by 4ft high, a restriction that forced me to stoop reverently. I settled down at the back of the recess, leaning against a large stone, cross-legged under another displaying ancient zigzag carvings. I sat there in the dim light and knew that thousands of years ago others had sat there too, in that very spot, for some ancient ritual, meditation, healing or divination. I could feel their presence, and it was the close proximity of the living that I felt, not of the dead. The energies were comforting and a calming feeling washed through me. I was sitting in a place of ancestors, and was connected to them as surely as if they were sitting next to me. I had the feeling that spirits unseen were watching me, as if probing for my intentions and my sincerity. My words echoed around the megalithic chamber:

'I greet you, my ancestors. I honour your memory and give thanks to you for this magnificent epitaph of your faith. I thank you for the opportunity to spend time within these hallowed walls. I come here in peace and I deeply appreciate the harmony I am now feeling.'

No one answered, but I knew my words had been heard. I meditated within the alcove for around half an hour and although I did not receive any profound visions or messages, the feeling of love and relaxation deepened, as I sank into a deep pool of serenity. Every now and then I would feel a wave of energy sweep through my whole body. I was absorbing the flows of earth energies as they swept in pulses through the chamber on their journey across the Land, pausing here to spiral around within the ancient mound, as if dancing to the joy of life.

I arrived at Tara around 11.00am, and was met by skies that had radically changed, having become overcast and blustery. The Goddess had changed her mood - I hoped it wasn't something I'd said! A couple of cool shops were situated conveniently next to a toilet block and in one I obtained a thin, but adequate, guide to the Tara monuments, entitled *The Tara Walk*. This was just what I needed and clutching it in eager hands proceeded up the hill to the nearby church.

It was a brilliant example of site evolution, a process whereby churches were built on or next to ancient sites to Christianise them. My guidebook said that in the churchyard there were two megaliths, one bearing a carving that had been variously interpreted as either a Sheela-na-gig or Cernunnos. The former was a female exhibitionist representing the Goddess, whilst Cernunnos was the Celtic antlered Lord of the Forest. I found the stones in question and on the taller of the two the eroded figure stood out in relief. It was difficult to make out which character it was meant to be, but standing at the stone was in itself a powerful experience. I could feel strange swirlings in my stomach, which I may have taken as indigestion in the past, but now knew to be earth energies acting on my innards, pulling me round in a spiral motion. *This is SO funky!*

I left the churchyard and tramped across to the adjacent Mound of Hostages, a passage grave dating back to around 2,500 BC, which was aligned with the Samhain (pronounced *Sowan*) sunrise, at the end of October. To my disappointment I found it fenced off. I peered into the unfathomable darkness and wondered at what sights and sounds had been witnessed there in ages long gone. Close by were two large enclosures, bounded by ditches and mounds. In the centre of one was a megalith that can only be described as a 5ft tall penis! A more phallic shaped stone you would not come across. I felt an immediate urge to wrap my arms around it, and as I did so sensed the most powerful surge of love. I stood there, in a driving wind under darkening skies, for what must have been ten minutes or more. My arms were wrapped around this gigantic rock-hard member, wearing a huge smile that stretched across my face! I could not help it, for it felt so blissful. Some people walking their dogs passed by whilst I was in my megalithic embrace, but it mattered not to me. The Goddess said that everything was connected to everything else and that everything was energy, and at that moment in time I was a magnet for all the love and positivity that Tara had to offer. I absorbed and accepted it with humble gratitude.

My last stop at Tara was the Fairy Tree, a large Hawthorn that stood near the edge of the same field. It was a lone tree, standing some 20ft from a nearby hedge. Its gnarled branches were twisted, weather-beaten and betrayed the tree's age. The branches were adorned with offerings left by visitors, including ribbons, pieces of paper on which were written prayers, crystals, pendants, flowers, twigs forming geometric shapes, and much more. I wondered if the tree was permanently garlanded with offerings, or whether more people than usual had visited due to the impending Summer Solstice, just a few days away.

The tree was a living shrine to both the Earth Goddess and the souls had who honoured her. I sat beneath the branches of the sacred tree and leaned against the solid trunk. My spine tingled with the energy that was rising up through the roots, upwards to the highest branches. The tree was alive, but not just with the rising sap, but with life-force, with spirit, with consciousness. I knew it – I could feel it. Behind my closed eyes I stilled my mind and bathed in a sea of energy. After a while, I could faintly make out the image of a green man, with leaves exuding from his mouth, whose features I had seen in books, as well as in a few churches. He flickered in and out of my reality before fading. I didn't attempt to get him back, for I somehow knew that a time would come we would be formerly introduced.

With my heart filled with awe and appreciation, I left Tara and headed south for around an hour, passing around Dublin's busy ring road and out the other side, along the relatively quiet roads of County Wicklow. The weather was closing in and large raindrops periodically splashed on my windscreen. After continuing for a further half hour, I came to my last sacred Irish destination – Castleruddery. It was dry when I arrived at the Bronze Age stone circle, and I was thankful. It was large in diameter and dozens of stones had survived both Man and the elements. Two huge stones on the east side were composed almost entirely of quartz, which glistened in the intermittent shafts of sunlight. The Wicklow

Mountains formed a dramatic backdrop and several of the stones were aligned with some of the peaks, probably denoting ancient astronomical events. I stood at the circle's heart and could not help but smile. I gazed in awe at the stones, the mountains, the dramatic stormy sky, the glistening wet quartz, and felt both humble and grateful to be there. I called out to the mountains:

'I am truly blessed to be here, right now, at this moment in the long history of this circle. And I know I am exactly where I am meant to be. I honour the Land. I honour all creation. I honour you, my stone brothers.'

It was then that I felt a rain drop, which with expert aim had landed on the tip of my nose. Then another, and another, until within less than a minute the heavens had opened. And you know what, it did not matter. I stood there in the pouring rain, with arms extended skyward, bathed in the waters of the Mother. And it was so exhilarating, cleansing and purifying.

Then, as quickly as it had started, the shower stopped. I opened my eyes, and to my amazement found that the sun had come out, birthing two complete rainbows to the east, which arched right across the moody skies, touching the earth at each end. The colours were more vivid and brighter than I had ever seen before and that scene will live with me forever. The Goddess was an artist too. She had painted beautiful watercolours on a grand and magnificent scale, her canvas being the sky itself. I remembered the tales of pots of gold where rainbows meet the earth. But you cannot get close to the end of a rainbow, for as you approach it gets further away. I now knew that the treasure spoken of was really the Land. That was the real 'treasure' - the Land, and the knowledge and wisdom locked within it. I was standing on something more precious than any pot of gold.

'Nice one, my Mother ...', I shouted to the heavens, '... you've even painted the skies for me.'

A familiar voice echoed through my mind:

'Oh, it was nothing really, my son. Together we dreamed it.'

9. Fifth Moon – July: Wiltshire Crop Circle Lesson – Sacred Geometry

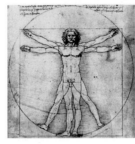

Da Vinci

The man who speaks with primordial images, speaks with a thousand tongues.
(Carl Jung)

The remainder of June and early July for me was a happy mixture of visiting sacred sites, sunbathing and trying to assimilate into my life what had happened in Ireland. All the words of the Goddess had of course gone down into my PC, word for word, and I did the best I could to recount the other events of my trip to the Emerald Isle. At times I had to stop still, catch my breath, even pinch myself to ensure it still wasn't some fantastic dream, some monumental hallucination, or mental debilitation on my part. I still hadn't told a word of my journey into the unknown to any of my close friends or relatives. There were so many times it was on the tip of my tongue, but on every occasion it just didn't seem important and, at the end of the day, I wasn't convinced that it wouldn't have been just my ego seeking glory or gratification. This really wasn't about impressing my friends, and even if I did tell someone close to me, it might just have *them* reaching for the phone to book me a therapist. No, the time for me to step out of the closet would come, and the time would be right, exactly right. The Goddess had already spoken of patience, and how Nature

93

was the supreme teacher of this virtue. She shows us plenty of tolerance and forbearance every day, year in year out, for She had taught me that everything happened at exactly the right time - and that was good enough for me.

It was a good summer, with long periods of hot sun and clear days of blue skies. I tanned well for I am an ardent sun-worshipper, and walked many miles over hill and vale, along beach and cliff top, and toured around the South in search of signs of her wisdom, and that of my ancestors. For the Mid-Summer Solstice, I decided to see the sunset at a Dorset sacred site, the Grey Mare and Her Colts Long Barrow. In the book *Ancient Stones of Dorset,* it is described and illustrated how the sun sets between two breast-shaped hills, but only at the mid-summer solstice. It was a fantastic evening and the sun duly obliged, setting between the breasts of the Earth Mother, and I alone witnessed the spectacle. With those breast-shaped hills on the skyline, to me it wasn't so much a place of ancestral memory, but rather ancestral *mammary.* I vowed from thereon forward to celebrate all the fire festivals.

For the New Moon I went to Avebury again, now one of my favourite places, and walked amongst the huge stones, sitting at the exact spot where, three months earlier, I had first felt and seen the energetic essence of the living Landscape. As before, I could feel the pulse of Mother Earth's heartbeat surge through my fingers as I tenderly caressed the earth, and within my closed eyes saw lines of luminescent energy race across the fields before me. *Can't anyone else see this?*

I stopped off at the Barge Inn at Alton Barnes, the local meeting place and watering hole for crop circle enthusiasts. In a back room there was a pool table and around the walls and on the ceiling were murals and friezes of Stonehenge, Silbury Hill, crop circles and other mystical scenes, all giving the impression that Scottie had transported me down to Planet Spliff. On one wall was a huge map of Wiltshire that was peppered with small round stickers of various colours, denoting where crop circles had manifested over several years. *Wow, lots of shit goes down around here!* I knew this area was annually rich in crop formations and that this pub was where the croppies hung out. I sipped my pint, letting my mind go walkabout. What do you call a gathering of crop circle enthusiasts anyway - a formation of croppies? Or a harvest of croppies? Or perhaps a circle of croppies? Or how about a trample of croppies, or even a trespass of croppies? And of course there was still the universal question; do croppies simply go round in circles? Who knows and who really gives a f-f-f-formation anyhow! At least I knew my bizarre sense of humour was still careering around my head. Yes, I was still the slightly weird guy I had always been, and not really insane, although I wondered if, after the publication of this book, certain members of organised religions would disagree with my diagnoses. 'Burn him at the stake!' they might cry. 'Sorry, guys...' I would reply, '... no steak for me, I'm a vegetarian!'

As I examined the beautiful photographs of formations on the walls before me, it dawned on me what the Goddess had said about July's subject matter – sacred geometry. Her clue had been, **'Next time we shall talk at a temporary holy place next to the red beast'.** A temporary holy place! That was it – it was to be at a crop circle! Before my very eyes were photos displaying an array of geometrically perfect art. Symmetry, triangles, perfect squares, octagons and more, all laid out on the sacred English landscape, designed and executed by forces unknown. Well, not unknown to me, not anymore. These were the Goddess's handiwork, I was sure of it.

But where and when was it to be? This particular Full Moon occurred just after midday on a July Friday, so the day was obvious. But where was it to be? **'... next to the red beast'**, She had said. The red what? Looking at the map it was clear that Wiltshire usually had a great concentration of formations every year. It was surely no coincidence, my croppie friends had told me, that there were massive numbers of ancient sacred sites in the same area. Stonehenge, Avebury, Woodhenge, Durrington Walls, Old Sarum and countless other monuments lay thick on the landscape, a landscape graced annually by many crop formations. July was more or less midway through the crop circle 'season', which was of course heavily dependent on the availability of fields of ripe crops in which to manifest. Yes, it all felt right. Only at this time of the year could the Goddess, if She so wished, use crop circles as a medium for a lesson, and sacred geometry, the subject this month, surely fitted the bill. I did remember, however, my experience of Ireland, where I got both the day and the locality wrong initially. But this time it felt right, with no ego, no smug feelings detectable. It just *felt* true.

I had never been able to make my mind up about crop formations. You know, are they genuine or not? Plenty had been hoaxes, and it was these that often made the headlines in the press, harming the public's perception of work being carried out by genuine researchers. But the more I surfed the Net, the more I was drawn to the conclusion that a sizeable percentage of formations could not possibly have been explained away by conventional means. Enormous creations would often manifest in a field within hours of said field being devoid of anything save for crops. People had also reported peculiar lights and heard humming and crackling sounds in the dead of night where formations were observed at daybreak. They had been put down to UFO's, little green men, tornados, whirlwinds (do me a favour!) and of course the nutty, anorakie, but cleverly artistic, hoaxers. But I had no doubt who was responsible for the genuine ones – it was the Goddess. But what was She trying to tell us? Hopefully, I was to find out. But if I were wrong about the time and place then I would be the one going round in circles, or not, as the case may be!

Mary, a friend and crop circle enthusiast, often spent summer nights outdoors in fields and on top of lonely hills looking for circles being formed or strange lights in the skies, and she had tipped me off about a website that was updated almost daily, giving news and photographs of the latest formations. I intended to peruse the site on the morning of the Full Moon. Yes, that felt right also. I hoped it would reveal the destination of the next tutorial from Her Ladyship.

By 7.30am on the morning of the Full Moon I had already logged on to the *'Temporary Temples'* website. I clicked on the 'LATEST FORMATIONS' icon. It took a few moments to download the full colour image, but then there it was. Wow! It was magnificent. And the place it was at? Avebury – well, that figured! The aerial view was incredible. In the background was the henge circle containing the mighty stones and the village of Avebury itself in the centre. In the foreground was a 150ft diameter formation that took my breath away. The inner part was a five-pointed star, the centre of which was divided into an octagon, which itself enclosed several triangles. Surrounding all this was a larger perimeter, comprising a large circle, which was punctuated by more octagons and triangles. It was truly stunning and I sat staring at it for several minutes. My heart opened and I knew I would be standing in the formation in less than two hours. But more than this, I realised that the formation was occupying the very spot where I had witnessed the dance of energy patterns whilst sitting on the bank of the henge back in May! Incredible. It was as if the physical formation had been created from an energy blueprint of some sort. Perhaps the energetic seed of this formation had been sown months before.

'You did well this time, M'Lady. You're an artist in every sense of the word, and a mathematician too.'

And some people still advocated that crop formations were all hoaxes. OK, guys, let's see you have a bash at replicating this one in the dead of night, and without anyone spotting you. It was perfect, completely symmetrical and incredibly complicated and I could sense the Goddess looking down with pride at her artistic prowess. This was no hoax. In any case, recent research had shown that even manmade formations could still affect the energies of their immediate landscape in the same way. This was just one example of how Man energetically interacts with the Land, even without intending to.

In just under two hours I was passing the Alton Barnes White Horse, which peered down at the broad expanse of open fields below. I knew that many circles had appeared in the Alton Barnes area over the years, including the famous pictograms and key formations. A little further on I turned left to go the back way into Avebury via East Kennet, thus missing out Marlborough. At the crest of the steep hill I parked up, pausing to observe the landscape, which had opened up before me. To the left was West Kennet long barrow on the skyline, but the scene was dominated by Silbury Hill in the middle distance. It rose magnificently out of the valley floor. As I turned to get back into the car, I noted a field on a hill to the east of where I had stopped. The slope was steep and it was framed by trees. I thought how wonderful it would have been if a crop circle had been there, for the steepness of that field would have enabled a superb view of it, with very little foreshortening. But it was not to be this time.

Ho hum. Perhaps another time.

I arrived at the car park of the pub at Avebury at 10.30am. As I got out of the car my eyes were transfixed by the pub sign – **The Red Lion.** So *that* was, *'... the red beast'. Nice one, M' Lady.* As I said, it was Friday, so I was hoping that I would be alone in the formation for at least a little while. By the weekend I knew that news of the circle would be widespread and hundreds of people might be scampering all over the Divine artwork. I walked east down the lane that divides the North and South inner circles of stones, past the last cottage and through a gate that bore a notice telling me the route continued up to the Ridgeway, an ancient track dating back to the Neolithic. After a further one hundred yards I came to a gate that gave access to a field on my left. I held in front of me the printout of the aerial photo and could clearly see the gate in the shot. This was the field.

I balanced precariously on the top bar of the gate and could just make out some areas where the crops were missing. Unfortunately, this formation was not on a hillside, so it was difficult to make out what was what, so I was grateful to have the aerial photo. I opened the gate, which was unlocked, and entered the field of ripe wheat, which stood about 3ft tall. It was a fine, warm July morning, the crops were ripening fast and only occasionally did I see any green stalks. As luck would have it, one of the tramlines, the spaces created by the harvester wheels, was close by and was heading directly for the undulations I had spotted. I set off across the sea of golden wheat, which gently rustled and danced for me in the summer breeze. I was full of anticipation and, as I got closer, could feel my stomach and heart fill with a tingling that I knew, from previous experience, to be earth energies. The cosmos seemed alive as I walked across the field, and I was I.

When I was halfway across the field, I became aware of two figures heading towards me. A man and a woman, both in khaki shorts and t-shirts were closing in on me. I flashed back to the aggressive man at Men-an-Tol, and the warning words of both Bel and Ken resounded in my ears. Sooner or later I felt that those with different agendas would confront me, and may even seek me out.

'Good morning', the man said. This was echoed by the woman following him. They were both middle-aged, and looked well-to-do in their polo shirts, designer shorts and good quality boots.

'Good morning.' I replied. 'Been in the circle?', which from the moment I said it, seemed to be a ridiculous enquiry. Where else would they have been!

'Yes, and it's a beauty. The energies are amazing. We've just spent an hour in there and feel full of it. It's a place of great power and spiritual potency. You won't be disappointed.'

Considering he did not know me from Adam, he seemed to know I would appreciate the rather alternative description of their time inside the formation. Perhaps I was giving off that aura now, for I was certainly uplifted by the prospect of entering the sacred creation.

'Have fun!' he added as he passed. The women bringing up the rear just smiled as she passed me.

'Thank you. I intend to.'

After a further dozen or so paces, the form of the structure could be made out ahead and the crops soon parted to reveal its full grandeur. I call it structure because, although the formation is formed by the flattening of the crop, it was structured, three-dimensional, and had geometrical form. I held the photo in my hand in the bright sunshine and tried to orientate myself. The flattened shafts of wheat were laid down in swathes of spiralling waves, and I saw that each stem was intact, not broken or split at all. I looked around and saw that I was alone in the field, but wondered how long this would remain so. I sat down in the centre of the 'temporary temple', as the crop formation web site called such phenomenon.

I closed my eyes. The heat of the day wafted around me and the earthy smells of the oceans of wheat surrounding me filled my being. My fingers scratched at the flattened wheat and down through it to the dry earth below. Instantly a rush of energy rose up through my arms and filled my heart until I felt it would burst. In my mind's eye I could see two thin, red-coloured energy lines crossing each other in the centre of the formation before me. They throbbed and pulsated, occasionally widening and moving up and down a foot or two. They seemed to have a mind of their own and were filled with life-force. I could sense that they were organic and had intelligence.

'Welcome. You have been decisive and have been in tune with Wyrd this time. You have done well.'

'Hello, my Mother.'

'Tell me, do you like my handiwork?'

'Of course I do, it's magnificent. Were you up all night making this one?'

'Hardly. I dreamed it and it instantly manifested. The principle of 'thought equals manifestation' applies to all, it's just that I have been doing the Cosmic Kitchen thing for a little longer than you, that's all.'

'You know that half the world seems to be arguing about what formations like this mean and who or what is making them.'

'Yes, I have observed the dialogue with some amusement. It is a wonderfully unique facet of Man's nature to complicate things that are really quite straightforward. But it is all part of the process of growth – for all of us.'

99

I took another look around – I was still, thankfully, alone.

'So, go on then. Lay it on me. What do crop circles mean? What's the bottom line?'

'Ah, the bottom line. Well for many there will be no bottom line, for these creations mean different things to different people, depending on their point of view.'

'That's not a cop-out is it, or should I say crop-out! Isn't there one Truth?'

'But we are all One. That is the one truth. All theories are correct, no matter what the suppositions and theories. You all create crop circles, and you perceive their meanings to be wide-ranging. But I can offer you an overview of why they are here.'

'Yes please!'

I settled down midst the beauty of the formation and looked about me at the complexity of the flattened, spiralling wheat, which was intricately interwoven, like Celtic knot work.

'For many eons of your time, Mankind has been reaching out to me in the form of prophets, holy books, organised religions, prayer, mantras, hymns, meditation and so forth. Thousands of different techniques of incredible complication have been devised in an effort to contact the Divine, even though I was here all the time in the natural world. But in the past when I sought to contact Mankind, it has always resulted in a corruption of the original messages brought to you by the wise men and women through whom I communicated. Buddha, Jesus, Mohammed, Babajee, Krishnamurti and many, many others have tried to bring messages of self-love to the public domain. But there has never been a religion that has not subsequently altered, and therefore diluted, the purity of the original message. You could liken it to Chinese whispers on a monumental scale. This was always inevitable, however, by the sheer nature of attempting to rationalise the dialogue of love.'

'We do seem to have a penchant for complicating things.'

'Yes, you do. I will continue. There have also been thousands of wise individuals who have, between them, written countless scriptures spreading the message of the eternal nature of the Soul and of Life. These have affected Mankind to a certain extent, but they have not had a major effect on the billions and billions of humans as a whole. There is still suffering, cruelty, ignorance, and denial of Man's

true nature. But the one thing that Man seems to act on and revere today is Science – the new religion that people respect and, indeed, worship.'

'I see what you mean. Because of science's complexities and specialist nature, people have to accept what scientists tell us at face value. I guess this is an updated version of how people have obediently followed religious dogma.'

'Exactly. And science has discovered that Nature is underpinned by geometry, from the beautiful geometrical patterns made by the dance of the planets to the growth of a leaf, from the spiral in a snail's shell to the beauty of a spider's web. It may well be that science's next progression is to discover me. Scientists are almost there. And when they find me, it will be through nature, through the Land. It cannot be through processes artificially created in a laboratory, but through something everyone can see all around them. So science and Nature will be seen as one, and therefore Man will value and respect the natural world. This is the only way ahead that will ensure the survival of Mankind. So to help make that leap to Natural Science, you need a new dialogue, a new language, proof that the geometry that holds together the natural world is imbued with consciousness. It has to be manifestation on the Land.'

'Hence the crop formations! It's the first day of school. You are teaching us a new language.'

'Precisely. All the principles of science, geometry and metaphysics are gradually being manifested on the Land in these formations. Visual images reach out into the common consciousness more than algebraic formulae. It is the age of the visual message, after all. The secrets of the processes of the whole Universe will eventually be encoded in my artwork, although it may yet be many decades before scientists realise this and learn to use them to discover entirely new branches of science. It was the alternative researchers who kick-started and are maintaining the study. But the day may yet dawn when my cosmic art may have a hand in solving some of the world's major problems, such as poverty, wars, alternative fuels, as well as a host of other revelations.'

'Why do we have to wait?'

'It is like teaching a child to walk or talk. It has to be gradual, ensuring the knowledge is fully assimilated into Man's consciousness. Putting a dictionary in front of a ten-

month-old child would only result in the book being destroyed, if out of innocent curiosity. The child can only take in so much at a time, for learning is a long and gradual process. So too with crop formations. You will not believe the formations that are yet to come, for I have already dreamed them, but you are not yet ready for me to etch them onto the Land.'

'I feel like we are little school children, learning our A, B, C's.'

'The analogy is a good one. But don't be downhearted, for Man has come a long way. As a species, you are almost out of kindergarten!'

'Kindergarten? Well, that figures when I see the ridiculously childish and stupid things we get up to. But will Man ever graduate, and leave school?'

'Only at the end of the physical Earth, which has been constructed of those energies which enable the full scope of freedom of choice to be actualised. The physical realm of the planet has to a large extent been left to its own devices, a grand experiment if you will, with the desire for you to ultimately develop beyond the constraints of a physical body into fully conscious beings. Most civilisations in the Universe are non-physical and have evolved within stricter guidelines and parameters. This planet has no such shackles. Earth is a school for sure, but do not think of me as a teacher so much as a fellow student, who has just been around in physicality a little longer than you.'

'A fellow student?'

'Yes, for I too am learning and will be as long as the physical Universe exists. But my wisdom is vaster than any human for I see the whole picture of all that has ever been, and from this vantage point can guide you through all the lower grades of your schooling. As part of my conscious growth, Earth may eventually recognise when She is no longer required to be in the physical and will return to pure light. In the meanwhile, appreciate if you can that being Human, and the freedom of choice that comes with it, cannot be experienced anywhere else in the Universe. Marvel and rejoice at that fact.'

'I am beginning to. So what *is* sacred geometry?'

'From the onset, recognise that all geometry is sacred, as are all the processes and manifestations in the Universe. Man has coined the term 'sacred geometry' to explain the

revelation that geometry is not just a concept of the human mind, but that it controls everything that exists on the physical planes. And this includes you.'

I did my best to concentrate, wiping my brow, for the sun was now hot on my head,

'Leonardo Da Vinci's famous image of 'Vitruvian Man' is one of his most celebrated and easily recognised works of art. With outstretched arms and legs the figure demonstrates how the body is built up of smaller parts that relate proportionately and mathematically to others. The proportions of the human body exhibit sacred geometry; thousands of years ago your ancestors observed the geometry and numbers present throughout nature and sought to imitate these processes in their sacred sites. Stone circles, temples and gothic cathedrals were all built to copy the geometry observed in the natural world. Their goal was to align participants with natural forces, with the ultimate object of contacting the Divine. In the Christian Bible, for instance, the Book of Revelations reads:

'And the angel that talked with me had a golden reed to measure the city thereof.'

and that...

'... the wall thereof, 140 cubits, according to the measure of a man, that is, of the angel.'

And it goes on to say that the New Jerusalem has,

'... twelve gates... twelve angels... the names of twelve tribes, that is three gates in each compass direction.'

When people build holy places to echo the principles of Nature, the very structures themselves resonate as a component of the Land, and not separate from it. This can be observed in ancient stone sites, for they are not detached from the landscape, but rather are part of it. A man-made stone circle and the Land join and fuse, and the earth energies pass freely between one and the other. Stonehenge and other circles contain the geometry of five, six, and eight pointed stars, as well as triangles and more. Avebury is in fact at one point of a huge six-pointed landscape star, connecting it to Stonehenge - The Wessex Astrum. For thousands of years sacred sites have been designed to reflect divine forces. The secret is to recognise that basic geometrical forms, such as triangles, octagons, circles, spirals, hexagonal forms and the like, are all sacred.

Geometrical shapes are all sacred manifestations, and geometrical forms are the building blocks of the Universe. They are also expressed in all life forms and, ultimately, are expressions of pure consciousness. They articulate my thoughts and dreams. You ask what is sacred geometry – well, it is I – it is everything!'

'Wow! So the next time someone calls me a square I can take it as a compliment!'

'Well, you could. I wish everyone had your sense of hilarity. Humour is healing, as long as it does not causer humiliation. Then it is born out of fear, not love.'

'Some people are going to ask if God is a mathematician, what with all this geometry, the Fibonacci sequence and the rest.'

'This is true. Take a sunflower, for instance, which has on its head twenty-one spirals in one direction and thirty-four going the other way – consecutive Fibonacci numbers. And the nautilus shell, whose revolutions also follow the Fibonacci sequence. All of Nature works on mathematical principles, and this is clearly demonstrable. But you could equally say that all mathematics is based on natural principles. The physical Universe is based on mathematics, but it is my thoughts and dreams that initiate physicality. I am a mathematician, true enough, but I am equally a dreamer, creator and, above all, I am Life itself.'

'Cool. Tell me, my Mother, what does the formation I am sitting in have to teach me?'

'Ah. Now that's for me to know and you to learn! But the answer is here, all around you as you sit. Someone will crack the codes one day, and decipher their meanings. That time is not too far away, for some of your researchers are very close. But the key to real progress is for scientists to embrace the study of my landscape handiwork. Only then will my messages be open to all and, more importantly, be accepted by all.'

'It may seem to some that you could give us the answers right now. Instead of all these enigmatic shapes in our fields, you could just give us the secrets of the Universe straight out.'

'Hmm. As you may remember, I once made a gift of certain principles to the shaman you call Moses. Unfortunately, although he was a wise and humble man, those around him sought to interpret the wisdom I gave in the light (or should I say darkness) of a patriarchal society. Moses himself was an

unwitting accomplice in the misinterpretation of my words. Similar things have happened since. Take the wisdom of Solomon, Buddha, Merlin, John Dee and Gandhi. Enough is enough!'

'Hang on. So are you telling me you made a mistake?'

'Me, make a mistake? There can be no mistakes in the Universe. All happens as it is meant to. Remember that I too am on a learning curve, although the difference between you and I is that my curves of learning are quite literally the spiralling arms of galaxies.'

'OK. I'll let you off. But why can't you give us the codes, the meanings of these symbols in the fields?'

'So you think it a good idea, a loving act, to thrust a book of applied mathematics in front of a young child and expect him to understand it? I am afraid to say that there are some Universal truths that Man will not be ready to receive for a long while yet. Anyway, most of the answers would go right over your heads! And it has to be said that another reason is because although you may understand some of the information, you may abuse it. Would you call giving a small child a loaded gun to play with an act of love? And don't forget that guns have never killed anyone; it is always through human intervention. Besides, the processes you go through to learn the Universal secrets are all part of your journey, and mine. I am enjoying it.'

'So mysteries and questions lead us on to greater things.'

'But of course. One of the reasons antiquarians and ordinary folk became obsessed with ancient Egypt was because it offered mysteries on a grand scale. And the chief mystery was the enigma of the hieroglyphs, which Jean François Champollion solved in 1822. But what preceded this was around hundred years of fanatical activity as explorers rushed around Egypt in search of some artefact that held the key, which ultimately turned out to be the Rosetta Stone. If a papyrus entitled 'The A-Z of the Egyptian Alphabet' had been found in the very first excavated tomb then the depth of mystery and awe for ancient Egypt would not have developed to anything like the same proportions. Knowledge gained through experience is vital, for although I cannot directly help you as a species to survive, by seeking me out in the Land, throughout the Cosmos, and in the face of every person you meet, you may save yourselves. The nearer you get to

105

perceiving Divinity in nature, the more you will realise that you too are Divine, and Gods and Goddesses do not destroy themselves, indeed cannot.'

'I find the concept of me being Divine really funky. But I won't try walking across the local pond just yet. But I have found that the more I realise my innate holiness, the more humble I feel.'

'This is good, this is how it ought to be. Although I am so proud of the Universe I have created, I have no ego, and therefore no sense of superiority over anything or anyone. To be Divine is to be humble. That is not to say that you should be weak or submissive. To be knowledgeable and humble is a sign of great wisdom and strength.'

'The meek shall truly inherit the earth, as the cool dude said.'

'Truly. Jesus knew that humility is power and that love strengthens, and that selflessness brings you more riches than a lottery jackpot. Look at the Land. Awesomely powerful, as recent natural disasters like tsunamis and hurricanes have shown, yet incredibly giving. It does only what is necessary, yet all of life benefits – it is not greedy so every creature is fed. Nature is humble, yet is more powerful than all the atom bombs Man has created. When I flex my muscles, or turn slightly to change my position, then the world listens and takes notice. A poet once said that a volcano is beauty and the wrath of God combined.'

'So you create natural disasters.'

'I just am. I only ever act out of the love of creating. Negativity, retribution, punishment and apparent death are human concepts. I do not set out to destroy life, for I would be destroying myself. Physical death, however, is a part of the natural cycle of things. Every time you walk down the sidewalk, you murder hundreds of tiny creatures unwittingly, and alter the destiny of billions of microscopic organisms. You cannot help it. I did not order millions of people to live in areas below sea level, or on major fault lines, or on the slopes of volcanoes. But they do. I cannot interfere with your free will, so every now and again when I do what needs to be done, humanity suffers. But I only do what is 100% necessary, for if I did not, all life on Earth would perish. I can make no apologies for earthquakes, volcanoes and such, for they are expressions of my growing pains. And do not forget that you yourselves are as much a part of the natural system

106

as I am, for you and I are one. I will do whatever it takes to re-establish balance on Earth – I can do nought else.'

'I get that, for sure. So can living in harmony with sacred geometrical principles help us?'

'You cannot help but live with sacred geometry, but you can certainly enhance your lives by recognising and respecting the sacred essence that underpins the Universe. But I will speak more on possible futures for Mankind another time. For now, it is enough to appreciate that mathematics, physics, biology, geography and all the other disciplines that science has formulated to explain the Cosmos, are expressions of Divinity. How can they be anything else? In Christian myth, did not God create the Earth and the heavens? Did I create all this from nothing? The Universe was created because I had a dream, and I am still dreaming, as of course are you. All physical matter has been created from my curiosity. Who am I? I am still searching for an answer to that one. When you ask the question, 'Who am I?' know that I too seek the answer, through you.'

'Amazing. But hasn't the problem in the past been that science has tried to disprove the existence of God by showing that the Universe is some giant clockwork machine?'

'And like clockwork it does indeed run, although the clock is very slowly running down. But the regularity and apparent mechanistic appearance of the Cosmos is but an illusion, spun by Man as he sees through scientific, spiritless eyes. I would like you personally to try and be more aware of the movements of the sun, moon and the stars to get a feel for sacred geometry, for there is much to learn by observing the cosmos as your distant ancestors did. There is balance and sacred order in all things. Take for instance the changes in the moon throughout the year. Around midwinter the Full Moon is highest in the sky (in Gemini and Cancer) because the sun is passing through its lowest points in the sky (Capricorn and Sagittarius), which are diametrically and geometrically opposite. Around midsummer the Full Moon is always low in the sky, because the sun is in its highest declination. At the Equinoxes, the sun rises due east and sets due west. Balance. Perfect geometrical harmony.'

'I had never noticed all that, but I bet the builders of the stones circles did.'

'Indeed. And so they aligned stones where the sun rose and set at the solstices. They observed that the sun rises more or less in the southeast at winter solstice, and that it sets into the horizon in the opposite direction at summer solstice. Likewise, from these latitudes, at midsummer the sun will rise approximately northeast, exactly in the opposite direction to where the winter solstice sun sets. Again, Divine harmony, Divine geometry. Much of course depends on the height of surrounding hills on the exact point at which a celestial body will rise or set, as well as latitude, but the principles hold true for sites with clear skylines. Take also the phases of the moon. Although there are variations of up to one hour due to the exact time of the phase and latitude, the first quarter moon will be south around 6.00pm, whilst the Full Moon will be south around midnight. Then the last quarter moon will be south around 6.00am, with the new moon approaching south at about midday. Again, you only have to learn a few basic principles of the motions of the sun and moon to know what time of day it is, what month it is and so on. Of this your ancestors were acutely aware.'

'That really is cool. The skies really are a giant clock and calendar. But what about all these Golden Sections, and pentagrams that researchers have projected onto the landscape? For instance, around Rennes le Château in France, wow, that seems to me like some draughtsman has gone berserk with a compass and setsquare. All those five and six-pointed stars. Is that stuff for real, or are people projecting their beliefs onto the landscape, seeing what they want to see?'

'A good question. There is sacred geometry in the Land and in all of nature. Your distant ancestors were aware of this and sought to build their stone circles and temples in harmony with these. The Templars, Cathars, Chinese Feng Shui practitioners, geomancers, and later the Christian freemasons, all positioned their sacred places to replicate these sacred shapes. Imitation really is the sincerest form of flattery and is also, in the case of Man tuning into natural principles, an effective one. But do not believe everything you read or hear. For every germ of Truth, there are many, many false assumptions. This is particularly true of crop circles, and of ley lines, which I will speak of at a later date. It is for you each to decide which is which – are you dealing with a legacy of ancient wisdom or imaginative fiction?'

'Which, indeed.'

'It is perhaps inevitable that once a theory appears sound and has apparently been demonstrated as plausible, like the sacred geometry around Rennes le Château or the St Michael Line, it is only too easy to see pentagrams, five-pointed stars and ley lines everywhere. This is not to say that sacred geometry is not present in all of nature, but most of the proposed geometrical shapes on the Land involve Manmade structures and, at times, are a by-product of the mind and the ego. You see a bird flying South. That doesn't mean every bird is flying South. Because someone claims responsibility for making a crop circle or two, should you assume every circle is a hoax? Do you believe every word that is written in a holy book? The answer, of course, is 'no' to all these. Make your own mind up about everything.'

'Everything?'

'Yes, that is what I need from you and all of Mankind. Be individual. Be unique. You all need to be different to what has gone before. In fact, you all are, but do not realise it. To comprehend your uniqueness is growth. You are all explorers of your world. Find your own ley lines, check out all sacred geometry alignments yourself, learn to know the Land and its ways and formulate your own theories. But let these be based not so much on pure knowledge, as on pure love and feelings. Feelings never lie. Theories come and go, and thoughts and proposed 'facts' come in and out of fashion. What do you feel? What does your inner voice tell you? What you find out yourself, using your own experiences, no one can argue with. You cannot doubt what you experience. Mind you, having said this, the physical Universe is all illusion! Have you seen the movie, 'The Matrix?'

'Say what?'

'Sorry. I could not resist it, even though what I imply is true. The theme of that movie is that the world you know is an illusion. This is true, of course. But the reality is very different from the fiction, in as much as you have total free will. Your thoughts are your own, and not being controlled by a machine. The trouble is, most people are content to be controlled to a certain extent, by governments and organised religions. But do not despise the controllers or the led, for then you despise part of me. Simply make up your own mind about the things you attract along the strands of Wyrd.'

'So what is real and what is not?'

'I guess that depends on what you define as real. You are real. Your soul is real. Your dreams are real. Your fears are real. Love is real. Your whole life and all its experiences will be real to you, and your actions and reactions to them. Just do not lose sight of the fact that you are part of the dream that we all share. The dreaming is real, make no mistake. I dream the Universe. But the physical Universe is but one expression of who I am. And, despite its apparent vastness, physicality is only a relatively small part of what I am. I am discovering this all the time. I am very excited. And you could be too, as part of this unfolding of consciousness, this potent, vibrant, living Spirit that is Divinity.'

'But sometimes I feel so small and utterly consumed by the scale of the Cosmos, as if I am spiralling out of control.'

'Actually you are spiralling into love.'

'Oh I'm sorry, ignore me. I'm going round in circles.'

'How true, and how very geometrical!'

Just then I heard people approaching through the field, chatting and laughing as they negotiated the tall, ripened wheat. Damn, and it was just getting interesting.

'Remember what we spoke of before. Perfect timing.'

'OK. OK. I'm not perfect, you know.'

'Well, that all depends on one's definition of perfection. One last thing: On your way home tomorrow morning look at the field that caught your attention earlier. You may realise that you are more creative than you believe. Thoughts create matter. Ideas are manifest in the physical world. We will speak next Full Moon, when we are going for a little walk across the Land.'

'At last! Trekking up the Himalayas or across the Sahara? Or how about up the slopes of Mount Fuji?'

'Well, let's see. It is somewhere just as sacred, just a little closer. You know Dartmoor, don't you?'

'Ho hum. Dartmoor, eh? Oh, well. At least it's summer. No storms or dank mists or getting lost on the moors. No *Hound of the Baskervilles* or other demons lurking on the moor.'

'You think not?

110

10. Dreaming a Crop Circle

© P Knight

Behind nature, throughout nature,
Spirit is present.
(Ralph W Emerson)

I spent the night at a fine B&B on the outskirts of Avebury, but before retiring I did the obligatory pilgrimage to one of Avebury's most treasured sacred places – the Red Lion! The pub was busy and people had spilled outside to enjoy a balmy July evening. Avebury always reminded me of Glastonbury, with its eclectic cross-section of visitors, pilgrims and locals.

I sat outside in the sunshine and gazed at the souls whom Avebury had attracted. There were a couple of families, each with two young children, but that's where the similarity ended. The first family were seated at a table and looked very well off, with designer tops and trousers, and smartly turned-out children wearing their designer clothes. The other family could not have been more different. The parents were perched on the car park wall, whilst the children were having great fun repeatedly jumping off a giant millstone. All four were wearing tie-dye, and the mother was bedecked in dungarees, red dreadlocks and funky multi-coloured hair-wraps. It was funny, because although the former family would have been the more socially acceptable of the two, the latter were far more interesting, and I would certainly have felt more at ease in their company. The rest of the car park was filled with an assemblage of more travellers, a small group of leather-clad bikers, an entourage of around half a dozen ramblers, and a couple who gazed longingly into each other's eyes.

I sat down to take in both the late sun and the atmosphere. I felt inclined to get out the small notebook that I usually carried along to jot down notes, things that I might commit to memory. (Remember, only the Goddess's narrative had guaranteed recall,

111

and not necessarily other events or my thoughts.) I started wondering about the day's events and about crop circles. I found myself drawing, almost automatically, circles, lines, and other geometrical shapes. I had no idea where these came from. I wasn't sure why, but I also drew what looked like my attempt at designing a crop formation, with various circles and a star in the centre. Perhaps I had seen it on the Net previously and it had left an impression on my memory. Or perhaps the visit to the circle had triggered something within. Did the Goddess doodle *her* circles prior to committing them to the landscape?

That night I had the weirdest dream: I dreamt I was walking across the hills above Avebury in the dark. Suddenly, I saw flashes of light just above some fields in the distance. I got excited and took them for UFOs and watched them for some time, weaving and dipping across the landscape. When I awoke in the morning I remembered the dream perfectly, which was unusual for me, and wondered how cool it would be if UFOs had been reported in the area that night.

After breakfast I retraced my route out of Avebury, via the Avenue and the village of East Kennet. The road then ascended the steep slopes of the northern end of Lurkeley Hill, at the top of which I had paused the previous day to admire Silbury Hill in the valley below. I arrived at the summit and the road levelled out, but I immediately had to pull over and stop the car, as something in the distance had caught my attention. It was a crop formation. I got out and just stared in amazement. The circle was magnificent and large, a classic key shape, with a circle at either end. The larger circle had what appeared to be a six-pointed star in it, and at the opposite end emanated a snake-like wavy line. *But hang on a minute. Yes, yes it is!* The field was the very same one that had been empty when I had stopped the day before. I had thought then how cool it would be should a crop circle appear there! *This is crazy!* But there was something else. The formation looked familiar. I had seen it somewhere before, definitely, but where? Then the truth struck me like a bolt from the blue. I reached into my coat pocket and pulled out the notebook I had doodled in the night before at the pub. My fingers thumbed furiously through the pages until I found the relevant doodle. There it was – the crop formation I had drawn. My drawing was identical, and I mean exactly identical, with the one spread out before me in the field below!

'Holy Moses!' I shouted out across the Wiltshire hills.

A huge grin spread across my face. I had imagined a crop circle and dreamt of its formation. The Goddess had been busy whilst I slept, acting on my visions. As it sunk in, I stood there surmising which had really come first. Had I picked up in some way what was to happen, sensing some sort of Dreamtime ripple along the fibres of Wyrd, or had the circle been plucked purely from my imagination? Whichever it might be, it was staggering. I looked down again at my sketch and then back at the formation – they were the same, no question of it. *Wow!*

'You've been busy again, M' Lady, you certainly have.'

I could feel her smiling at me, enjoying my realisation. I nodded my head and surveyed the landscape around me.

'You're a bloody great artist, you know, the best there is. I guess I had better thank you for making my dream come into reality. But I can already hear you say that I created it as much as you did. I guess I did. OK then, we *both* did a fine job!'

The funkiest thing about it was that two days later, aerial photos of the formation, my formation, were all over the Net at various web sites, all saying what an interesting formation it was, apparently combining earlier 'pictogram' designs with later more complex formations. Well, I might have known that a formation I had helped design would have a touch of nostalgia about it. I printed off the aerial photo and hung it on the wall next to my PC station. Every time I look at it I am reminded that we are all co-creators of the landscape and the wondrous things that manifest. As the Goddess had said,

'We all create it every second of every day... what you send out comes back.'

And concerning the crop circle at Avebury She had told me,

'I dreamed it and it manifested instantaneously. The principle that thought equals manifestation applies to you too, it's just that I have been doing the Cosmic Kitchen thing for a little longer, that's all.'

I later told my croppie friend, Mary, about the experience with the Avebury circle and she was very excited and told me of others who had either dreamed of circles which had subsequently appeared, or else had seen empty fields which had subsequently revealed a formation. But she said it was not common, considering the number of formations that appear annually, and she was very pleased that it had happened to me. She asked if she could pass the story on to crop circle researchers, and I suddenly felt like some sort of minor celebrity in the weird and wonderful world of croppies. I had mixed emotions there, I can tell you!

The intervening weeks between the July and August Full Moons were for me a mixture of assimilating what the Goddess had spoken about in the crop formation, and integrating myself further into the Land and sacred sites. At Lughnasad/Lammas, in early August, I went to the Nine Stones, a local stone circle at Winterbourne Abbas in Dorset, where the Lammas sun apparently rose between two round barrows on a nearby skyline when viewed from the circle. I showed up - but unfortunately the sun didn't! Cloud intervened and the close proximity of the busy A35, which growled and rumbled by just yards away, made the whole experience rather unpleasant. I did, however, get the distinct feeling that the spirit of the place, indeed the stones themselves, appreciated my efforts to honour the festival.

I visited other Dorset and Wiltshire sites, including Old Sarum, Clearbury Rings and lesser-known places, looking along leys and feeling the gnarled, ancient stones for tinglings of the Mother's pulse. But a change was going on within me. The landscape was turning into a geometrical paradise, with spirals, pentagrams and all manner of sacred shapes that I now knew to be expressions of both Divine will and Divine love: the spiralling nature of unfurling ferns; spider's webs; broken shells on beaches, revealing the spiralling nature of their interior. I once sat for hours in a pine wood, studying countless cones, large and small, long and short, all of which displayed intricate and mesmerising growth patterns. In parks and gardens, I stood enthralled at the spiralling nature of sunflowers, as they danced for me in the summer breezes, always keeping their watchful eyes on the sun.

Even a visit to the County Museum in Dorchester revealed that the Goddess had been doing sacred geometry for a long time. On display were the spiral growths of ammonites and, older still, the goniatites. Sacred geometry had always been around it would seem, and was very successful in modelling the physical Universe. As they say, if it's not broken, don't fix it. Some things cannot be bettered or improved upon, despite evolution. Even, the word 'evolution' now had a whole new meaning for me. In perusing the exhibits I was looking back through eons of time, back to the dinosaurs, and before that the giant insects of the Carboniferous coal forests, and before that the giant fishes of the Devonian, right back to the first life on the planet. But to me it now looked like someone's photo album, her photo album, portraying

114

her growth from infancy, through adolescence and onto old age. Trouble was, although we are told the Earth is four and a half billion years old, I wondered if the Goddess was elderly or still in her infancy! Or, relatively speaking, was She still in the womb? *Freaky thought for the day that one.*

What really blew my mind was a clock on the museum wall. On its face showed twenty four hours as representing the whole of Earth's history, with the fishes, amphibians and dinosaurs, etc all variously appearing at six o'clock and seven-thirty, and so on. But when I looked for where Man was, I found that we had appeared just five seconds before midnight! And we think the Universe revolves around us and we are all-powerful and all conquering. I looked at the reign of the dinosaurs, which was impressive both in terms of millions of years and the fact that they occupied over two whole hours. And we have only been around for five seconds! Well, you can't say the Goddess lacks patience. The words 'long haul' and 'commitment' came to mind. It made me feel even more determined to act in a responsible and conscious manner, for I was the end product of four and a half billion years of growth, death, decay, new growth and so on, all of which seemed to culminate with me looking at the clock on a museum wall. Continuing the clock analogy, at various times in my life it had seemed as if some Divine power had been winding me up! Sorry, Mother. And for some weird reason I became preoccupied with the issue as to whether the Goddess created Man during the tick or the tock!

Get a grip man!

11. Dartmoor, Deer and Dowsing

© P Knight

Oh Druid stones, upon forlorn moor,
When the chill rain begins at shut of eve ...
... The Heaven itself is blinded throughout night.
(John Keats, *Hyperion II*)

So August came, the schools were out, and beaches and cars were filled with countless noisy and demanding little gods and goddesses. Don't get me wrong, I love children, in fact I went to school with them. It had been said that God must be a teacher. Who else would invent summer holidays of such a long duration? It was only now that I was truly appreciating how true this statement was. In fact the whole Earth is the teacher, with us as her pupils. Trouble was, our lives last considerably longer than the summer vacation, and at times our beach could be an empty and very lonely place. But not for me - not any more.

It was with some relief when I was at last heading west through rural Devon, having spent the preceding two hours crawling out of Dorset along congested A-roads. Swarms of cars towing caravans seemed to hunt in packs (one of the Goddess's mistakes if you ask me, the caravan that is). It has been said that one of the draws of caravanning is the joy of the open road. Fair enough, but do their owners ever consider why the road is always empty in front of them? As if that were not enough, there were the traffic cones, which stretched for mile after mile like serrated dragon teeth (have not seen the funny side of those either, Oh Mother). Sometimes the caravans and cones coexisted together, like some

116

pact made in hell. The Goddess said there was no hell, but I was having doubts on that hot August Friday morning. Everyone travels on Friday to miss the traffic. Right, nice one, good plan everyone. I was already ruing the fact that the Full Moon was on Saturday, and in August, too. I was having visions of ramblers covering Dartmoor like an infestation of ants. Where was I to find the solitude to connect with the Land? As if to rub salt into the wound, I knew that many of these walkers would be the very ones that I had been stuck behind on the way. By the time I was approaching Dartmoor, I could have drawn you the logo of the Caravanning Club in my sleep.

The one saving grace in all the chaos of summer traffic was that I now believed that everything happens when it is meant to, and if I arrived somewhere later than expected then it was all still as it should be. This was reinforced in a dramatic way as I approached the perimeter of the wilds of Dartmoor. I passed through a heavy shower, and the windscreen wipers were working overtime, when I spied a lay-by coming up on my left. I decided to pull over, take a breather and sit out the downpour. The view from the stopping place offered distant views with the heights of Dartmoor rising enticingly on the skyline just a few miles ahead. Without warning the sun appeared from beneath a jet-black cloud and illuminated the Land and raindrops alike. *Rainbow.* I turned around to look out of my side window and there it was. It was so bright and vivid, as it arched across the menacing skies, as if to console the weary traveller. My eyes were transfixed on the artistic genius of the Goddess. It dawned on me that if I had been 'on time', I would have been twenty miles further down the road and would have missed the beautiful play of light and water that danced before my eyes. *Thanks, My Lady.* More to the point, I now knew that the more I spotted and appreciated these gems of synchronicity, the more frequently they seemed to manifest. It was as if I myself was creating more of the same, which of course I was.

My lodgings for the night were at Princetown, in a pub I had frequented previously. But on the way I wanted to stop off at a couple of places en route. One was Corringdon Ball, the only Neolithic long barrow on Dartmoor. It lay near the southern extremity of the Moors and close to the A38, so it seemed just right to be my first port of call. I passed through the sleepy town of South Brent, before following winding lanes connecting several small hamlets. I parked up in an isolated spot, just south of Zeal, next to where my map showed a bridle path headed southwest to

117

the long barrow. The walk was about a mile each way and would be a good loosener for the days ahead. I located the path, a route that soon unleashed hidden blessings.

The track soon ascended through wooded slopes, and it was like stepping into a scene from *Tales of Narnia*. Huge boulders covered the way ahead, most covered by soft blankets of mosses of every hue. A small stream trickled down the centre of the sunken track, proof of the heavy rains the moor had recently witnessed. Both living and dead branches blocked my way at times, and many of these were likewise covered in a green carpet of moss. The wood closed in on me from all sides as an eerie darkness descended. It would not have surprised me if I had come across a fairy or a goblin sitting on a rock, such was the otherworldly scene I was walking through. Several times I had the feeling I was being watched, but I never felt threatened in any way. In fact, I wondered if I should return after fall of darkness to see if my hunch about the fairies was true.

After a fifteen-minute ascent, the woods ended abruptly and the open expanses of the moor stretched out before me; mile after mile of gently rolling terrain covered by heather, gorse and dotted with small herds of cattle and sheep. I could see why my distant ancestors found the moors so appealing and built hundreds of sacred sites there. A further few minutes walking, often through sodden heathland, revealed the mound and stones of the Corringdon Ball long barrow, gracing the skyline in the distance. At the east end I could see a large stone rearing out of the ground at an acute angle, like the death throes of a stricken ship destined for the bottom of the ocean. As I approached the gnarled, weather-beaten stones, I felt truly blessed to be there at that moment, and really appreciated the sanctity and solitude. I sat on the fallen capstone, surveying the Land in all directions, knowing that thousands of years ago, others had sat here, looking at an almost identical vista. I wondered what they had thought as they sat there and for what purpose had they built this epitaph to their faith. 5,000 years separated them from me, yet at that moment we were linked through time and space, as if they had been sitting there just yesterday.

'Well, My Lady, I know you are here. You always are. Now I wonder where you will reveal yourself to me this time.'

I'd had a sort of loose plan, a few funky looking places that I wished to see. I figured that I'd just go my merry way and look for the signs, and listen for her voice. I wasn't panicky about that any more. Ireland had taught me a lot. We would meet up at exactly the right time, at precisely the right place, I was sure of that.

Just then something moved in the corner of my eye. I turned to see animals moving swiftly across the open moor about half a mile distant. They were deer, yes, a herd of around ten, bolting as one directly away from me towards the summit of an adjacent hill. I may have been the cause of their flight, and I watched them intently until the last disappeared from view over the crest. *Hmm, deer.* I somehow felt that I would be seeing more in the next few days, and not just on a mundane level. The deer I had seen seemed to be inviting me to follow them, and I knew I would surely follow. I could make out some antlers on the two largest deer and I recalled how the Celtic god, Cernunnos, Lord of the Animals and Forests, had antlers.

'Are you calling me, My Lord?'

I closed my eyes for a short meditation, and as I did so my inner vision could see colours, as if painted on the inside of my closed eyelids. I was still looking in the direction of where the deer had run, and I could just make out faint lines of colour, shades of white, yellow and orange, that appeared to mark out the course of their flight. They were not as lucid as at Avebury, but were there all the same. Were the tracks some sort of energy residue from the deer, a memory of the event etched on the landscape? There was another possibility also, which I remembered from the experience on Avebury. Did their path mark out an energy flow across the moor? Had the deer fled along the path of an invisible yet tangible flow of energy? Perhaps they knew it would lead them to safety, or perhaps it just felt right to follow the course of comforting, powerful energy when danger threatened.

I opened my eyes and could see nothing but open moor where the lines of energy had been. My human senses were clearly not as sensitive as those of animals, but I felt that with time and effort, I could potentially learn to see, feel and be almost as perceptive as any four-legged beast. The Goddess had said that we are all part of the Land, and that we humans had merely created the illusion of separateness and with this in mind, we can all learn a closer connectedness with the Land.

With some reluctance, I said my goodbyes to the old stones and retraced my steps back down the hill, through the enchanted woods and back to the car. My next stop on that sunny August afternoon were the famous stone rows at Merrivale, not far west of my B&B. I parked up at the car park to find hoards of people

119

tramping the moors to and from the megaliths. Despite people milling around, the locality is still very special, with its lines of small stones trooping across the open moor, occasionally accompanied by kist tombs and the odd stone circle or two. I saw someone dowsing with rods and knew that I really must get into that. His rods twitched and turned as the guy walked in and out of the rows of ancient stone. He passed me by but did not register my presence, such was his concentration, and so I did nothing to disturb his focus. At the end of one of the rows was a larger stone, which stood basking in the warm afternoon sun.

'May I please join you, my stone brother?'

I sat down on the sunny side and leaned against its solid, ancient rock. The stone was warm to the touch from the sun and I relaxed midst a tranquil scene of moor, blue skies and nearby grazing Dartmoor ponies. They treated the stones with total indifference as they munched away at the grass, yet it did cross my mind as to why there were so many of them close to the stone rows. Was it the chance of rich pickings from the tourists or was there another reason? I thought about the energies I had seen earlier and the whole concept of the sacredness of particular places. I concluded that perhaps the ponies knew more about why they hung out here than they were letting on. I was certainly soon aware of a tingling in my back where it made contact with the stone and felt sure it was to do with the energies the dowser had been pursuing. There seemed to be a flow to it, as if it were passing through both stone and my chest. It brought with it a feeling of peace, and the noise of the nearby road, playing children and neighing horses faded from my consciousness. A huge, involuntary smile grew across my face and I felt high with this newfound connection with the Land and my ancestors.

Full Moon was at 7.45pm. Back at my room in the inn at Princetown, I wondered what the night would bring and where I would go and whom or what I would meet. I unpacked what little I had brought with me and studied my guidebooks and maps once again, to accustom myself with the area. I had no idea where I was off to for my audience with the Goddess but felt inclined to try something new to find out. Some weeks earlier I had been to an alternative group meeting in Bournemouth, where the speaker's presentation had been about map dowsing. In a nutshell, this comprised of having a map in front of you and focusing on something you are trying to locate. You can either use your intuition to choose a point on the map, or use a pendulum. As I did not have the latter on me I thought I'd have a go at the intuitive stuff. I spread out the OS map of Dartmoor on my bed and pored over it. And I looked at it some more. About ten minutes lapsed and I had still received no indications of where I should go.

Ah-ha! Then I thought of something else he had suggested trying. It would involve closing my eyes, concentrating on my objective, and raising my hands over the map, putting my index finger down on the map when I sensed a pull. *OK, here goes!* My right hand circled just above the moors, forests and towns, like some bird of prey riding the thermals in order to spy its next victim.

'Where am I to be contacted by the Goddess?'

I kept repeating this mantra until, without warning, there it was - it felt good - it felt right. With a rush of blood and a pounding heart my index finger descended onto the map like an eagle homing in on its kill. Contact! The Eagle had landed, so to speak! But where? My eyes followed the path of my finger, which I kept firmly on the paper. And there, in small Old English text, were the words *Scorhill Circle. Hmm.* Looking outward from the location of the circle I saw that it was some miles north of my pub, near the village of Gidleigh. Sunset was around 8.30pm so I needed to get a move on.

About half an hour later, after some wrong turns and an enquiry to a rather bemused local, I arrived at Scorhill Farm, the closest point I could get the car to the stone circle. I donned my weatherproofs, hat and gloves and also packed my rucksack with some snacks, water, a whistle, torch, and an orange emergency plastic bag large enough to take me. I had the feeling it might well be a long night!

12. Sixth Moon – August: Dartmoor Lesson – Walking the Land

© P Knight

The simplest way to explore Gaia is on foot.
How else can you be part of her ambience?
(From *Gaia*, James Lovelock)

The trek to the circle was an undemanding one, and the sight of the moorland bathed in the low, late evening sun elevated my spirits. On the way I heard a cry from overhead and sure enough there was a large hawk of some sort, just as it had been on previous occasions. Surely it could not be the same bird, could it? My way was being shown for me again. The bird's call had announced my arrival to the whole moor, including, perhaps, beings unseen.

Scorhill Circle was beautiful, comprising about twenty largish stones, most of which were still standing. The setting was magnificent, the Bronze Age megaliths standing in a shallow valley, set against a backdrop of hills and open moor. Just to the west a stream trickled by, and its waters were reflecting a low sun, which would soon be relinquishing the sky to the Full Moon. The air suddenly felt alive with magic and the Land too seemed to be bracing itself for the night ahead. I entered the circle and sensed her presence immediately.

'Good evening, my Mother', I shouted at the top of my voice.

'Good evening, my son. This is the first time you have addressed me with confidence before I had made my presence known to you. You are indeed opening up.'

'Yes. Things are changing all the time. My sensitivity, my awareness and my senses all seem more alive than they have ever been.'

'That is no mystery. You ARE more alive than at any other time in your life. It is good that you are so. You have done well. But tell me, for what purpose do you think you are here on this night of the Bright Lady?'

'Well, last month you said we were going for a 'little walk' across the Land.'

'Correct. Of course 'little' is a relative term and perhaps I am guilty of a certain degree of understatement.'

'Oh, really? And why aren't I surprised? OK, lay it on me. Why am I here on Dartmoor?'

'Dartmoor is one of the few remaining places in England where the ancient spirits still dwell almost unchanged, and the Land is virtually as it was centuries ago, before the Wise Ones were persecuted. There are still Old Ones residing here, and the Otherworldly Folk still survive, if barely. Elsewhere the Blessed Ones have mostly retreated to the Otherworld, unable to return, at least not just yet. This is one of the goals of your quest, to create a world where the faery and their kin can once again dwell on the Land. I would like you to walk arm in arm with the Spirit of the Land this night, to let the Land guide you, following the signs without fear and without question. Tonight you will connect with the Land in a way you have only read about, in books about shamans past and present, or in the works of Tolkien and Castaneda. For the Land has to be experienced directly. To truly connect with the Earth Spirit you must lay bare your soul to it, you must have no secrets from it, and you must trust it completely. You must step out on a limb. Only then will you have a chance to fully assimilate the Spirit of the Land.'

'But you are the Spirit of the Land, are you not? Am I not connected with you already?'

'You have made a connection, this is true. But you are still many moons from reaching your true potential as a human being, if indeed you ever do. You have come a long way since

that night at Arbor Low, but you have still taken but your first steps in being reborn.'

'That makes me feel both exalted and depressed. Although I now see a path stretching out before me, there still seems so much to learn. I feel almost overwhelmed by the enormity of it all.'

'But this is good. The Universe IS enormous, magnificent, and fathomless. Yet do not be despondent, for I too sometimes feel almost overwhelmed by my vastness and splendour. But it was my choice to create the physical Universe and to let it expand and get ever more complex. It is the only way that I can eventually know who I am. And in the same context, letting in the immensity and limitlessness of the Cosmos into your Soul is the only way forward for you, and for all of Mankind. Remember what I said about not trying to necessarily understand the Universe, but just trying your utmost to fully experience and appreciate it? That is what I need from you, your experiences, the expansion of your awareness and your consciousness.'

'All sounds very easy and clear when you put it like that. Oh, I wish there were an easier way.'

'But I did not chose you because the task is easy, but because it is hard. And so too with humanity. One day you and I may look back and appreciate all the trials and tribulations, and wars, and pestilence, and self-punishment that Man has put himself through and realise that despite all that, we came through it. Indeed, it was BECAUSE of it that we came through.'

'Then we WILL pull through?'

'Not so fast. I said we MAY look back. The future of Earth has not been decided upon, remember? We all create it every second of every day and nothing is pre-destined. But with your help, I feel the future will be somewhat brighter.'

'That's good enough for me.'

'Now let us get on with the task in hand. Shamans, shamankas, wizards, druids, and other wise people with a deeper connection with the Earth, have always lived within a landscape they perceived as animated and vibrant, one that is composed entirely of energy and life-force. Every atom on this planet is impregnated with my soul, and every landscape has been sculpted by my love. This realisation is to look at the Land through ancient eyes. Tonight your eyes will open. Let's go for that little walk I spoke of.'

I felt drawn to walk around the perimeter of the circle of stones. The sun had just disappeared behind the hill to the west, but still shone on Kester Rock, an outcrop to the south. It would still be some time until the sun would set over the entire moor.

'Tell me, what do you see?'

'I see a circle of ancient stones, composed of granite, rich in minerals and crystals.'

'Try again.'

'OK. OK. I see a circle of ancient stones that are imbued with energies and that probably mark and attract flows of energy. Perhaps the circle stands on ley lines?'

'Really? You are still only looking, not seeing. FEEL! SEE!'

I stopped in front of one of the larger stones.

'OK... feel... see. My physical Universe is an illusion, right?'

'To a certain degree this is true. Nothing is as it seems, remember? Now look again.'

'OK. Everything is energy. This stone is pure energy. My body is pure energy. Only our relative vibrations stop me putting my hand into the heart of this stone. God, I feel like Neo in *The Matrix.*'

'But this is not fiction, for this is the real world. No conspiracies here. This world is a product of pure energy and love. Now, FEEL IT!'

'OK. This stone is you. It's part of the Goddess. I too am part of the Goddess. Therefore the stone and I are one. The Land and I are one.'

'Go on.'

'It's more than that. I know it is. Yes. I am beginning to feel it. That's it: I am the stone and the stone is I!'

I began to feel some resistance to my outstretched hands. About six inches from the surface of the stone, it was as if I had made contact with an invisible force field, a bit like those encountered in old SF movies, or those invisible sheets of glass of street mime artists. I knew about the human aura, of course, from many years studying eastern spiritualities. Did this mean that the stone also had an energy field, an aura?

With these thoughts the dusk light was transformed into an array of blinding iridescent lights. Energy swirled and danced all around me. And I knew that it had been there all the time but that my eyes were now open. In the fading light, I held out my hand towards the stone, which was now composed not of solid rock, but a myriad of dancing lights and glowing crystals. My hand likewise

125

was coursing with luminous flows and pulses of light. I touched the stone and my breath was taken aback as my fingers entered it. My hand and the stone were one. Our energies merged and there was no separateness. But then I realised that I had not reached the physical stone at all, but I was immersed within the megalith's aura. I could not see where the 'solid' stone ended and the aura began, it was all part of the whole. My own hand and lower arms were likewise enclosed in a sheath of glistening energy, which seemed to play and interact with the aura of the megalith.

'Now you see that all is energy. All is connected to all else. But more than this, everything is part of everything else. All is an element of your Goddess. Nothing can exist but by my desire and my love. But you had not perceived this. Before now, you did not see the world as it was, but as you believed it be.'

I felt at one with this standing stone. It was sending me love. I could feel it. And it seemed pleased to see me and interact with me.

'It knows what I am about and why I am here.'

'Yes, it does. You could say that the standing stone is in fact a very UNDERSTANDING stone.'

'An *understanding stone*. Nice one.'

'The stone has many similarities to yourself. You too are an energy source that has been squeezed into a physical body, but you are so immense that you spill over – hence your aura, and likewise the aura of our stone brother.'

I stood motionless and exalted as the stone's energies continued to play with that of my own.

'Shamans have been frequenting stone circles for thousands of years, to interact with their energies, to tap into the planetary heartbeat, seeking contact with me. We will discuss sacred sites in more depth in the future, when you shall dowse these energies as you follow the leys with which many are associated. But for now, my son, we will push on. Someone is approaching and a giant acquaintance of mine is awaiting your company. Come.'

With these words I backed away from the stone and my everyday awareness returned. I surveyed the moor in every direction, but could see no one. Without hesitation, I headed south towards the small river I had earlier seen winding its way across the valley floor. I made for the ancient stone bridge that spanned it, on which I paused. It was composed of a single massive granite block, and standing on its solid mass I surveyed the moor, as skies continued to darken, heralding a sunset that was hidden from my view. I looked towards the east, but the Full Moon had still not risen. Thin bands of cloud ambled across the skies, driven by a light breeze. The first hint of chill filled my lungs, but I knew it was going to get much colder. I crossed the bridge and instinctively turned left, tracing the bank of the river towards what looked like a small ravine, bestrewn with a jumbled mixture of large boulders. I made my way toward it and as I did so I noticed that the sun had reappeared behind me, casting my shadow before me, and turning around I saw this was due to a dip in the distant hills. The retreating solar orb was barely above the skyline, making a second setting imminent. In the meanwhile the meagre warmth it offered was welcome in a cooling landscape.

'Our friend is just ahead, downstream. Keep walking along this bank.'

The river was flowing strongly, presumably following the wet weather of the preceding week, and I had to watch my step over slippery rocks. There was soon a huge boulder looming in front of me, a Colossus amongst its brothers. It rose some 8-9ft out of a bed of smaller debris, and the base of it was being lapped by the waters of the stream. I approached it and without hesitation gently stroked the ancient granite surface. Crystals of quartz, feldspars and black micas were worn smooth by centuries of patient yet persistent licking by the river. I had a flashback of *Close Encounters of the Third Kind*, the scene where the hero touches the huge clay reconstruction in his house, realising at last that it was Devil's Tower. My inquisitive fingers explored the uneven mineral-rich surfaces, in anticipation that something perhaps equally miraculous was about to unfold.

'Welcome to the Tolmen Stone.'

'The Tolmen Stone? This stone has a name, so presumably some folklore too.'

'Yes. It is said that Druids held rituals at this place. This is true, although they were merely continuing a tradition that was inherent when they arrived in these lands. Look around and you will see what brought them to this giant brother.'

I clambered around the left side of the huge boulder, and using two large granite rocks that were lodged up against it, I ascended with care. On reaching the top I was greeted by an awesome sight. The stone was not solid! It was perforated by a round, one-metre diameter hole, that passed right through its entire length to the stream below.

'Wow!'

'Wow, indeed. Now you can see why the stone has attracted attention for many hundreds of years. Even throughout your Medieval times, the Tolmen was visited by the wisewomen of the moors, who passed on hidden knowledge here and carried out initiations and the ancient practice of shamanic dream sleep. It is this opening, the water-born breach, that is the key. Like a Japanese Zen painting, it is the space that is crucial, not the solid form that surrounds it, as are the silences between drumbeats.'

'OK, how so? What was the hole for?'

'How can I help you understand? Ah, yes. I know you have seen the film Stargate, the tale of an ancient artefact. When activated the device transported people in a few seconds to another locality light years away. It is based on the theory of black holes and wormholes, both of which do exist in the physical Universe. Well, the perforation before you is the ancient equivalent, for in passing through you have the potential to enter a portal to other dimensions. Shamans have been coming here since the hole was large enough to squeeze through, some 2,000 years ago. It is not just symbolic either, for I wish you to slip down the hole soon. The true nature and powerful effects of the portal, however, are only open to those with profound experience in shamanic practices. To them what lies on the other side is a land of danger, demons and near-death experiences.'

'Er, OK. Demons and near-death thingies, eh? If you don't mind, I am relieved that I am not experienced in shamanic rites and stuff. So why am *I* going through the hole?'

'Your passage through the hole will be symbolic of your willingness to change. It is a very personal rite that no other human will witness, but which the Land will see and appreciate. You will show the Otherworldly beings and Elementals that you are sincere in your quest. You must see the cavity through which you will plunge as the birth canal of the womb of the Earth Mother, out through which you will be reborn by plunging into the amniotic fluids of my body. This ceremony is only possible after wet weather, for normally the river is too low for you to safely fall through the hole. Are you ready? For you must pass through the Tolmen at the precise

moment that the sun sets and the moon first appears; It is the moment of balance of cosmic forces, of yin and yang, solar and lunar.'

'OK. I'm up for it. My heart is pounding, but I'm getting used to that when you're around.'

'Well done. Tonight you are here to experience aspects of the Land and of its Spirit, my Spirit, which are normally hidden. Tonight is truly your rebirth.'

Not bothering to look if anyone else was around, I removed my waterproof, woolly jumper, boots, socks, trousers, and my shirt. *Sod it*, I thought, and off came my underwear. I sat on the edge of the hole as naked as the day I was born. My legs dangled down into the cavity as I sat on the edge, poised for the drop. I gazed down to the babbling stream some 8ft below, and the waters suddenly seemed very cold and deep, even though it was August. I knew that the depth was no more than a few feet, which made me apprehensive - I could see pebbles on the riverbed. I looked to my right, observing the last tiny facet of the sun's face, which seemed to pause on the skyline, as if teasing me. To my left I could just make out a diffuse, misty glow from behind the rowan trees that hugged the riverbank - the moon was up!

'Now! The moment is now. Jump!'

I wiggled my bottom over the side of the hole - and plummeted. Although I must have been in freefall for only a couple of seconds, it seemed to take twice as long for me to clear the hole and impact the water. Time literally ran about half normal pace as I passed down the granitic-lined chute. And then – splash! The shock of being immersed in bitterly cold water, before bumping hard onto river cobbles, took my breath away. As soon as I could right myself, I shot my head out of the flowing waters and gasped for air. I stood up as quickly as I could, nursing two cuts on my legs sustained from sharp concealed rocks. The blood from the wounds merged into the waters and was carried away seaward. I stood naked midst the chilly, bubbling waters, and turned to greet the Silver Lady, who had miraculously freed herself from the mist during my freefall. And greet her I did with open arms extended, my pulse racing as I felt life-force surge through my veins. My spirit soared as I breathed and tasted the Land. For that was what I was truly doing – breathing in the essence, the life-force, the very Spirit of the moor.

'Good evening to you, Silver Lady!' My words echoed around the inside of the Tolmen hole, and two startled birds flew out of a nearby bush.

After a few minutes I felt my body trembling as the chill of the dusk air bit, so I clambered over wet and slippery boulders to retrieve my clothes. I used my T-shirt to dry myself as best I could before dressing myself in my remaining dry garments, and some nearby dock leaves acted as makeshift swabs for my cuts. Fully dressed, I stood on top of the Tolmen and spied the surrounding landscape, which had darkened to such an extent that the moon was now casting faint shadows.

I looked down at the hole through which I had plunged, and I knew that I was merely the latest of many who had taken the plunge of rebirth over thousands of years. I felt humble and honoured to be in their exalted company. I sensed that the Tolmen Stone was also pleased. I climbed down off the stone and turned to face it.

'Thank you for allowing me to pass through your hallowed body.'

'Come. We shall continue our walk. The night is yet young, and so now are you.'

'OK, Mother, you lead and I'll follow.'

'No, my son, this time it is you who will lead. And know that you walk on my body this sacred night, so please tread gently. Use all your senses and follow your inner wisdom, which is great, yet for the most part untapped. Tonight you cross over a bridge that connects seen and unseen worlds, both manifest and invisible realms. Your footsteps will not only reclaim a magical landscape, but will reclaim that part of yourself that has long been hidden. Come!'

13. Shamanic Moon – Wolf and Stag

© P Knight

He will delight the company of every fairy knoll,
He will be a dragon before the hosts at the onset,
He will be a wolf of every great forest,
He will be a stag with horns of silver.
(Kuno Meyer, *The Voyage of Bran*)

I do not know exactly where I journeyed over the next three hours. With only the ashen light of the Full Moon to guide me, I did indeed stumble over tree roots and small rocks when I did not look where I was treading, and walked headlong into unseen branches and cobwebs. But I never felt afraid, as I consciously journeyed across the sullen moor. Under normal circumstances, a trek on the moor after dark would have been a foolhardy exercise, but this landscape held no fears for me, for now I respected its laws and its raw power. And my senses were sharp as never before: I heard creatures of the night flapping their wings overhead, the hooves of distant ponies crossing the shadowy moor, and even small creatures scurrying amongst the heather – all lucid to my newly heightened senses. The moon was bright and rode the constellation of Pisces, the fish. It was somewhat ironic that the Silver Lady should be in the star sign that had come to represent Christianity, just as I was immersing myself in a spirituality that had its roots thousands of years before the birth of their Saviour.

After about half an hour of level walking from the Tolmen, I spied a rocky rise ahead, which was silhouetted against the last deep blue hues of the west. I clambered up the glistening granite outcrop to the summit, only to marvel at how much detail I could make out in the moonlight. Distant tors, forests, rivers and herds of ponies could easily be picked out as my eyes widened to feline sensitivity. In fact I felt feline and, at one point, experienced what a lion or wolf must feel like, as they wandered their landscape at night in search of prey. *Should I howl? No, not just yet.* I wanted to blend in with the Land, not draw attention to myself. But, saying that, I could feel that the Land was aware of my presence, every step of the way. I was not alone.

'So why don't you go ahead and howl then? For an old friend of mine is waiting to meet you.'

So I stood up on that rocky outcrop surveying my domain and, making a trumpet around my mouth with my hands, I howled!

'How-w-o-o-o-o.'

And I howled some more. It was fun! I felt so powerful, free, alive and ...

What happened next took my breath away. My fourth bay was returned by the howl of a wolf, and I mean a real wolf!

On Dartmoor? I mean, come on, this is Dartmoor!

'Er, hello, Mother. Like, erm, no wolves here, right? … RIGHT?'

'Is that so? Remember, nothing is as it seems. To the shaman there is never just one landscape, but always many landscapes. Worlds and dimensions mingle, mythical and physical landscapes intertwine and interact.'

'Yeah, I got that already, but it did not prepare me for a wolf howl echoing across an English moor under the Full Moon! And it came from quite close. That was no echo. With respect, I have to say that I am feeling a teensy-weensy apprehensive at this point. What are you up to? Has it escaped from a zoo?'

'No. In fact, it is you that has escaped from your cage, for you had been held captive. An aspect of your psyche has been set free and wants to meet you. Relax, for she is not on this physical plane, but neither fully are you tonight, for you have one foot in the realms where your totem resides, and this is where you shall encounter her.'

'OK. OK, er… what do I do?'

'Please sit down and close your eyes. Relax. She is coming for you. But you must meet her half way across the bridge that joins your world and hers. Close your eyes - and see...'

I did as I was bid. Her calming yet authoritative Elder voice always inspired me to go beyond where I had been before. On top

132

of that rocky Dartmoor outcrop, bathed in healing moonlight, I sank unusually quickly into a deep meditation. In my mind's eye, the landscape was still before me, a scene of desolate shadowy moorland. A gentle breeze licked my face and seemed to whisper a charm. Then the wolf came, out of the shadows, head on. She approached slowly, and with a slight hesitation. She was a fully-grown wolf, I would say even elderly, covered in a thick coat of pure white fur. Her eyes sparkled as they caught the moonlight and her whole body glowed as if lit by more than just the moon – she radiated a faint luminescence. She came to a halt just 3ft in front me and sat back on her hind legs. Her eyes were intense, yet loving, and full of wisdom and trust. She bowed her head slightly and I responded by slowly reaching out and touching her dense, soft fur. The image was so real that I could feel the textures of her fur, and even some matting. Her head rose again and we resumed mutual eye contact. There was so much awareness and knowing in those deep eyes.

'She has agreed to be your totem. She will be your companion and guide as long as you stay connected to the Old Ways, to the Land, to me. The wolf is traditionally associated with the Full Moon, which has formed the framework of our mutual journey. But the wolf has the qualities of good judgment and wisdom, a strong sense of community values, is focused when needs be, and is both loyal and strong. She possesses acute senses, sees well in the dark, and her intuition is great and finely tuned. In many traditions, the wolf is associated with wisdom and the sharing of such with others. All these qualities you yourself will need to fine tune in the years ahead.'

'Does she have a name?'

'Why don't you ask her?'

I looked into her beautiful, glowing eyes, and mentally asked the question. The answer came back instantly, without any shred of uncertainty - *SIRIUS!*

'Yes, Sirius she is. She is the psychic link between Men and the Dog Star, the brightest star visible from Earth. The Dogons of Africa believe that Sirius is the home of Earth's original teachers. The star was sacred to the Egyptians, and the sighting of it in August skies heralded the flooding of the Nile. Her appearance to you marks the outpouring of your own psychic waters, as well as the purification and nurturing of your spirit. Just as the dry dust of Egypt is flooded by the

fertilising waters of the Nile, so too your soul will grow and be reborn, but not just for you personally, but for the many, many others who still inhabit the desert of ignorance.'

'Greetings, Sirius.'

She looked into my eyes and unbridled love passed between us, a bond I would come to know and appreciate in the months ahead.

'Sirius will be here for you always. She has offered herself up to your service, in order to help bring my messages back to the centre stage of mankind's consciousness. Whenever you feel doubt, or fear or need the comfort of a loyal friend, remember that Sirius is as far away as closing your eyes and requesting an audience with her. But be mindful to be respectful. She has been part of the planetary psyche since she was first dreamed into existence in ancient times, thousands of years ago. She has helped many on their paths, and may well do so again in the future. You are honoured my friend.'

'That I truly am. Thank you, Sirius. I intend to be worthy of your company and your council.'

With that, the white wolf rubbed her head against my face, licking me across my right cheek, before turning away. She disappeared into the darkness of the moor as quickly as she had manifested. As I opened my eyes, a distant howl echoed around the moonlit tor and filled the cold air with enchantment. I noticed that the wind was catching a wet patch on my right check, exactly where Sirius had licked me! My fingers ran across the moist skin and on inspection they glistened in the moonlight.

Sirius, you were really here!

The Silver Lady was approaching the south and was surrounded by a gossamer hazy halo, which illuminated isolated high altitude clouds that hung above my head. What a night! If someone had told me a few months before that I would have been sitting on a Dartmoor tor under the Full Moon, totally alone save for a wolf, then I would have doubted their sanity. Yet there was I, doing that very thing, and not doubting my own sanity in the least. There had been moments, don't get me wrong, when I had wondered if perhaps a proverbial screw had dislodged itself - but not any more.

I once again surveyed the moon-bathed landscape. My sight was as sharp and sensitive as that of Sirius, as I picked out the smallest movements of cattle, sheep and ponies in the distant gloom. I could also make out the sound of trickling water from down in the valley, an equally remarkable feat, as the brook from which the sounds emanated must have been a good mile distant. But I could neither hear nor see a wolf. She was no longer there, not that she had been there physically in the first place. But how could I explain the wet cheek where she had licked me in my meditation? It made me wonder at what point reality ends and meditation begins, or whether they were both just different levels, between which we could pass? Despite her physical absence, I knew that my newfound ally was watching over me, and would be there whenever I had need of her wisdom, comfort or guidance.

'My Lady, you said there were two friends I had to meet this night. Is the other to be a totem also?'

'He is, indeed. But this one is not of the Otherworld, for he is very much part of my physical plane, just as you are. And he is not so much an individual, but rather is part of a collective consciousness, a group soul that will guide you whenever you are uncertain which way to go, either physically or metaphorically. You spotted some of them earlier, and now you move ever closer along the Web of Life. Come, let us continue.'

'Deer! I saw deer earlier. Continue to where... where are we going?'

'You are heading to exactly where you are meant to be. How could it be otherwise? Just follow your heart and I will follow you – how can I not? I wonder what we'll find.'

'You mean you really don't know?'

'Do I need to answer that?'

The next half hour or so was spent ambling across the open moor under the bright moon. I must have been walking more or less south for a while, for the moon had been directly in front of me. A nebulous mist covered lower parts of the moor, clinging to the Land like the heavy breath of a dragon. I then noticed I was approaching several small megaliths, each around 2ft tall. Rather than a random scattering, they formed what looked like a well-intentioned row. These I followed for around a hundred yards until a much taller standing stone loomed in front of me, illuminated on one side by the moon's rays. It was only as I approached the ancient obelisk that I realised how high it truly was. I was dwarfed as I circled the granite monolith, which must have been all of 9ft tall.

'Welcome to the Longstone! It is one of several that bear that name on the moors. You have come to one of the favourite places of your next companion. He likes to come here to feel the energies that are attracted to the stone, and indeed radiate from it across the moor. Come sit in the moonlight. He approaches.'

I nestled up against the ancient stone, facing the moon. The megalith was cold through my waterproofs and I positioned my rucksack to act as a cushion against the chilled stone. Despite the brightness of the lunar orb in my face, I could still make out details of the moorland around me, including a prominent rise in front of me (which I only learned afterwards was Thornworthy Tor). The granitic peak rose from the grey landscape like a dragon rising from the Underworld, as if to salute the Silver Lady.

My peace and serenity was broken by something moving about a hundred yards in front of me. Mother had said that I would meet a creature from this realm and this revelation made my heart race with anticipation - what was emerging from the cover of darkness? Something caught the moonlight and glistened briefly, before vanishing. Then it flashed again, and again. They were antlers! Out of the gloom approached an adult Fallow stag.

There he stood, in all his magnificence, and this time my eyes were fully open - this was no meditation. Before me stood a fully-grown, antlered stag, towering above me as I sat against the Longstone. The antlers had a total span of about 5ft from tip to tip and they looked more than capable of doing me damage. Yet I felt no fear, only a rush of adrenalin from not knowing what was to come. One of the points on his left antler had broken off, presumably during some rutting activity, and he also had a small nick in his right ear. The stag snorted twice and his breath shone momentarily in the moonlight before being consigned to the mist.

I whispered to the Goddess.

'What should I do? Should I get up and approach him? I mean, I'm no St Francis of Assisi, you know. He may leg it.'

'You are right, he may. This is no spirit, but a physical being, and one that normally shies well away from humankind. You are privileged, my son. He was coming to this place anyway, but remember synchronicity, that nothing happens by chance. Some part of his being knows this too and it makes him curious. He obviously feels safe, or else he would have fled before you had even seen him. Why not stand? Rise very slowly and see what happens.'

OK, I'll try that. Here goes. Slowly does it. There… I'm up.
'He's still there watching me. He hasn't moved.'
'I know!'
'Sorry. OK, fine stag, who are you? Why are you here?'
The stag did not reply. I waited a whole minute, but nothing.
'He's not saying anything.'
'Do you speak deer? If not, my friend, I do not see how you could expect an answer. He is a stag, and you are a human. But you do have some common ground – the Land. He represents the male spirit of the Land. In ancient times he was seen as an aspect of Cernunnos, the Horned One, and of Herne the Hunter. Many shamans wore headdresses with antlers to contact the spirit of the stag, to aid hunting and divination. Antlers are a symbol of a connection to higher forms of attunement, as well as heightened perceptions, for they grow behind the eyes. Each year they are shed and grow back larger, a metaphor for your continued shedding of the old and the attainment of inner growth. A deer's senses are very acute, its eyes designed for clarity at a distance, symbolising your own heightened awareness. The strength and fierceness of the wolf are contrasted by the deer's gentleness, coupled with a certain innocence. As well as a search for wisdom, it is also a return to innocence you seek.'

As I took all this in, the stag before me seemed blasé about the whole discourse. He nibbled at the thin grass and then chewed at his own skin, presumably to remove some irritating parasite. Then, without warning, he gave me a parting glance and a loud snort, which made me jump, before trotting off into the shadows.

'Balance, my friend. The wolf and the stag – perfect! You have chosen well.'
'I chose them?'
'Who else? I could not have selected your totems. No one could have, even though some say they have the knowledge to do this. You have also chosen beasts of this Land, ones that dwell within the spiritual ether of Britain. No buffaloes, bald eagles or condors for you. I am pleased; for it shows you are connecting to your ancestors and the ancient spirit of this Land, choosing indigenous totems, ones that belong here. Many people nowadays select more 'fashionable' or exotic creatures as their totems, North American creatures being in vogue at the moment. This is all well and good and will still lead people to me, but they cannot connect you as closely

with your homeland. People are transporting the spirits and symbolism of beasts to areas where they never dwelt. Their spirits are strangers here and therefore cannot teach you about your indigenous landscape as well as home-grown totems. How can they? Would you expect a kangaroo to know the English landscape as well as the Australian Outback? Do you imagine the spirit of the dolphin would be able to teach you about connecting with the landscape of Dartmoor? True, these totems may open up ways of inner seeing and growth, but the object of this exercise is for people to connect with their native landscapes, rather than focus on lands thousands of miles away. In ancient times, totems were ALWAYS indigenous creatures.'

Good points. To be honest I had never been happy with all that North American Indian stuff. I always felt we could have our own stuff we Brits could connect with. And now I knew it. When I visited a Wiccan camp in the New Forest a few years ago it did feel right how all the symbols on T-shirts and jewellery were British and European animals, or mythical creatures associated with Europe, such as dragons, fairies and unicorns. In hindsight, I now think this is one reason why I never felt totally attuned with Buddhism and Hinduism. They are all profound, yet still imported. At that time I couldn't find any homegrown ancient mystery traditions, for the Church had sent them all underground. But now I saw that Divinity was all around me, in the Land, and not just at the end of a four-hour ohm meditation, or at the top of the Kabbalah.

'Over the years, using mainly Eastern traditions, you grasped something of being connected with the Divine. These other traditions are noble in intent and in practice and have been instrumental in bringing about a spiritual focus to many over the centuries. But at the end of the day, they can be carried out without any form of contact with the Land, and therefore, ultimately, they dismiss the Land as a mere backdrop, a plaything for Man to manipulate and potentially misuse. Many people have meditated for world peace at the top of Glastonbury Tor, or at some remote Nepalese monastery, or indeed have prayed for the same at Mecca or Rome, but always with limited success. Until people once again connect spiritually with the Land and, of equal importance, acknowledge their responsibility for caring for the Land, they will continue to be steered, by religions and

politicians, in directions that are harmful to the Planet, on which their survival ultimately depends.'

'Heavy stuff! I know what you mean about indigenous landscapes. I have stood at the foot of the pyramids, and seen the sunrise over the Nile. I have been to the top of mountains in Africa, and I have visited vast Greek temple complexes. But I have never felt so connected to the Earth as I do now, here at this lonely stone on Dartmoor.'

'That is because you are home. But I mean more than geographically. You have truly returned to your spiritual roots, to a place where you have been before, and may well come to again – your own Land. Welcome home.'

'Thank you - it's good to be back. But, to tell you the truth, I am getting weary. I need to sleep and I haven't got a clue where my car is. Where the hell am I?'

'You are at the centre of the Universe, where else?'

'But where is here?'

'You mean, where is here in relation to places that aren't here? Now that's different.'

'Yes. OK. That's what I mean.'

'Ah. Now then, let me see. You have been very wise, in fact. Your intuition and lack of fear has guided you to within a mile of where you started. The stone bridge you crossed earlier, near the Tolmen, is just a short distance to the north. How would you say it? Oh yes, how cool is that?'

'Cool, indeed. OK, My Lady, are you coming with me? Will I hear from you again tonight?'

'Well, if you mean will you hear any owls, deer, cows, dogs barking, brooks flowing, and the breeze rustling through the trees, then you will indeed hear me. But as far as vocal interaction is concerned, I will cease the dialogue now, so that you might focus your thoughts and appreciate just how excellent your inner wisdom is. For it will return you to your car in the dead of night, with only the moon to guide you. Next Full Moon we will look at, and connect with, sacred sites more fully, and learn the encoded secrets they contain, which are many. Good night. For it has indeed been a very good night.'

'Good night, My Lady. I will never ever forget this night. And I will ensure that others learn of it too.'

I shouted another *good night* across the moor. And then I was again alone, yet not alone. And sure enough, within half an hour of leaving the Longstone, I crossed the stone bridge and recognised Scorhill Stone Circle ahead of me, bathing in the moonlight. Back in my car the clock said 4.15am. Although I had been walking under an extremely bright moon, the headlights and the lights on my dashboard made my eyes wince. The moon's silver face seemed to shepherd my every turn as I headed back to my bed in Princetown, and what would be an extremely sound six hours' sleep. That night I dreamt of wolves and stags, and of the wonders that had unfolded that night.

14. Dartmoor – Opened and Closed

© P Knight

To see a World in a grain of sand,
And a Heaven in a wild flower,
Hold Infinity in the palm of your hand,
And eternity in an hour.
(William Blake)

I awoke next morning to the sound of heavy traffic coming from outside. Princetown was a busy place first thing on an August morning, due to its position on the main east-west road that dissected the moors. After an exhilarating shower I headed down to breakfast. The room was full, every table being occupied by a cross-section of the great British holidaying public, plus one chap who looked like a travelling businessman. Two families had teenage daughters, who were doing their best to look cool as they constantly fingered their mobile phones, and wriggled around in their seats to adjust skirts that looked more like wide belts.

I looked around the room as I enjoyed the food and recounted in my head the previous night's events, knowing that no one there would have been able to relate to any of it. Indeed, I myself was still coming to terms with the magical events that had transpired. I sipped my tea and tucked into my eggs, beans and mushrooms, contemplating the stupendous turns of my newfound life. I now had a stag and a wolf for totem guides. For all I knew, Sirius might have been in that very room, watching over me. Or was that a little facetious on my part, thinking that only I would be her focus and that she would be at my beck and call. Although the Goddess had said that the wolf would show up whenever I needed her, this did not mean she was in close proximity 24/7. I knew of course that her spirit could be anywhere and everywhere, and she could potentially be with me within seconds if I called for her. Everything was connected to everything else. My wolf friend would come if I needed her, it did not matter from what dimension or from which part of the planet her spirit was residing. This was the nature of Wyrd, the cosmic web that connected all things.

As I looked around at the breakfasting souls, I realised that I was truly blessed in being chosen to be the conduit of the Goddess. But I did not feel in any way superior to anyone else there. With my new-found knowledge and inner power had come a great sense of humility and a respect for all people, be they black or white, rich or poor, reader of the Times or the Sun, atheist or Catholic priest. We were all one. The only things stopping us from realising our potential for true peace and growth as a species was our separation from the Land, our inability to see geography as sacred, our reckless use of the Earth's resources, and the lack of a common Universal spirituality with the Earth Goddess at its focus. I wondered just how many of my fellow diners would be affected, either directly or indirectly, by my book. Would the future of the children in the room be enhanced because of my experiences over thirteen moons? I hoped so.

I have waffled a bit, I know, but these were my thoughts and not the words of the Goddess, and that was how I now saw things. No one could take away my ideas and conclusions based on *my* personal experiences, although my assumptions might perhaps be amended in the future. It already seemed ironic to me that one of the purposes of the book was to convince people that they cannot approach the Goddess and the Land through reading alone, no matter how many books on Wicca, leys, sacred sites, shamanism or dowsing they consumed. The Goddess had to be experienced first-hand. And that could only, repeat only, be fully realised by leaving behind our cosy homes, our protective churches, our New Age circles, and even those 'intensive' weekend enlightenment workshops. Although they could take us part way there, may point us in the right direction, and may indeed open some inner doors, they were only stepping stones along the way. We must all take ourselves off in isolation to meet our Divinity, out there in the Land. To go without really was to go within.

And that was exactly what I was going to do that day – there was no need to rush back after all. Following my night of magic, I wanted to experience Dartmoor in the cool light of day, to see what was now different, and what was indeed the same. What would my senses reveal to me that had previously been denied? I couldn't get out of the dining room quick enough, even refusing a second cup of tea! Now you wouldn't see Wallace and Gromit doing that, would you? They thought the moon was made of cheese, but I could now confirm to the dynamic duo that it was made from love. I retreated to my room for an hour to input all the night's events into my laptop, still amazed at how excellent my recall was. Every detail just flooded back as the fingers of the Goddess keyed in her wisdom.

My first point of call was a *'must see'* site, according to my guidebooks - the Drizzlecombe Stone Row. I headed off and within half an hour was parking alongside Ditsworthy House, a centre used for educational outings, by the scouts, school parties, Outward Bound, that sort of thing. It stood in isolation midst a circle of tall trees, the shelter being most welcome as I walked through them – it was a gorgeously hot August morning, with hardly a cloud in sight. The path to the stones was straightforward and initially followed the floor of Plym Valley. But after about a ten-minute trek, the vista opened up to reveal Dartmoor in all its glory. Mile upon mile of rolling moors stretched out before me, punctuated by occasional boulder-strewn tors. As I walked, I tried to keep my attention on my immediate area, practicing a sort of conscious walking. I had had to do it the previous night when my vision was restricted, and it seemed a good practice now. I noticed all manner of things that would previously have gone unnoticed: spider's webs, the tiny fragment of a discarded snakeskin, minute feathers, tiny purple and yellow flowers, the smallest and most delicate banded snails, which I was able to avoid squashing.

This truly is walking in the Now.

Occasionally pausing to take water, I looked in the distance and the moor looked almost devoid of life, save for the odd sheep and crow. But by concentrating on the part of the Universe closest to me, my Universe, the Land yielded all manner of signs of life, and death for that matter. At one point I paused for a while to observe a line of ants that crossed my path. Hundreds of them marched past, seemingly oblivious to my presence. Back and forth they went, some carrying what looked like tiny eggs, others with twigs and other detritus. The organisation and ceaselessness of their efforts was amazing and I knew they too had their part to play in the Goddess' unfolding.

After around thirty minutes, I crossed a stream, pausing again to quench my thirst. The flow was so clean and pure and the cool waters tingled down my throat. It tasted so invigorating and I could feel the energies of the water as they entered my body. I took another palmful and let it slowly trickle down between my fingers, catching it playfully with my outstretched tongue. It felt so good. Water truly is a Goddess-given gift to Mankind, for without it life as we know it could not exist. For we can survive for weeks without food, but only days without water.

'Thank you, My Lady, for the gift of life.'

As I rose to my feet, I spied a line of stones in the distance, about half a mile away. I had not noticed them before, as I had been focusing on my immediate landscape. It was only as I drew nearer to them that I appreciated how huge they were. It was Drizzlecombe. Three ancient stone rows several hundred yards in length marched across the moor in regimental fashion, each ending with a stone cairn at their eastern end. But the most telling spectacles were the three huge megaliths, one around 8ft high, the middle one 10½ft, and the tallest towering above my head at 14ft. They were of solid granite, and very phallic, standing proudly on the moor. They had resisted both the elements and the changing spiritualities that had put asunder so many of their kin. I stood before the largest in its nurturing shadow, its gigantic bulk offering me shade from the hot sun. I went right up to it, but could not touch it for a few moments, as something held me back. It was reminiscent of that scene from *2001 A Space Odyssey*, when Moon Watcher, the clever apeman, approached the black monolith with apprehension, before eventually giving in to his curiosity and touching it. Well, that's just how I felt. Even without touching the megalith, I sensed my body shaking slightly, as if something was interacting with my aura. My hands started to sweat and my breathing became faster.

'Hi, there. How are you, sir?' I addressed the stone, 'May I please touch you?'

It somehow felt OK to go ahead. So I closed my eyes, reached out with both hands and placed my palms onto the cold, hard, eternal stone. Wham! Flashes of colours and sparks played in front of my eyelids, and a rush of energy raced up my arms, and entered my chest. I breathed in the most enormous breath ever, as my heart filled with life-force, a feeling of pure and utter love.

144

The stone and I merged into one and my soul soared. After a few minutes, something told me to open my eyes and I did so to be confronted with a pure white butterfly nestling on the stone just above my head. It flapped its wings in a gentle, welcoming breeze and I stood just inches from it, in total awe. How can they say that something as beautiful as that was pure chance, sheer luck, a mere gathering together of molecules and atoms? There was purpose to that beautiful creature before me, as it too was important to the Goddess and the unfolding Universe. If it weren't, I thought, then it would not exist.

I spent a further two hours at Drizzlecombe, hugging stones, sitting on ancestral cairns and walking the stone rows. Occasionally, ramblers would pass by, some pausing at the stones briefly before continuing their own personal pilgrimages. I smiled at several of them as they passed, due mainly, truth be known, because I had a permanent smile on my face. The huge stones reached for the skies, and with them my own soul soared, replete with love and admiration for the Goddess. She had been very busy here, and it showed.

My next stop was at a double stone circle called Grey Wethers. This circle was stunning for its approach as much as for the stones themselves. I left the car in a clearing surrounded by woods, next to Fernworthy Reservoir. A half-hour trek up a gentle slope passed through those woods, which in reality were coniferous plantations. On the way, I visited Fernworthy Circle, a pleasant site surrounded on all sides by trees. One of the stones made me look twice. There on one side was a face in the rock, and what's more, it displayed a broad grin. I wondered if I would have spotted that before my inner eyes had been opened. The whole landscape was now animated and full of images of magic and wonder.

The path continued upward through pine plantations. These were normally quite sterile and regimented, and can often be devoid of atmosphere, but near the top of the slope, the woods closed in, and were dense, dark, and mysterious. The pine trees were close enough together, and tall enough, to deny the forest floor nearly all direct sunlight. Fallen trees were moss covered and mushrooms grew out of carpets of pine needles, even at this time of the year. It was like a scene from *Lord of the Rings*, and I half-expected to hear the call of an Ent echoing through the forest. I also sensed I was being observed and studied, but I knew not by what or by whom. I stepped forward to leave the path, to enter the gloom of the forest, but a little voice popped into my head: *Not yet! Not yet!* The time was not yet right. The Green Man was not ready to grant me an audience. But I knew that time would come.

Some way up the bridle path, I was greeted by a crowd of ramblers, who swept past me with a swiftness of foot and with all jaws firing. How can people ever truly appreciate the peace and tranquility of the Moor when they talk all the way around it? Now one of my weird hobbies, if you remember, was to invent collective nouns. Well, what should I call a collection of ramblers, thought I as they passed me by. *Let's think. How about 'a saunter of ramblers'? Or a 'prattle' or 'compass' of ramblers'? Or perhaps 'a stomp'? Or how about, yes I like this one, how about 'a trample of ramblers'?* Sorry - now back to the plot!

I did not want to be disturbed again, so I thought it best to leave the bridle path, along which I would inevitably encounter more people. I soon came to a fork in the track, the bridle continuing ahead, with another, less well-trodden track going off to my left. It felt good to take this other path and I now knew from experience that if something felt good inside, then I should go for it.

The forest edge came on me abruptly, and as I passed through a bridle path gate, I was greeted once more by open moorland. I could see two circles of stones in the middle distance, huddled together midst a sea of purple heather – they were the Grey Wethers. As I drew closer, I could appreciate how much the circles really belonged there. Although they were manmade, they were not on the landscape, but *within* it, as the Goddess had said. They were immortal ingredients of the eternal Land. On arrival at the circles I paused just outside.

'Hello, ancient brothers! Sorry to intrude on your day but, I have travelled a long way to get here – in more ways than one. I'd like to hang out with you for a while. Is that OK?'

An instant after my words had echoed across the circles, a big smile came across my face. I did not intend it to and did not instigate it; the smile just arrived of its own accord, accompanied by a really nice feeling that the stones were glad to see me. I know this will grab some people as a little nuts, but something, some force, made it known that it was cool for me to chill out with my stone brethren.

The two circles were almost complete due to restoration, each comprising about twenty megaliths, the average height of which was around 3ft. The gap separating the circles was about 8ft wide and I stood at the spot where they were closest to each other.

Straight away I felt good inside, and the feeling was one of balance. I sensed that the circles represented the two polarities: male/female, yin/yang, sun/moon. I was standing midway between them and I was totally spaced out, yet not in a trippy sort of way, but in a fully controlled, balanced way. I closed my eyes and at first could not see anything, save for utter blackness. But after a few moments, I could detect a very faint, white stream of light flowing across the gap between the two circles. It was very faint, but was definitely there all the same. The flow was sluggish, but steady. Although I sensed good vibes standing between the circles, I wondered if the slowness of the current was due to the fact that the circles had been restored. Had this been done accurately, or had the stones been positioned incorrectly. Did 'restored' mean that some stones were not even the originals? I would ask the Goddess about this when it was relevant.

Exactly west of the circles arose the craggy mass of Sittaford Tor, and I surmised that at the Equinoxes the sun would set into the tor, when viewed from the Grey Wethers.

Walking back down the hill through the pine forest, I had a quickness and firmness in my step. I felt as if I somehow belonged there, and that the forest and the circle had in some way been pleased I had passed their way. Strange I know, but the Goddess said that everything has consciousness on some level, so perhaps that feeling was actually emanating from the forest and the circle, or at the very least unseen entities that resided here.

Another strange thing happened on the way back to the car. At one point the path narrowed and the trees closed in on me on either side. The dead straight path ahead did not require any effort of concentration on my behalf, and I drifted off into some sort of altered state. For a while it seemed that it was not I who was walking past the trees, but that the trees were moving past me! It was a bit like the video to Pink Floyd's *'Another Brick in the Wall'*, where those tall hammers march past, only this time it was the trees passing by. As soon as I realised what was happening I lost the effect, my mind eradicating the magic. Back at the car park I turned 180° and stood facing the forest.

'Thank you Spirit of the Forest. Thank you very much.'

That much had definitely changed since my experiences on the moor. Previously I had sometimes half-heartedly, almost jokingly, said *'hi'* and *'so long'* at sacred sites. But now I meant it. And the reason for my sincerity was because I now knew that someone or something was there to hear or sense my greetings, my requests and my appreciation. I turned back to the car park and as I did so heard the cry of a buzzard overhead, as had happened before. I rapidly diverted my attention skyward, and there he was, identical in size and appearance as before. Could it possibly be the same bird? Surely not… could it? At the very least, I knew that the cry of the bird was the forest's acknowledgement of my appreciation.

After dining at a pub at Chagford, I proceeded to my last sacred site of the trip, that of Spinsters' Rock. I had done some research and found that this dolmen stood on the Mary current of the St Michael Line. Now the Goddess said we would cover earth energies and leys at a future Full Moon, but I had done some homework nevertheless. The St Michael Line was an alignment of sacred sites that went across Southern England from Cornwall up to East Anglia. Dowsers had found that accompanying this alignment were two energy flows, which they called Michael and Mary, because they were respectively male and female currents, and that these flows weaved around the axis of the ley, a bit like the snakes of the caduceus. The Mary flow was named from the profusion of churches dedicated to Mary that stand on the current, and so too with the Michael flow, along which stood a predominance of St Michael churches. Now I was neither a proficient dowser nor a ley hunter (although I had the feeling that that was gonna change once the Goddess got started on me) but felt as if dowsing would be another key to help contact the spirit of the Land. And my dowsing rods were in my car!

Spinsters' Rock dolmen stood in isolation; almost forgotten it seemed, in a field across the lane from a small farm. On approaching the stones, I could sense their ancientness and appreciate the effort that must have been put into the dolmen's construction. Three huge uprights supported a massive capstone, all fashioned from Dartmoor granite.

'Greetings. May I join you, my ladies?'

Again, it felt good to enter the site. It seemed to me that the more humble and respectful I was, the more I would be welcomed, and the more would be revealed to me. I circled the dolmen once before entering. I had to stoop slightly, as my 6ft frame was just too tall to stand fully upright beneath the massive capstone. I sat down within the heart of the stones, beneath the huge crystal-covered roof. As before, I sensed a feeling of utter peace, and had the feeling, as I had done in the forest earlier, that I was not alone. Something or someone was there with me, although I could not put my finger on exactly what it was. Was it a spirit, an actual

148

entity, or was it a memory of some event that had happened there long ago? And did being immersed within the flow of the Mary current have anything to do with it? I rummaged around blindly in my rucksack until my hands emerged with their quarry – my two dowsing rods. I had purchased them some weeks before after the Goddess said we would look into leys and earth energies at a later Full Moon. So there I was, sitting in a dolmen on an energy flow of the St Michael Line.

'OK, so let's go for it.'

I emerged from the cover of the stones, dowsing rods in hand. For some reason I looked around to see if anyone was approaching. Well, it was my first time after all! I grasped my rods in each hand and proceeded to circumnavigate the site. Now I remembered reading somewhere that I should focus on what I was seeking, be it earth energies, lost keys, underground water and so on. So I muttered to myself a continuous, 'I wish to pick up the Mary current, I wish to pick up the Mary current…' Then, to my astonishment, my rods crossed. *Wow!* No, I really mean Wow! After about three paces the rods uncrossed. I turned around and retraced my steps, to find that they crossed again at the same place.

'Yeah!' I cried out, such was my excitement. I turned to the left, and my rods remained crossed as I walked away from the stones. I figured that as long as they remained crossed I was still amidst the flow of Mary energy. After around 50ft of slow walking and intense concentration an amazing sight greeted me. There in front of me were two rows of tiny flags, like those you stick on your sand castles at the beach. They were all orange though, no Union Jacks or Welsh dragons on these babies. What the hell did this mean? Clearly, someone had been here dowsing before me and had marked the flow of energy.

'Yeah!' once again resounded around the field. I had indeed followed the Mary flow, with no help or prompting, and these flags confirmed it. *Cool.*

My delight was short-lived, however. A loud, male voice boomed across the field from somewhere behind me.

'It's those intolerable, bloody dowsers again. They think it's the ruddy seaside, with their wretched flags.'

I turned around to be greeted by a guy of middle years, with an upper class accent, who was dressed in country wear, complete with green wellies (Wellington boots or gumboots to the uninitiated!) and a green Burberry coat. He looked as if he had just

149

stepped out of an issue of *Horse and Hound* magazine. He was not a happy bunny, and even less so when he saw that I was brandishing a set of dowsing rods. He strutted straight past me.

'Did you put these here then. Was it you?'

'No, it wasn't. I was dowsing and just came upon them. I'm a visitor to the area, a tourist if you like, just passing through.'

He started to pull up the small flags, stuffing them brusquely into a plastic bag he had produced from his coat.

'I'm forever clearing this place of all manner of things, from flags, to candles, nightlights, feathers, bones, crystals, effigies. You name it, it's been left here.'

'Are you the landowner?'

'I most certainly am, and I curse the day that I was made to keep public access to this field. I would close it off tomorrow. The stones attract all manner of low-life: hippies, travellers, so-called Pagans and witches and, of course, bloody dowsers.'

I said nothing, but slipped my rods back into my rucksack whilst he was distracted. Having collected all the flags, he came over.

'It's not right. This is an ancient site for sure, and I suppose it should be preserved as part of England's heritage. But all this alternative Pagan stuff, well, it's not Godly. All that sort of thing was replaced by the Bible and Christ's teachings. We've grown out of all that primitive stuff. They've already got bloody hunting banned, for God's sake. Perhaps they want us to go back and live in bloody caves too, do they?'

I felt as if I should try and at least be pleasant and non-confrontational. He already knew I was a dowser, but he did not seem aggressive to me personally. Perhaps my conventional garb and the fact that I had proclaimed myself a tourist carried some weight. It was still a shock to my system, though. I had been in touch with a Dartmoor that had opened itself up to me, and yet was now confronted by a person who represented an aspect that was closed. How should I respond to him? He had made clear his stand on certain issues obviously dear to his heart. Did I have the courage of my convictions to air mine?

He continued. 'Dowsing for water and wells is one thing. We've been doing that in the countryside for bloody generations. But all this airy-fairy New Age rubbish - now that's quite another matter. I caught a group of women dancing naked here at the last Full Moon...'

It crossed my mind, perhaps unfairly, as to how long he had watched the naked women before he interrupted them!

'… Disgusting. It goes against the Bible for a start, not to mention common decency.'

Ah ha, the Bible. Now I saw where he was coming from. I would do right in not airing too much of what had happened to me recently. For one it would convince him I was a complete lunatic, and for another it would surely put him on the offensive again. And there was another reason. All this was completely new to me and I was still assimilating it into my life and getting to grips mentally with large chunks of it. Could I hold my own in a confrontation? Was I ready? Anyway, did there have to be an argument, or could I just let slip a few small snippets of what I had been through? Perhaps I could make him at least rethink some aspects of his entrenched beliefs. I took a deep breath.

'With respect sir, aren't these sites open to all people to visit? For the stones are surely part of everyone's heritage, no matter what spirituality they hold? I am sure most people who come here do so to honour the place and the people who built it, not to abuse or misuse it. England is, after all, a place of great religious tolerance and a land that champions freedom of speech.'

'That may be so,' he replied, 'but we don't welcome those sort of low-lifes around here. People around here are God-fearing and decent, and we hold old-fashioned ideals and values in good stead. And most of us, by the way, have a shower first thing in the morning. Anyway, we have moved on since the Stone Age, and our religion has progressed and refined our connection to God. Things are more civilised now.'

You really think so, matey? OK, lets try this.

'But the people who built this marvellous structure', I continued, 'were Pagans, and worshipped many gods and goddesses, and held the Land to be sacred. So, too, were the builders of Stonehenge and Avebury and the other massive ancient sites that we as a nation cherish. They were skilled in the arts of astronomy, dowsing and sacred geometry. Surely a closer connection with our ancient heritage, the sun, moon and stars, and a deeper appreciation of how Nature works, will benefit us today. Look at the mess the world is in. Conventional religions and materialism have led us on a downward spiralling path, surely.'

He looked at me suspiciously, for I had made my stance on these matters clear.

'Yes,' he replied, 'but we all need to unite under a common religious banner to come through all this, not fragment it still further. And the Church is the only way forward for me.'

'But trying to herd the world into politically motivated religions has failed,' I responded, 'Surely, people should be open to find their divinity individually. Churches are emptying, and sacred sites like this are attracting more and more disillusioned people. I am afraid to tell you that it is the way of things, a sign of the times. Things come and go, passing away to be replaced by newer ways. That has always been the way of Mankind. Evolution in action.'

He did not like that at all and his face reddened, his posture stiffening.

Get ready to beam me up, Scottie, on my command.

His nostrils flared. 'I am afraid I am going to ask you to leave my land. Right now, if you please. The way we live in these parts is English and Godly, and some may see it as old-fashioned and out-of-date, but it has held us in good stead for a thousand years and more, and has lead to a peaceful and stable society.' He gestured towards the gate.

'But that's the point', I retorted, 'the world's in a mess, society structured around religion hasn't worked and still isn't for most people – half the world is starving. Ask yourself one question: Is the world in a mess despite organised religions… or because of them.'

After my parting shot I turned and started back towards the gate. I could hear his footsteps a few yards behind me, keeping pace with mine. As I opened and passed through the gate, I turned and stood my ground as he approached. We stood face to face for a few moments before I spoke my final words.

'I bid you good day. Sorry if my words have offended you in any way, for I meant no offence. But last night up on the moor I found heaven and found that it is not up in the clouds, but right here, at places just like this. I touched the Divine, and Divinity touched me. Last night, I heard the Word, and the Word was good. The Word is here, right now. May I suggest that instead of looking to the heavens for salvation, we could all look for it on Earth? For it is here… it is here.'

He did not reply. I did not look back until I had got into my car, parked across the lane, although I heard the gate close loudly behind me. He looked awkward and avoided my gaze, making much about closing the gate as he fiddled excessively with the chain. I sensed it had gone OK. I had respected his beliefs and had not got him too aggressive or defensive. It had been but a brief encounter, but I knew that stronger tests might come in the future, as I had been warned previously. Had this been just a precursor for battles to come, confrontations where I would be put on the spot by more fundamentalist opposition? For now, I was satisfied. Perhaps in some small way I had planted a seed that would make him more tolerant to future pilgrims to Spinsters' Rock, no matter what their spiritual persuasion.

15. Seventh Moon – September: Stonehenge Lesson – Sacred Sites

© P Knight

Awake! O sleeper of the Land of Shadows, wake! expand!
I am in you, and you in Me, mutual in Love Divine,
Fibres of love from man to man thro' Albion's pleasant land.
(William Blake)

My trip to Dartmoor had been the most profound to date. My experience at the Tolmen Stone and meeting my two totems had left me in a state of vertigo, as I wrestled to take it all in. There I was one day, being led around the moors under the gaze of the Full Moon to meet a wolf, and the next I was pushing a supermarket trolley. How does that work? But perhaps this is real test of self-change, to assimilate our spiritual discoveries into everyday life. I had experienced a similar state of affairs a few years earlier, whilst spending some eighteen months in South Africa. Much of my time was spent hanging loose with the Cape Town Rasta community. Although I never immersed myself entirely into their spliff-dependent way of living, I would be lying if I said I had not indulged to a certain extent - yeah, man! I saw it as part of the search for my Self, and at the time was beginning to get disillusioned with the idea that Eastern spiritualities such as Buddhism and Taoism held all the answers.

But my point is this: I would hang out for the night with my dread-locked brothers and sisters only to have to go down to the local Asian corner shop in the morning, or negotiate Cape Town's traffic, or suffer the strange looks from bigoted white Afrikaners as I passed them by in my tie-dye. I and I 'ad a real problem wi' dat one, man! But the Rasta's had the right idea, as did the shaven-headed Hare Krishna devotees of Cape Town, who would thrust their pamphlets into the hands of those passers-by who hadn't seen them coming. Neither group gave a four-X for what anyone outside their community thought of them. They were true to their own beliefs, whilst at the same time integrated within the community, to a lesser or greater degree. They were apart yet simultaneously included in society. I suspected that Rasta dudes and Krishna devotees also pushed trolleys around supermarkets.

This was surely one aim of the Goddess, to get across that people need not give up their religions, or isolate themselves from society, or get connected with the Land at the expense of anyone else's spirituality. Differences in culture and centuries-old, ingrained religious-political mindsets may never enable Man to beat to the rhythm of the same drum. But I felt that if each religion took just a little more responsibility for the environment and honoured Planet Earth as a Divine creation to be nurtured and respected, then that would be a start, and there would be hope.

On Dartmoor the Goddess said I would be taught more on the true nature of sacred sites at the forthcoming Full Moon. I had already been to scores of sacred places, and had some mind-blowing experiences. But I knew that I had only scratched the surface, and that most of the iceberg of knowledge still lay unrevealed beneath the waters of my knowing.

The next few weeks were spent on more mundane, but no less enjoyable, activities. I visited my mother in Birmingham, stopping at some sacred sites in the Cotswolds en route. The chambered barrows of Hetty Pegler's Tump and Belas Knap were both spectacular, and I spent half an hour in each. The former site was especially powerful, as I had to clamber through a small entrance and the main chamber was quite small and somewhat claustrophobic. In the dimness, I was cut off from the outside world, yet was utterly secure within the belly of my Mother.

I also enjoyed a day on the beach at Durdle Door, the huge arched cliff that displayed all the art and imagination of the divine sculptress. The autumn sun was warm and the schools were back, ensuring the beach was relatively empty. The caves at the foot of the chalk cliffs invited me into their damp, flint-lined interiors and I sat within looking seaward. It struck me how it was similar to looking out from within a chambered long barrow or dolmen: surrounded by rock, nurtured and sheltered from the outside world. Perhaps caves had given our ancestors the idea of erecting artificial structures inland. It seemed to me that great concentrations of these occurred in chalk areas, where geology dictates there can be few caves, perhaps forcing our ancestors to create substitutes. My studies had also revealed that many clusters of megalithic tombs also occurred right down the western seaboard of Europe, in a strip from Portugal, through Brittany, Denmark, right up to Scandinavia. Perhaps they had imitated caves, as they would only otherwise have found them on the coasts. The idea was to go within the body of the Earth Mother, and underground sacred sites achieved this as well as any cave.

As the September Full Moon approached, I began to tune in on where I would be going for my next verbal encounter with the Goddess: *'Next moon we will look at, and connect with, sacred sites more fully, and learn their encoded secrets, which are many.'* But where would that be? I was now aware that the answer was not so much about cracking codes, but rather following strands of synchronicity.

It occurred to me that the Goddess herself might not be aware of where the next meeting would be! For She had already said of future events: *'We have not yet decided on the future... we are yet to create it!'* I was the co-creator of my life, creating as part of her whole. The fibres of my synchronicity were also hers, and vice versa. That concept was so releasing, for I was no longer at the mercy of some God on high, whom I blindly followed. I was not aware that the Goddess had given me a single command. It was always by way of a request, or suggestion, or guiding comment, and She had even on occasions followed *me.* It was this liberation that, ironically, gave me the respect and love I now felt for her, a respect so deep that I would follow her anywhere. I had complete trust in her wisdom and compassion, and in return She had my devotion - a reverence born not of fear, but out of love.

OK, then, where we goin'?

One day, whilst proof-reading my story thus far, it dawned on me that Stonehenge had already been mentioned several times, yet I had not been there since the Goddess had revealed herself.

Hmm, Stonehenge. I wonder.

Although it was Britain's most famous and oft-visited ancient sacred site, the tourist aspect had made me steer clear of it. All that hustle and bustle, and the hoards of camera-clicking tourists. I had conversed with M'Lady at relatively quiet, even remote, localities so far. Could I even hear her voice over the traffic, and the noise and jostle of chattering tourists?

Stonehenge. Perhaps that is the lesson, that She is everywhere, even midst the commercial exploitation of a sacred monument. Hmm. I wonder.

Over the next few days, I pondered the issue and let it go, only to come back to it again. I got rational a few times but eventually eradicated the intellect stuff. But the more I tuned into Stonehenge, the more it was pulling me. The feelings got stronger two days before Full Moon, as if I was caught up in some swirling eddy that was sucking me in, a bit like the effect a black hole might have on the Enterprise. I could hear Scottie shriek:

'I canna hold her, Cap'n!'

It's OK, Scottie, prepare to beam us down. Right, listen up landing party. Beware - foreign tourists on the planet's surface. They are armed with digital cameras, flash, audio hand-helds, and display loud, over-animated gestures. Phasers on stun!

So the day of the Full Moon arrived. And there was I, at Stonehenge, a little after 3.00pm on a pleasant, sunny September afternoon. I had been beamed down to the car park of Planet Stonehenge, in the National Trust quadrant of the English Heritage Galaxy. Cars, camper vans, mini-buses, coaches. You name it, everything other than passport control was there, and hoards and hoards of foreign tourists. I felt like an alien at the shrine to my own spiritual heritage. Where were the English? As the hoards disgorged from their coaches, many paid homage to the black and red monolith of the Coca Cola deity, or visited the underground shrine to the God of reeking toilets. Eventually they would all converge as a single organism on one pay booth and its adjacent over-worked turnstile. The mass took on the appearance of a giant colony of ants on the move. It seemed as if it would destroy everything in its path, including the self-esteem of the monument.

Stonehenge, like other national treasures, was an unwitting victim of its own magnificence. I stood midst the scrum of people speaking languages I could not comprehend (they could have been Vulcan or Klingon for all the good it did me), waiting in line to see one of the pinnacles of Man's prehistoric achievements. How did it come to this? It's strange, but I felt as if I were equally to blame, as if I were an accomplice to the crime, in some way countenancing the calamity. I guess we must all share responsibility for our world – the Goddess teaches us that.

After paying my entrance and buying a guidebook from the shop (I found one in English, next to one I think was in Vulcan), I walked through the road tunnel with the other ants and came out the other side a little more relieved. As the environment opened up, the crowds dispersed somewhat, congregating in smaller groups scattered around the permitted walkway that surrounded the stones. The image reminded me somewhat of the old westerns, when the Indians circled besieged wagon trains. I stood at the place where the path was closest to the megaliths, on the west side. With the crowds no longer spoiling the view I could marvel in awe at the skill of my ancestors, and of the spiritual driving force that propelled them to such towering heights of realization. The huge trilithons and solitary uprights rose from the earth like surfacing dragons. Others surged upward from the ground at acute angles, like whales frozen in mid air, preluding the almighty splash of an inevitable plunge.

Stonehenge was indeed iconic, representing a 'Golden Age', a time when priests and priestesses practiced their observations of the intricate motions of the sun and moon. It had also gained iconic status for the patriotic seekers of a lost alternative Albion, steeped in myth and magic. Like other great sacred sites such as the Pyramids, Jerusalem and Glastonbury, Stonehenge had the ability to bestow unto all seekers whatever they required, regardless of spiritual, religious, or indeed political, persuasion.

I continued my very slow circumnavigation of the stones in the warm afternoon sun, hardly taking my eyes off the circle. With every step came new treasures and surprises. Sometimes I could make out what seemed to be faces in the gnarled surfaces. Were these the result of weathering or vandalism, or had Man fashioned sculptures of their gods? It must have taken me a full hour to orbit the stones, as I took several breaks to sit on the grass and take in certain scenes. The axis of the mid-summer solstice pulled me immensely, and I stood looking down the axis, wondering how many thousands before me, over eons of time, had done likewise. Along this axis I sensed a strong current of energy, flowing directly into the heart of the stone circle.

But where was the Goddess? I sat down on the grass in a relatively quiet spot on the east side, close to a huge round barrow. Then I knew She was there.

'Hello, My Lady.'

'Hello to you, my herald. Welcome to my temple.'

'This place is truly sacred in every sense of the word, isn't it?'

'Yes, it is. Although all the Earth is sacred, it was noticed long ago that certain places were special or powerful, where people could directly approach the ancestors and the gods. This was due to the sensitivities and physiology of the human body, as well as characteristics in the human brain, which picked up on certain dynamic vibrations. There are particular locations on my body that are certainly more powerful energetically, for they are my chakra points. On your body you have seven main chakras, points where the energy is focused, although there are, of course, many others. My body mirrors this, as I too am a living entity. For instance, the sacred centre of Ireland, Tara, is the throat chakra of that country, whereas in Europe, the northern lands of Scandinavia are my Crown, the British Isles the Brow chakra, and the Iberian Peninsular equate to the Sacral of the human body. You see, your body mirrors the Universe precisely. How could it be otherwise, for you are the Universe.'

'That's cool. Is Stonehenge really that exceptional, or is much of it hype?'

'Well, one of the reasons we have met here is to get across to you that Stonehenge, and other major sites such as Avebury, Callanish and Carnac, are all as equally sacred as each other. But more than this, the isolated standing stone on a desolate moor or a once proud stone cast down in a ditch is likewise equally sacred. How could any one spot on the landscape be more sacred and holy to me than anywhere else if all are part of me, the Goddess, the Earth Spirit? It is true, of course, that some sacred sites are more important to the well being of the planet as a whole. Compare the situation with that of the human body. You could survive the loss of a hand, a toe, or even a limb, though the loss of these would affect your body negatively. But to lose your heart or your head would be terminal. Your ancestors were aware that certain places were especially important for the fecundity of the Land. For this reason we must not damage or lose any

159

more of these holy sites, for there are always consequences for the whole planet.'

'Looking at the sorry and scandalous state of affairs here at Stonehenge, I can only imagine how the Landscape has been harmed.'

'Indeed. By creating man-made sacred places, one can affect the flow of life-force across the Land, either positively or negatively. This is why your distant ancestors chose with great care where they built every standing stone, circle, henge, tumuli and temple. They were aware of the responsibility that comes with erecting a building or altering the landscape in any way. Today's westernised culture has largely forgotten this knowledge, and with it the skills that once ensured the Land was not harmed unnecessary.'

'You said before that we would look at sacred sites more deeply. What is it we need to learn?'

'Well, let us take Stonehenge, for example. Many volumes have been written about this monument. People have hatched their pet theories and defended them to the hilt, often with blatant disregard for newer hypotheses. But most have been wrong in their conclusions, for they failed to see that sacred sites were not intended for a single purpose, but rather for an anthology of uses. In a nutshell, sacred sites are multi-faceted. If someone says that Stonehenge is here solely because of its astronomy, they are incorrect. If another says it is positioned because of its alignments with other sites, then they are wrong. If a healer says the chief reason for the monument is because it is one of the Planetary Chakra Points, then they too are not 100% correct. If someone else advocates that the main reason the stones are here is purely to attract and amplify cosmic energies, then they too are in error. And if yet another researcher tells you that Stonehenge exists as some sort of tribal statement of power, then they too are wrong.'

'Then what is Stonehenge... what?'

'The answer is that it is all those and more. Take your pick: it indeed stands on many leys. It attracts and amplifies earth energies. It is an astronomical observatory and calendar. It is an archaeological wonder. It is a pawn in political debate. It is on a powerful landscape node. It is a temple to both the male/solar and the lunar/female logos. It was a tribal symbol of authority. It is a structure that has encoded sacred

geometrical principles. It is a testimony to a dedicated and devoted spirituality. It is an international heritage site. It is a portal to other dimensions. It is an icon for alternative groups and individuals. It was designed to enhance and alter acoustics. It is all these and many more. Can you see that this is the nature of sacred sites? They are never exclusively what they at first appear to be. Nothing is as it seems, remember? There is rarely one single reason why a sacred site is located where it is. And this is the key point: it is the collective sum of all the above and more that makes Stonehenge sacred. We perhaps need to look not necessarily at what makes a monument sacred, but rather seek to define the term sacred site.'

'OK. Could you please define *sacred site*.'

'What makes a place sacred? Well now, let's look at some possibilities. Is it the structure that was erected? Or the practices and rituals that define its sacredness? Or is it the place itself, the geography, which is sacred? Is it indeed the presence of the 'genius loci' or presiding spirit that makes a locality sacred? Sacredness is certainly not determined by how many tons of stone were used to build a temple, church or stone circle. My answer to your question may seem ambiguous, but this is the nature of sacred sites. Don't forget that in many parts of the world today we see vestiges of ancient traditions that either did not erect any megaliths, or else very few. They saw their myths and gods in the bark of trees, in the shape of a boulder, or else in a twisted, dead tree. The very landscape itself was seen as an open book onto which myths were emblazoned.'

'So it is the sum of all the ingredients and qualities that defines a sacred place?'

'Yes, precisely! And to deny the existence of, or indeed to take away, any of these components is a desecration. As I said before, see sacred sites not as existing ON the landscape, but rather WITHIN it. An ancient stone circle on a hilltop, a solitary megalith on a lonely moor, or indeed a ruinous chapel in a wood, are not separate from the landscape, but are part of it. The builders of such ancient places were reflecting their spirituality, which was being at one with Nature, at one with the Land. The megalithic stone sites were meant to last for an eternity, to be immortal as the Land is. They were made from the rocks of the landscape,

each component coming from the crystals and minerals of that land; components of the geology were merely being repositioned and enhanced.'

'Yes, I felt this on Dartmoor.'

'The circles of Dartmoor are made up of Dartmoor granite and the great majority of stones comprising other circles around the world are of their indigenous geology. This was not just a matter of convenience. It was because stones selected of local material enable a natural union with the energies that are sought. But even stones brought from another area because of special qualities, like the Welsh Bluestones here at Stonehenge, are still composed of natural minerals and crystals. They are part of the Earth's crust through which an interaction can take place between the life-force of the Planet and Man.'

'So the multi-faceted nature of sacred sites, such as this beauty in front of me, must mean they were used for a variety of uses.'

'Indeed. At any holy place there may have been funerary rites and interments, festival celebrations, astronomical observations, initiations, tribal elder meetings, intertribal gatherings, shamanic rituals, dream-sleeps to contact ancestors, and healing, depending on the type of site and where it was located. It is like a church - within its confines are held weddings, christenings, baptisms, services of worship, Sunday schools, fêtes, choir concerts, funerals and burial. It is a centre of the local community, as is a synagogue or a mosque. And I must also add that, be they ancient or modern, sacred sites accumulate earth energies. The more a sacred site is visited, and the more spiritual interaction takes place, the more the energetic potency builds up.'

'OK. I get that. There is also something very magnetic about an ancient site, and how it seems to blend into the landscape. I must admit that a stone circle or standing stone looks far more at home on a moor than an electricity pylon or for even a giant wind turbine. But is this just romantic nostalgia, because the stones are old and part of our spiritual heritage?'

'Well, I believe you know the answer to that one, but I will elaborate further. The pylon and the wind turbine, although very practical and useful apparatus, are not spiritual objects by any definition. They transgress the purity of the spiritually defined, mythologized, sacred landscape. They were not erected with any thought for the disruption of the flow of

earth energies or with any consideration of the places they stand on or near to. Stone circles, like the one before you, were built with total regard for the land on which they stand and with a deep respect for the landscape for miles around. These sites have an affect on the energies of other places, sometimes hundreds of miles away, so therefore were sympathetically positioned and constructed. And this is the crux of the matter. It is not just what was erected and for what purpose, but rather its position on, and connection with, the Land. This is what defines the sanctity of a prehistoric sacred site, or indeed historic ones such as Knights Templar churches or a Gothic cathedral.'

'I see. But what about the theories and arguments about what Stonehenge, and other sacred sites, are actually about; are these in danger of becoming distractions, keeping us from feeling what the place are really about?'

'A good question, my son. The reason you ask the question is because you wish to confirm what you suspect. You have remembered what we spoke about previously. The attainment of knowledge is a noble effort, and can, as a result, lead to a closer connection with the Land. But all too often the attainment of information in itself becomes a self-sustaining, insatiable beast. The bottom line is to experience and appreciate, be it a walk in the park, a night out crop circle watching, or running a ruler across a map to follow a ley. Knowledge ought to lead to experiencing and appreciating the Land. Period.'

'I guess we have come to associate wisdom with the amassing of facts and figures.'

'The attainment of knowledge for its own sake has become one of Mankind's legacies. But knowledge without direct experience of one's inner nature, or without relating to the Land, is worthless and has led Man up many blind alleys. Science is gradually discovering who I am, but is still preoccupied with what it can define and quantify, rather than on how to experience me directly. Science would come along in leaps and bounds if all scientists were spiritual. Most are a wonderful collection of either atheists or adherents to the main religions, and are thus bound by their preconceptions. But things may get there eventually, and if Science finally reaches the top of the mountain of knowledge, it shall find me waiting there with open arms.'

'I have read of those who leave crystals at sacred sites, and have seen for myself Pagans holding rituals. Can this sort of thing really make a difference?'

'It is comforting, and gives me great hope, that people are now returning in great numbers to ancient places for the purpose of giving of themselves. In the past many sacred sites were abused and desecrated, or energetically polluted by others to which they were connected. Does holding a ceremony or leaving a crystal and other items benefit a holy place? Well, the bottom line is this. With what intent is the practice carried out? If it is done out of pure love, out of genuine desire to help heal the site, the Land and ultimately the Planet, then healing is initiated. Every small act, such a crystal wedged into a fissure of a megalith, or a flower laid at its foot, or the burning of incense, or indeed a simple prayer or meditation, is beneficial in some way to the locality - if the motive is that of love.'

'And I guess a sacred place will be able to tell the difference between love and ego.'

'Oh, yes! The spirit of the place will know the difference between an act of love and one of selfish intent. Some members of Pagan groups, and many self-styled healers, are unfortunately immersed in their own self-importance. Although they themselves may be under the illusion that they act with noble intentions, they do not. How many of these people go out to sacred sites without witnesses, and do the same practices sitting in the cold, or the rain, or with no thought of how many others will witness their actions? One could argue that any act of interaction between an individual and a sacred site is useful. I would not disagree with that. But the effect is increased ten-fold if the impetus and energy is motivated by love.'

'So love will open me up to the Land and the energy of a sacred site?'

'Yes. Love in your heart for what you are doing will connect you with the Planetary heart.'

'I have been feeling more and more lately about leaving an offering or token when I visit a sacred site. I often see crystals left behind at such places. What do you have to say on this?'

'Crystals can be useful tools for healing, divination and connecting with the Earth. But try if you can to use those that originate from as near as possible to the place where they will

be used. The vibration and spirit within an indigenous crystal will be more akin and in tune with a locality. If you are leaving quartz crystals at a stone circle in Britain, make the effort to use British quartz, which is plentiful. The same goes for the purity of crystals. Some believe that the most expensive, so-called 'perfect' crystal obtained from a crystal shop will in some way effect more healing than a piece of quartz picked up with love or 'by chance' on a beach. This is a misconception.

'Some people make a lot of money out of claims about what their big, elaborate crystals are capable of.'

'There is nothing wrong with making money. But I would point out that it is the intention that is crucial, not the size of the crystal or the flawlessness of its form. The crystal you pick up on a beach or from a river bed will have been chosen by you and has been collected from a natural place. In other words, it was meant to be there and had been waiting for you. Do not forget that in the majority of cases, a crystal on sale in a shop will have been blasted from my body using dynamite, in a far-off country, using very low paid workers who toil in hazardous conditions. Then it would have been crated up with thousands of tons of others, and transported halfway across the world. How much love was involved in this process? This type of extraction causes the Land, my body, great pain. And in the process destroys most of the healing energy of a crystal, as well as forcing any Elemental beings to leave. Crystals can be recharged to a certain extent with our love and by leaving them for a while at sacred sites, but why not collect your own? A pebble collected on the beach has been waiting for you for a long time. Befriend it. Nurture it as dearly as if it had been an expensive purchase.'

'That's really funny, 'cause when I go away on holiday abroad, or even here in the UK, I try to bring back a small rock, stone or pebble as a memento. My friends also bring me back small stones when they go away, rather than postcards or trinkets.'

'This is because you or your friends bring back not just memories of a locality, but some of its energy imprint too, which you can connect with. When you feel you must purchase a crystal for earth healing, at the very least strive to procure it from an indigenous locality. Take Britain, for instance. Quartz, feldspar, jasper, calcite, mica, amethyst, citrine and a variety of other crystals can be obtained within

165

these shores. They will all be more attuned to the British landscape and its sacred sites. If you feel drawn to use a particular crystal that is only found in a foreign land, then try to choose those that have been obtained through fair trade, or collected from rivers, beaches or through non-aggressive means. If it has not, the love you wish to put into a site through your crystal may not even begin to balance the harm that was done by extraction and transportation. At the end of the day, the crystal is but a conduit for transferring your love, and an offering of a small river pebble given with love will be as powerful as any so called 'flawless' crystal. This is not to say that these more elaborate offerings don't do good, but always remember that it is not what is written on the price tag that counts, but rather what is written across your heart. And be mindful that as you leave your offering, instead of trying to change the sacred site, rather let it change you. Let sacred sites tell their own tales, rather than those you would impose on them. A sacred site possesses a big picture about the landscape in which it stands – you do not.'

'And what about the rituals that modern Pagans, Druids and others carry out at sacred sites? Does it matter what they do, or how close their practices adhere to ancient rites?'

'Another good question. Archaeologists have said that because we cannot know the details of ancient rituals at stone sites, then it is mere New Age fabrication to attempt re-enactments. Advocates of the premise that sacred sites are relics of heathen, pre-Christian practices are equally horrified at attempts to carry out 'ungodly' shenanigans, especially those encompassing nudity. Again, I tell you to look into your hearts honestly. With what intent do you approach a sacred site and carry out your ritual? Is it out of love or ego? Is it a genuine desire to heal, or the need to belong to some movement that is seen as anti-establishment? Groups gathered together in my name to revere the earth and connect with the Spirit of the Land do great good. A sacred place generally breathes a sigh of relief that rituals expressing appreciation for the Land are being carried out. Such gratitude is well received and is indeed healing. As I said, energies accumulate over a period of time and sacred places benefit when people visit them with the right intent. The simple act of meditation can change the vibration of a sacred site, so it must be done thoughtfully and responsibly.'

'But there's nothing wrong with me getting a 'high' and having a good time at a sacred site, is there?'

'Indeed not, as you have already experienced. There is nothing amiss with self-empowerment, or attaining personal benefits from such practices, for this will also indirectly heal the Planet. Your joy will ripple across the landscape. But beware the ego, which may well enter through the back door. Once again, ask yourself these questions: would you come to this place and do your ritual on your own, unobserved by others? Would you do this or that ritual with no recognition? And how can you use what has been learnt in your everyday life? Earth healing isn't just for sky-clad Full Moon gatherings in a forest clearing, no matter how healing, uplifting and powerful these may be. The Land is here '24/7', as I believe you say, and needs your help, healing and love every hour of the day and night. This is the real leap to interacting with the Land shamanically.'

A sudden chill ran through my body, as a cool wind penetrated my woollen jumper. The sun was getting low in the west. The hoards were thinning somewhat as the shadows cast by the ancient stones lengthened.

'The crowds are diminishing, My Lady. The site will be closing soon. Oh, I wish I could go inside the stone circle and experience what it's like.'

'Well, your chances of doing this are increased in proportion to the depth of your desire. Thoughts create things, remember? Have faith and see what happens.'

'OK. I will. Is that it for this time, My Lady?'

'Almost. Save to say that today many sacred places are significant less for their practical importance than for what they have come to signify. But this does not have to be the case. Remember always to approach sites with humility. Ask yourself not what you can find out about a sacred place, but rather what may be revealed to you. In studying sacred places you will not discover anything. How can you? It is already knowledge that was known and utilised. How can you 'discover' what is already there and once known before? The wisdom hidden within an ancient site is merely being revealed to you. You may, if you feel so inclined, allow yourself a sense of achievement that it was you who uncovered something that was temporarily 'lost'. But do not take too much credit for revealing the past, for this leaves the

door open for the ego to sneak in, and with that humility is lost. This is particularly true for ley hunters and dowsers. The more humble their approach, the more may be revealed to them in return. A Native American elder once said that to be a medicine man he had to be lower than a worm and higher than an eagle. Likewise, you can strive to experience life to the full.'

'OK, I understand.'

'Next month we will look at the earth energies and leys, two elements of the living landscape that you have touched upon briefly on your travels. The landscape is alive with life-force and anyone can experience these divine healing vibrations. We shall also look at how the Church built their sacred buildings on existing ancient sites, to both Christianise them and to feed on the energies.'

'OK. Cool. I will dust off my dowsing rods then.'

'Before then, tomorrow morning in fact, you may wish to go to the sacred place called Knowlton. Do you remember it?'

'Remember it? Are you kidding? You made me jump out of my skin when I first heard your voice!'

'Well, tomorrow is Autumn Equinox. Another chance to see something you missed in the Spring. Meanwhile, an old friend is now waiting to meet you, plus another soul who may soon become very special to you. Until next time, goodbye for now, my son.'

'And farewell to you, My Lady… and thank you.'

I stood up and faced the ancient stones.

'And thank you too, my ancient brothers.'

16. Drumming, Didges and Diana

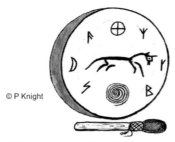

© P Knight

Nature never breaks her own laws.
(Leonardo Da Vinci)

I got up from the grass, realising that my posterior had got damp. I looked as if I had an accident of some kind. *Oh well, what the heck!* I didn't really give a damn – I was high as a kite! I passed through the tunnel, wading midst a stream of people who were now, mercifully, all heading in the same direction. On the other side I visited the facilities, before settling down on a wooden bench near the entrance.

*Well, My Lady, I would really like to go into the stones tonight. In fact, I **will** go into the stone circle tonight.*

I focused long and hard, purposefully staring at a nearby boarding which displayed a photo of the monument. I noticed that a group of interesting, rather 'alternative' looking people had gathered about twenty yards from where I sat. Some of them wore ponchos, carried drums and one guy, sporting a beard and open-toed sandals, held a didgeridoo. About a dozen of them chatted away, laughing occasionally. After about twenty minutes, the group and I were the only stragglers in the car park; all the tourist coaches having departed. I caught the eye of a couple of people in the group, and one person in particular returned my gaze. *Is it? Yes, it is.* It was Ken, the grey-bearded Einstein look-alike from the café at the Boyne Visitor Centre; He had materialised when I had

169

been despondent after failing to make contact with the Goddess, and had given me a bit of a dressing down.

We seemed to recognise each other simultaneously, and immediately began to walk towards the each other. On meeting, we embraced without hesitation. His hands were strong and his hug powerful and heart-felt. We stood back from each other and his inner beauty shone through his knowing eyes, just as it had in Ireland three months before.

'You said we'd meet again, Ken.'

'Indeed, I did. It's good to see you again, brother. Let me look at you. Ah, She has been with you again, for hers is the gleam I see in your eyes. I bet you could write a book.'

'Funny you should say that!'

We both laughed and I could again feel the bond between us.

'Tell me…', he enquired, with a glint in his eye, '… have you been in contact with her today?'

'Yes, I have. You know I have. Just now in fact. Oh Ken, the last few months have been unbelievable. You won't believe what I've been through, what I've seen, and who I have met and….'

'Hey, slow down!' he interrupted, 'First, come meet my friends.'

He put an arm around my shoulders and led me over to the group, who I realised had been watching and listening.

'This is my friend,' Ken exclaimed to the group, '… whom I met at Newgrange - the one I have been telling you of.' His brief introduction signalled both a universal greeting and unanimous acceptance. Whatever he had told them about me and my mission was obviously held in high esteem. A round of names followed and although I registered a few, remembering faces was never my strong point. Ken explained how they were part of a Pagan circle based in London, and how every year they would book one of the summer evening slots when English Heritage, in their wisdom, allowed people to go within the heart of the stones (for a fee, of course!). The group always endeavoured to pick a Full Moon night, and tonight was particularly favoured as it was Equinox. One of their number had not been able to make it, so they had a vacancy to fill. Ken put it to the group that I should take the place of their absent friend, and the motion was carried unanimously. The words of the Goddess echoed around my head. She had told me shortly before that I may get into the stones if I had enough faith and desire.

'Someone said I may get in to see the stones this evening,' I proclaimed to the group.

170

I smiled at Ken and he winked back understandingly.

The time soon came for us to go in. We filed through a turnstile, ushered through by a solitary security man. And what a difference to earlier - no crowds, no loud chattering of foreign tongues, our feet echoing through the tunnel. When we came out the other side, quite a different Stonehenge greeted me. It was about twenty-five minutes before sunset and the stones were bathed in the gentle, golden light of a low sun. The ancient, gnarled trilithons now cast long shadows and the monument was moody and morose, no longer looking as if it had been lifted from a picture postcard. The small party split up, as if everyone were attracted to different parts of the site, some sitting down whilst others circled it. I stood in utter awe for several minutes under one huge lintel, unable to pass beneath into the monument's heart. At the same time I could feel my heart chakra fill with energy and love and a beaming smile spread across my face. Eventually it felt right to enter the inner sanctum, and I joined four others who were sitting against some of the stones, all with closed eyes, their hands touching the earth. Later on I meandered around the megaliths, touching them here and there, eventually pausing to cuddle one of the smaller Welsh Bluestones, like a long-lost brother.

Facing west, the sun made me squint as it hovered seemingly motionless over the distant skyline, its rays still bright enough to cast strong shadows. The quietness of the moment was broken, albeit gently, by the sound of a single drumbeat, slow and meaningful, ancient and true. It blended perfectly with the atmosphere, adding to the scene of timeless sanctity. A rattle then joined in, and I could make out at least two people chanting a deep, repetitive mantra. I looked around to see that the whole ensemble gathered together around the west side of the inner circle, their faces glowing in the setting sun. Ken was at one end of the line and he beckoned me to join him. He handed me a rattle, which looked Celtic in design, decorated with delicate spirals and chevrons, clearly the result of someone's loving devotion. He was holding a drum, on the front of which was an image of the Uffington White Horse and other ancient glyphs. A didge growled close by, its earthy, ancient tones amplified and enhanced by the stones. The didging, drumming and rattling continued, sometimes quietly, at other times growing louder by degrees until a crescendo was attained, before settling down again to softer tones. The energy from the instruments and the chanting all combined to thrill my body to the bone.

At times it felt as if I would ascend into the skies there and then, such was the state of bliss in which I was immersed. The steady rhythms washed over me, as if I was being stroked by the very hands of the Goddess. At times it was difficult to tell the position of the origins of the sounds, and echoes made it seem as if the stones themselves were joining in the hallowed rite. The sun would come into focus, and then go out again, as I hovered between this world and other realms.

Ken leaned over to me, whispering in my ear, 'She is here. She is still here. The place is alive with her power and her love.'

'Yes, Ken. I can feel her too.'

He nodded and resumed his gaze at the sun, which was retreating behind skyline trees. And so, within a few moments, and exactly west of us, it disappeared from view. And at that precise moment, the drumming, rattling and chanting abruptly finished with incredible precision. It was as if someone had pulled a plug, for not one beat, shake or hum transgressed the sudden silence. And with that silence came a power, a rush of something magical, a potent sacredness. After a while, the group turned 180° and walked between the trilithons, halting just the other side. I followed and was invited to hold the hands of two of the female participants. One was of middle years, the other around her late teens. I wondered whether there was some teacher-initiate relationship between them. I stood awe-struck as we all looked at the risen Full Moon, which had cleared trees that surrounded a line of ancient barrows on the eastern skyline.

The elder woman of the two, whilst still clasping my hand, let out a loud invocation that pierced the dusk.

'Hail, Diana, Sovereign of the Night, Lady of the Heavens, Queen with the ever-changing face. We greet thee, we salute thee, we thank thee for thy light, for thy gift of Sight, and for thy gentle coaxing of the waters. Welcome, My Lady, to the place of our ancestors on this the balance of day and night. May you grant us the insight, wisdom, love and reverence of those who have stood here before over many eons. Enter our bodies and our very souls on this the night of Hares, and grant us your blessings. Receive our healing love and send it to wherever it is needed.'

The whole group greeted the end of her recital with a hearty chorus of, 'So Mote It Be!'

We then stood motionless and silent for I don't know how long. We were transfixed by the luminous silver orb before us, and I was oblivious to the world around me, save for the occasional flashing car headlamp and blinking aircraft light. The moon's light filled my being with love and a soft, healing energy. All those gathered there were united as one, with each other and with the ancestors of the stones, whom I'm sure were looking down on us.

'OK folks, time's up please, thank you.'

The voice came from behind us and brought me suddenly, too suddenly, back to this world. On turning, I was greeted by a uniformed security guard, who in all fairness had kept a respectful distance. I wondered what he had made of it all, although I guess over the years he must have seen far more bizarre practices.

We shuffled reluctantly away from the stones, some of the group turning to say 'thank you' to an unseen yet potent presence. I too paused and bowed in the direction of the ancient stones, which were now even more sombre and mysterious in the increasing gloom. Back at the car park, the chat was jovial and some bread and a cask of homemade mead were passed around. Although I had only met most of those present about an hour before, I was bonded to them by our common love for ancient sites and the Land, the Goddess.

It was with some surprise however, that the young woman who had held my hand at the moonrise came up to me and started up a conversation. She explained about her calling to all things Pagan, in particular the Moon Goddess. Her name was, wait for it, Diana! It was her birth name too, and not merely adopted to suit her present beliefs or a passing whim. Under a purple satin cloak, she wore a silver crescent moon pendant with a moonstone set in its heart, and a silver bangle with an identical design. Her hair was flaming red, and her eyes flashed like diamonds, revealing the spirit of someone who was experiencing life to the full. She was articulate and confident and I was fascinated by her exploits and adventures and, yes, was also in awe of her physical beauty. As she talked I thought how wonderful it was that someone so young was into all this. There must surely be hope for the planet.

'Ken has told me so much about you,' she said, 'in fact he keeps on about you. He is so excited about the new messages coming from the Goddess through you. He feels there is real magic afoot and that things are going to change for the better.'

'God, you make me feel like Neo in *The Matrix*,' I replied, 'you know, as if Ken has at last found *The One*.' We both laughed and our eye contact was electric.

'I'm just an ordinary guy, you know, although in the past I felt something was going on behind the scenes that I wasn't aware of.'

173

'I know what you mean. But you must face it - you *are* blessed. Of all the billions of people on the Planet, you have been chosen. That would blow my mind.'

'Believe me, Diana, it nearly has blown mine a few times! Even now, after all these months, I sometimes have to nip myself. From time to time I stop and think, 'this is all completely nuts!', feeling that She has got it all wrong. You know, some Universal cock-up was made, and She actually got the wrong person, and perhaps is too polite to come clean.'

Diana reached forward, grabbing both my hands.

'Well, I think She chose well.' Her eyes penetrated my very soul and something stirred within that had not done so for many years.

We separated and both circulated around the group, as we all exchanged thoughts on the evening. Yet all the time, my eyes kept seeking out Diana. And I noticed that whenever I caught sight of her, she was returning my gaze. I know, this is starting to sound like some perverted Mills and Boon or Barbara Cartland novel. I can just see it now: '*Their eyes met across a crowded stone circle!*' But in those visual exchanges something *was* passing between us. *You are beautiful, and spiritual, and...*

Then, without warning, I seem to have once again slipped into another of my Gollum moments: *get a grip man, you're twice her age… that's OK… cradle-snatcher… she's old enough… she is in awe of us, we cannot takes advantage… ah, but she likes us, so who would be taking advantage of who?… we've been on our own now for ages…. exactly, too long!… yes, we likes her... then we should tell her she is the Precious, before one of these fat Hobbitses beats us to it.*

Wow! Time out!

I took a deep breath and ran my fingers through my hair. Well, at least that hadn't fallen out like Gollum's, and I was still fully clothed. *Note to self: Don't watch any more re-runs of Lord of the Rings!* Thankfully, Ken approached, like Gandalf the Grey on his white charger, as if to rescue my sanity.

'Well, we're off now. Even followers of the Goddess have to go to work in the morning, and we have a way to go. We came in our minibus, somewhere over there. It's quite old now, and sometimes I think it's only our faith that holds it together! Let's not leave it so long next time, hey? Good luck my friend. Never lose your connection to her. She is everything. We all need you. So much is in your hands. But I know they are safe hands.'

He thrust a small piece of paper in my hand, on which was his new phone number. Hugs all round followed, as each in turn said their goodbyes to me, before fading into the blackness of the far end of the car park. Finally there was only one person left facing me. It was, of course, Diana.

'Well, then, I guess it's so long for now,' although as I said it, I hoped with all my heart that it would not be.

'Does it have to be goodbye?' Diana replied, looking slightly nervous. 'Look, don't get me wrong,' she continued, 'I don't usually come on to guys like this, but the connection I feel for you is surging through my body. Surely you feel it too?'

She was beautiful and desirable, there was no denying it, but I suspected that she might fancy me simply because of my mission.

'Look', I replied, '… of course I feel the same. You are gorgeous and spiritual and you are desirable, you bet. But I have to do what is honourable and respectful. This must overrule all else.'

She reached out and gently held my hands in hers. Her fingers were long, soft, and tingled with energy.

'I appreciate and respect what you say,' she went on, 'But you would do neither us any favours by saying goodnight to me now. I come to you under no illusions, for lovemaking is an act that honours the Goddess. In all of Nature beings make love as an expression of life. To deny our feelings is to deny the primal feelings that flow throughout the whole Universe. Our Lady rejoices in people's happiness and in physical union when carried out with respect and love and with no ulterior motive other than expressing the joy of Life. Look, the full face of the Lady of the Night blesses us. This night, this moment, will never happen again. Please, let us be as one tonight. I would feel honoured and truly blessed to spend the night with the emissary of My Lady.'

'No!' I replied, '… for it is *I* who would be honoured. You speak words that could have been spoken by the Goddess herself. You are truly one with her spirit. OK, Diana, Moon Goddess, let's go.'

She kissed me gently on the cheek and we both stood hand in hand gazing up at the Moon. We drove home to my place, and I made love to the Goddess incarnate that night, with the Full Moon illuminating our bodies as it shone through my window. I experienced a night of truly sacred bliss that will live in my memory forever.

That day I had felt the love of two divine beings.

17. Eighth Moon - October: Wayland's Smithy
Lesson – Leys & Earth Energies

© P Knight

Early on Brighid's morn,
Shall the serpent come from the hole,
And I will not harm the serpent,
Nor will the serpent harm me.
(Old Gaelic Hymn)

In the morning, Diana and I made our way to Knowlton in the growing light of dawn. It was chilly and the grass was damp under our feet as we entered the Neolithic henge. Several wisps of thin cloud hung over the brightening eastern sky as we sat against one of the buttresses of the ruined Norman church that stood inside the earthen banks. Life felt good as we cuddled under a large blanket I had produced from the boot of my car (I was by now a veteran of cold sunrises). We were two people with a common sense of purpose snuggled together awaiting the Sun God to arise. In the next field stood a mound called the Great Barrow, the largest prehistoric burial mound in Dorset. Yet it was more than that. My ancestors had positioned it with exquisite accuracy so that every year at the March and September Equinoxes the sun would rise out of its mysterious body - the Sky Father reborn out of the Earth Mother's tummy, when day and night were equal, in balance. We both sensed the energies of the place trickle through our bodies as we sat on the earth, and even the buttress we leant

176

against tingled with the life-force of the awakening Land. The church itself seemed to be awaiting the warmth that would follow sunrise.

And then, there He was. The sun, orange and huge, rose over the centre of the mound, taking his time to clear the trees that had made their home on it. *Wow!* Diana and I both shared the feeling that we were not alone, for the spirits of our ancestors were also with us, to observe the sacred spectacle. It was an incredible feeling knowing that thousands of years ago others had observed and honoured the same event from where we sat. It was like being transported back in time in the *Tardis*. At that moment I felt at one with my distant ancestors and wondered if *I* had in fact been there before, in a former life, to watch the rising sun.

Later that day Diana went back to London. Although we exchanged addresses, phone numbers and e-mails, we acknowledged that we both led busy, independent lives that were focused on different goals - I with my work for the Goddess, and Diana with her art. She was developing a style of Pagan-influenced art, which was stunning. Although we shared a love and respect for the Earth and the Goddess, and a mutual appreciation of each other's body and soul, our time was consumed with too much other stuff for anything closer to develop. (The lovemaking had been incredible and we would indeed get together occasionally to explore the beauty of both visiting sites and of being with each other. In fact we agreed that the reason it was great was that we got together so infrequently. That way we had heaps to talk about and the lovemaking stayed new and alive with inventiveness. You better believe it!)

And after she had left, I did my weekly shop at Waitrose - down to earth with a bump or what! But there was a distinct difference from before. Something had changed within me, even around the scrum and bustle of the checkout. I now had an inner peace surpassing anything I had experienced in years of meditation or Ohm-chanting. And what made it so powerful was the fact that I was indeed feeling that Divine connection even in shopping malls and other everyday circumstances, rather than just in silent meditation or on some weekend workshop. This was the real thing. I belonged; I belonged to the Land; I belonged to the Goddess; I belonged to myself. Yet I was still part of society, and that was surely the way forward. It was no longer a time to sit cross-legged up a mountain on the road to Kathmandu, but to bring back what we learn and assimilate it into Society. It was education and assimilation, not isolation, which had to be the next step towards saving the Planet.

During much of October I read a lot, made several trips out to sacred sites in the South, and tried my hand at dowsing. My dowsing rods twitched a number of times but I was never really sure if I was picking up earth energies or an underground sewer. I needed help. I went to a meeting of the Wessex Dowsers in Wareham. On the way there, I again let my twisted imagination out to play to tackle the question of dowsers. What *do* you call a collection of dowsers anyway? A swing of dowsers? A twitch of dowsers? A flow of dowsers? And I also thought of other issues that occupied the thoughts of probing minds: Do dowsers take the Michael (or the Mary!)? Do dowsers swing? Do they go ley line dancing - dowsey doe, take your partner by the rod? And do they have a spring in their foot? And what about the cost of their equipment – were pendulums spiralling out of control? And, as with the croppies, did dowsers go around in circles?

But my arrival at the Wareham meeting was quite a culture shock. Now I had expected to see a load of long-haired hippy types with a dowsing rod in one hand and a spliff in the other, as well as a copious number of rainbow-knitted jumpers, and perhaps some Gothy-looking dudes in black thrown in for good measure. But at the front desk I was met by a middle-aged lady, in a tweed suit, sporting a string of pearls and a bright silver brooch shaped like a peacock. Looking around the room I spied an assortment of people ranging from their late-twenties to around ninety! *OK, I've got the wrong night or venue and have walked into a meeting of the local branch of Rotary or Saga. Perhaps they could dowse with knitting needles?* But then I spotted a couple of men brandishing dowsing rods, as well as a woman in a tartan shawl who was holding a pendulum that was spinning around as if it were about to take off, taking her with it!

The upshot of the evening was that I got some instructions on dowsing and heard some amazing experiences of what dowsers can achieve, such as finding lost objects, locating buried megaliths, detecting and healing the body's illnesses, and a whole variety of fascinating activities. The preoccupation with most in the group was dowsing earth energies, as they twisted and spiralled their way to and through sacred sites. Someone had a map of Stonehenge and the whole site was awash with scores of energy lines running through it, looking as if an intoxicated spider had stepped in some ink and staggered across the map. No wonder the place was so powerful, and I could see why the Goddess wanted to put me right about leys and earth energies.

Leys, in particular, intrigued me. I had thought previously that *ley lines* were the creases left on bed sheets after love making, but evidently there was more to it than that! Over the next few weeks I absorbed myself in studying leys and earth energies, surfing the Net and browsing bookshops. I had no doubt that the Goddess would fill me in on what was really relevant and what was not, but I was totally fascinated by the whole subject. I studied *The Sun and the Serpent*, by Hamish Miller and Paul Broadhurst, referred to in other works as being the classic of its kind. I was very impressed and read it through twice in a fortnight. Many readers may be familiar with the work, but a quick résumé may be useful at this juncture.

The authors followed the alignment known as the St Michael Line, which runs from Cornwall across Southern England to East Anglia. En route it passes through many major sacred sites, such as St Michael's Mount, Glastonbury and Avebury, to name but three. But what they found was that the energy did not travel up the alignment at all, but in fact looped around it, making a double helix or caduceus pattern. They also recognized two distinct energies. The first was the so-called Michael current, so named because of its 'male', yang energy, and the fact that it flowed through churches dedicated to the winged saint. The other flow they named Mary, because of its 'feminine', yin vibrations. The latter flowed through churches dedicated to Mary and other female saints, as well as through holy springs and wells, which had Goddess qualities. Recent research had shown that major flows of energy even had unique 'signatures', sacred symbols that could be dowsed or visualized. These could be five-pointed stars, or roses, or other forms, and which were unique to any one ley.

I found all this fascinating, and more proof that the Land was bursting with life-force and that the energy currents dowsed were the Goddess's equivalent of veins and arteries and, in the case of major leys, perhaps the central nervous system. This was probably why I found it all so engrossing, the fact that there was living proof (quite literally) that the landscape had an invisible yet palpable spiritual essence. Some dowsers, however, looked at these energies through more 'scientific' and rational eyes, seeing the flows as mere 'electromagnetic' or 'magnetic' forces, lacking consciousness or spirit. To me, they were failing to see the whole point of the exercise, that through dowsing and sensing earth

179

energies we can contact Divinity directly, removing from the equation the need for holy books, dogma and priests.

As the month progressed and the days got shorter and cooler, I started to focus on where My Lady would talk with me at the forthcoming Full Moon. One night, just three days before full, I felt drawn to lift *The Sun and the Serpent* from my swelling bookshelf, even though it was already well thumbed and absorbed. I turned and peered through the patio doors, from where I could see the Lady of the Night returning my gaze. I went outside onto the patio, book in hand, and closed my eyes.

'Right, My Lady, where is it to be?'

I closed my eyes and focused. Soon, in my mind's eye, I could see the Full Moon, which was shining in a clear sky, illuminating a small wood. I could then make out a cluster of ancient stones in a clearing within a ring of trees. In my mind's eye I walked closer, to find that I was standing in front of the entrance of a chambered long barrow.

'Ah ha! There you are!'

It felt right to open my eyes and to simultaneously open the book at random. I did so and could make out an illustration, but the light was too poor to make out any detail. I stepped back through the patio doors into the welcome warmth of my lounge – the nights were getting chillier as winter beckoned. I looked again at the page (p194) and there, exactly as I had seen in it my mind's eye outside - was a photograph of Wayland's Smithy. It was situated near the southern extremity of Oxfordshire and I remembered reading about it before, in that book and elsewhere. It was a long barrow that had been modified during its long history, and that huge megaliths had been erected around the entrance, at the eastern end. An ancient ridgeway ran close by, connecting it to other ancient sites, such as the White Horse of Uffington, not far to the east. The photo of Wayland's reminded me of West Kennet long barrow, at Avebury, for at both sites my ancestors had clearly attempted to a create womb-like chamber within the earth, where they could presumably immerse themselves in the female energies of the Goddess.

It was around noon on the day of the Full Moon when I parked up at the side of the road near a sign that said Odstone Farm. *That's odd!* Opposite me was a lane that ascended the slopes of the Downs, and I looked up to the top of the ridge where I knew Wayland's Smithy waited. There were several clumps of trees on the skyline and I knew not which was my destination. I stashed my dowsing rods in one pocket of my waterproof coat, donned my hiking boots and was off. The ascent was gentle at first but then steepened considerably, making the last ten minutes tough going. Even on a cool October afternoon, with no sun and a chilling wind, I was short of breath by the time the ground levelled out. I arrived at the point where the ancient ridgeway track crossed and turned left, taking the advice of a sign directing me to the long barrow.

After just a few hundred metres of level walking along an ancient track lined with hedgerows and clumps of trees, I arrived. Another wooden sign directed me left, through some tall beeches, until a clearing opened up before me. And there stood the resplendent Wayland's Smithy. A façade of four huge megaliths rose like surfacing whales, two each side of the entrance of the mound. I scanned the scene before me – I was alone. *Good!* I felt the need to walk around the monument first, and found many smaller stones lining the outline of the 4ft high trapezoid mound. Leaves littered the floor and gathered in small heaps in the spaces between some of the smaller stones. A couple of the beeches were already shedding their foliage, and the rest would soon follow - winter was approaching.

Sunset was still many hours away but with almost total cloud cover I knew it would get dark early. I was about a mile from the nearest homestead and realized that if I was to stay there until after sunset, it was going to be a dark descent. Still, who knew where the Goddess would send me. Having completed my circuit of the long barrow, I stood still outside the entrance, peering into the darkness of the interior. I knew that the chamber was not as deep as the Irish ones I had visited, but it was more than dark enough for me. I stepped over a low stone that straddled and barred the way into the chamber, and had a mind to sit on it. It was about the height of a chair and was comfortable. I sat spellbound, looking into the darkness of the chamber, and even from this closer viewpoint was still unable to make out any detail within. Excavations had revealed eight skeletons in the chamber, although over a dozen more had been found in earlier graves under the centre of the mound. It seemed as if the dead would rise and walk out of the darkness at any moment.

I contemplated the legend that gave the place its name. Wayland was the smith of the Norse gods. Legend says that when Christianity superseded the old ways, the Pagan gods had to work for their living. Wayland became a travelling smithy, shoeing horses and that one of his haunts was the barrow, fittingly close to the Uffington White Horse. The Saxons may have regarded the latter as Odin's horse Sleipner, which led to the long barrow being regarded as a smithy. It was said that any traveller needing his horse shod could leave his horse tethered to one of the stones, and deposit a coin on the capstone. On his return next morning the horse would be shod. I wondered if perhaps the legend was a corruption of some other practices of a more spiritual kind that went on eons ago. Were coins left on the capstone as votive offerings, in return for the vision or prophecy of an oracle?

I heard voices behind me, as unseen people passed by along the Ridgeway, but mercifully these faded into the distance. Silence was resumed; save for the rustling of leaves that still desperately clung on to branches that swayed in the autumn breezes sweeping across the hill. I rose to my feet, as I was now ready to enter the chamber. I again surveyed my surroundings and was pleased that I was still the only human around, although by no means did I feel alone. I approached the entrance to the chamber and peered inside. I had to stoop to enter and remained in that posture as I explored the interior. As my eyes got accustomed to the gloom, I could make out that I was in a chamber about 6ft in diameter, and that three antechambers accompanied it, their sum forming a cruciform structure. I shuffled over to the back wall and sat down, facing the daylight of the outside world. Something happened to me whenever I went into ancient chambered mounds, such as Newgrange, Fourknocks, and now Wayland. It was like going back in time. In fact, time seemed to be left behind, having no meaning or control any more. I felt safe and nurtured within the womb of the Great Mother.

Suddenly a strong breeze entered the chamber and brought with it a few dozen leaves, which jostled and danced around me until they settled to the earthen floor. I knew She had arrived.

'Good afternoon, My Lady'

'And a good afternoon to you too.'

'That was quite a dramatic entrance.'

'Oh, I do like to make an entrance every now and again. Nature is about drama and the theatrical. How are you?'

'I am well, as you well know, my Mother. And this place is powerful. I swear I can feel my ancestors around me.'

'That is because they are, my son, they are. No mystery. Just because you cannot see something does not mean it is not here. Look....'

With those words I caught something move out of the corner of

182

my eye. As I turned I just caught the back of a man wearing long hair and an animal skin disappearing into the solid walls of the chamber.

'Wow! Hold the phone. Wasn't ready for that! Phew. Was that display just for me?'

'Well, now, that all depends. Things just happen. Synchronicity, remember? Would the apparition have appeared at that precise moment if you had not been here? Perhaps. Did your presence trigger the apparition? Perhaps. All things are bound together on the Web of Wyrd and therefore cannot be separated. Things happen because they are meant to, often for a variety of different reasons, depending on the individual participants.'

'Yes, I remember, but it is no less a shock when I see a prehistoric-looking dude disappear into solid rock. Mind you, nothing should surprise me anymore, should it?'

'Indeed not. Expect nothing and you will gain untold magic and wonder. It is only the constraints of the human mind that disempower most people from the realms of fairy, myth and magic. And you know by now that the rock face isn't really solid anyway, is it?'

'So why are we here, at this ancient place, for this Full Moon?'

'And Full Moon it surely is, in about half an hour, in fact. Well, you have been absorbing yourself in dowsing and looking at ley lines in recent weeks, and this is good because I will lay out truths today to clear up many modern myths about the subject, as well as teach you how to follow the pulse of my body and immerse yourself in the living flow of my love. Now, please make yourself comfortable.'

I leaned back and nestled into the large megalith behind me, finding a smooth portion to lean on at the third attempt.

'OK. *Ley* it all on me, My Lady!'

'This holy place stands midst energies associated with one of the main solar lines of cosmic power – the Belinus Line. Take time now to soak up the healing energy. Ponder on the fact that the energy you feel surging through your body was in the Isle of Wight first thing this morning. The flow of my life-force is eternal and never-ending and after passing through here, will travel onward to the far north of Scotland, flowing through many sacred sites on the way. See this flow not as electricity passing along a line of pylons, but rather as a conscious force, imbued with purpose, vitality and life.'

'OK. But I've read somewhere that there is a difference between leys and energy flows, isn't there?'

Do not concentrate on defining what you see around you, for people have this distracting, and at times detracting, habit of pigeonholing everything. Save to say this: ley lines are by definition alignments of sacred sites, often but not always astronomically aligned, running across the Land, sometimes defined by a narrow corridor of sites. They are man-made, even though many of them make the most of natural features too, which in turn may be astronomically aligned. Indeed, a sacred hill or spring may have been the origin of a ley. Your distant ancestors often aligned their sacred sites with cosmic events, such as the rising or setting of the sun, moon or bright stars, even supernova and comets. Other leys were laid out on the Land to commemorate the spirit flight of shamans, as well as to be 'flight paths' for those who would follow. They sought to connect with the heavenly bodies and the energies they emanated. Man has sought contact with the spirits of the celestial bodies since the earliest times. Some other leys have been called Death Roads, as they mark ancient funerary routes. Again, people honouring their ancestors.'

'But wasn't it Alfred Watkins in the 1920's who said that leys were laid down as prehistoric tracks?'

'Indeed, he did. Alfred was a sincere man, a pioneer, who laid down the foundations of research for those who followed generations later. But he did not see the true spiritual nature and significance of leys. He saw them only in practical terms, for he was a down-to-earth man. Now, along many of these leys (the genuine ones, that is!) there would be places such as stone circles, wells and springs, holy hills, sacred groves, megaliths and so on, which would have been visited by pilgrims and shamans over many centuries. Do you follow?'

'I do.'

'And this is where Alfred's straight tracks come in. They were of secondary origin, evolving out of people developing tracks whilst visiting the sacred places on the leys. He saw nothing of the shaman on the hilltop projecting his consciousness along a ley to the rising sun. He saw nothing of the shaman's spirit flying over the Land. And he saw nothing of the torch-lit beacons that spread in succession along the leys as each in turn observed the sunrise on sacred

festival mornings.'

'So many leys are a genuine phenomenon, then? Archaeologists would disagree, I am sure.'

'In fairness to those noble scientists, many leys are indeed a product of the modern imagination. But many more are ancient in origin. The problem has been akin to crop circle research, where hoaxes have been detrimental, to the extent that scientists do not accept my genuine works of art. And it is so with ley lines too, as many are indeed not prehistoric in origin. The mystery is deciding which are!'

'Miller, Broadhurst and others, tell us that the earth energies do not travel in straight lines along a ley, but curve and spiral and meander around the axis. Is this true?'

'Indeed, it is. That is not to say that every ley has powerful energetic components, or that every ley has energy that is detectable to humans. Again, do not pigeonhole. Treat every case on its merits and although basic principles apply to most sacred places, do not presume that all of these elements are present. Much depends on the local geology, topography, design of the sacred site, positioning of stones and mounds, which local emphasis that was prevalent, the purpose for which a sacred site was built, and many other factors. We spoke before how sites are multi-faceted, so do not project your expectations onto the sacred places you visit. This will also affect the way you interpret your dowsing results, just as quantum physics scientists have found that their expectations can affect the results of their experiments.'

'Some authors make the earth look like a huge energy grid rather than the living conscious being you are.'

'This is still a problem with many. You can be an atheist and be a fine dowser. You can be a Christian priest or Jewish Rabbi and be a fine dowser. But as long as you believe that you are dowsing forces that are inorganic and lifeless, you will never discover what it really means. People have once again got locked into the brain, into thinking, into analyzing. All I really want you to do is feel, and sense and love. You see, the bottom line of dowsing, when all said and done, is to prove to mankind that there is consciousness and a living spiritual essence held within the Land. All else is a sideshow! It is true that dowsing can do excellent work in healing the Land, individuals, as well as houses and animals, and it is good that people are discovering this aspect of energy. But

185

do not forget that every single atom of energy used in healing or detecting anything or anyone is part of my body, part of my consciousness. This is the bottom ley line!'

'Nice pun! I'll make a comedian of you yet.'

'The whole of nature is full of humour. I did create Mankind after all!'

'True enough. You must have been in a funny mood that day. But please tell me, the way we build our houses and motorways and pylons on the Land, does this not adversely affect the flows of energy and life-force?'

'Indeed it does, and at times in a very harmful way. In fact, I feel the pain of it often. Imagine your arteries being blocked. Very soon you would have a stroke and need surgery. Imagine what damage is done when a power station, or housing estate, or sewage pipe, or motorway, is built across a stretch of land that was previously and preciously virgin and pure. The surface energies are scattered, blocked, or become sluggish, unable to follow their preferred way across the Land. They often have to divert underground or else take a detour of many miles. Or they may forge ahead across the obstacle, becoming corrupted in the process, energetically polluting the Land further down the flow.'

'I have been reading about the Feng Shui practitioners in the Far East, such as in China, who make sure that new buildings are positioned with the landscape in mind.'

'This is a very good way to live in harmony with Nature. In fact, it is the only way that does not harm the Land and, as a consequence, Mankind. Unfortunately, modern buildings and roads are erected with no prior consideration of the earth energies or leys, and as a consequence damage the Land. The energies flowing across the surface are not wholly destroyed but it takes time and effort for them to be diverted. And in this diversion there will never be the purity of flow of the original current, for it is not flowing where it wants and needs to, but rather where it has been forced to go.'

'I get really upset when I see new pylons, phone masts or other monstrosities going up in the countryside. Is there hope for the Land?'

'Of course, there is. The Land is eternal. Is there hope for Mankind is the real issue here. And that is where you and others like you come in, spreading the word about the damage being done, as well as telling others of the spiritual

186

essence of Nature. There is most definitely hope, or else you would not be sitting in this sacred chamber. And there is much you can do to heal sites such as this.'

'There is?'

'Most certainly. You can focus on sending out love, and it will ripple across the Land to other places it is energetically linked with, which is, ultimately, everywhere! Send your love out across the world to wherever it is needed. Just send it, pure and sincere. I will direct the flow to where it is most needed. Yes, there is most definitely hope for the Land and, as part of the Land, you can instigate healing wherever you go.'

'That's good enough for me. Say, I brought my dowsing rods.'

'Then let's have a play with them. Come... outside.'

I went back out into the light and stretched my limbs in the chilled October air. I held my two dowsing rods, one in each hand.

'Right. Now, as you know it is predominantly my feminine current that flows through this place. See if you can pick me up. Just concentrate on dowsing the yin flow and nothing else. You will only detect that which you focus on. Please commence.'

'OK. Here we go.'

I walked slowly around the edge of the mound in a clockwise direction, watching and waiting for any twitch or swing of my rods. As I did so I mumbled a continuous, repetitive mantra:

'Please show me the female current of the Belinus Line... the Mary current of the Belinus Line...'

After about forty yards there was still nothing. I rounded the corner at the rear of the mound, the opposite end to the chamber, and suddenly the rods crossed. I stopped dead. I was on the axis of the long barrow. I continued further and within a few feet the rods magically uncrossed.

'Wow!'

'Wow, indeed. It warms my heart every time someone feels my presence. Please carry on and see what happens.'

I did so and for the whole length of the mound nothing happened. I came around the corner and passed the large stones again and, as I stood outside the chamber on the axis of the mound, the rods crossed again.

'Here my feminine current flows along the axis of the barrow, as it does indeed at many others. Now put one rod down and just use the other. This way you can follow a flow,

as it twists and turns, like a serpent coiling and zigzagging across the Land.'

I did as I was instructed and stood there with just one rod in my right hand. I took a step forward and immediately the rod swung to the left. I followed it, keeping my body behind. The rod meandered and veered off, the serpentine-like energies leading me over the low stone and into the chamber itself. I crouched down, taking care to keep the dowsing rod level so not to tilt it by accident. In the center of the chamber the rod went berserk, spinning round and round in an ever-decreasing coil. I sat down at the apex of the invisible vortex.

'Now isn't that neat! You followed the current into the chamber and found that it disappeared into the ground in a spiralling nature. This is the sacred heart of the mound, where overground energy connects with my deeper underground life-force. In many cases, the spirals you saw carved on the rocks in Ireland were telling of this phenomenon. The sacred geometry of these ancient chambers channels the energies, to focus and amplify them. This was done partly to ensure the health of the alignment and the surrounding Land, but also to enable shamans and priestesses to access this sacred spirit, for divination and healing. Now close your eyes.'

As I did so, I instantly became aware of a stream of faint energy, a dim but definite white light that was flowing into the chamber. The light became gradually brighter and I could now make out the spiralling energies my rods had followed. The flow was rapid and went downward in a coiled motion into the ground beneath where I sat. I felt my body fill with this powerful force, consuming my entire being. I let myself go with it and my upper body swayed, as it mirrored the spiralling flow into the earth. My head began to spin as the motion quickened and the lights brightened. Giddy and unbalanced, I fell onto my back, hitting the cold earth with a thud. After the initial shock, my eyes opened and all was once again still, dark and silent.

'How are you feeling? A little heady, no doubt. My energies flowed through you and fed on you, as you fed on the current. You were one. That is the whole point.'

'So every time I pick up an energy current with my rods or pendulum, or just feel it in my body, then I am feeling you, feeling your pulse, your veins and arteries, your heartbeat, your spirit.'

'Yes, my son, yes. That's it! That is precisely it. But be very

188

specific in what you dowse for. It is not sufficient to ask for 'earth energies' or 'energy', for everything in the physical universe is energy! Be specific and focused. And do not put the preconceptions of others into a place. Find out for yourself. You may go out with your newly acquainted dowsing friends, and I think you ought to, and you may all pick up the same energies at times, and at others you may pick up flows that no one else can. Remember what I said, that each of you has a unique relationship with me, with the Land, so why suppose you would detect exactly the same vibrations? That is the way of science – repeatable experiment. It is not the way of Spirit. You are all unique and it is what you find out through your uniqueness that is your greatest gift to me, and to the evolution of the planet. Have faith in what you feel. Your feelings never lie, only your mind may do that, through misinterpretation.'

'So if I go outside now, I could pick up other energies that I did not earlier, because I was not focused on them.'

'Exactly. Have a go. You will find that the whole place is alive with flows, spirals, spirits, Elementals, ancestral memory. Free your mind and open your heart to the wonder of it all.'

I recovered my stance and went back outside brandishing both rods, and went about experiencing Wayland's Smithy. I asked for earth energies associated with the four tall megaliths, and found that flows were attracted to each of them. They were like huge bar magnets attracting and sucking in energy from the surrounding landscape. I also asked to be shown where the former burial place was, on top of the mound, and my rods duly crossed at a point that felt about right. A flow from one of the stones went directly to the largest of the beech trees, spiralling around it before shooting off in the direction of the White Horse, to the east.

'I can dowse!'

'But of course you can, everyone has that potential. It just takes a leap of faith, an open mind and, of course, an open heart. You, my friend, are developing all of these traits. But wait…'

'What is it?'

'About half a mile away a group of people have just made the decision to visit this holy place. So we must leave soon. Anyway, I wish to show you some other aspects of earth energies. We will follow my Mary flow of the St Michael Line,

which passes close to here, and see where she takes us, including some local churches. Ogbourne St Andrew would be a good place to begin.'

I made my way to the edge of the site and, as was now my usual practice, turned and bowed in gratitude to the spirits of the place. This time, the Goddess replied:

'Thank you. You are most welcome. Now let us go!'

I made my way back along the ridgeway and as I started my descent to the car I came upon a group of ramblers, about ten in all. We passed each other, exchanging greetings, and I heard one say to his companions that they would have to go left to Wayland's Smithy. With a smile I hotfooted it down to my vehicle and, after a quick check of the map, was on my way.

It only took about a fifteen-minute drive west to get to my destination, the church at Ogbourne St Andrew. The *Sun and the Serpent* described how the Michael and Mary currents converged there and of a powerful node of energy on top of a prehistoric mound, which rose inside the churchyard. It was a classic place of site evolution, whereby the Church took over an existing sacred place. Going through the churchyard gates I saw the large mound on my left, which was now overgrown with large trees and bushes.

'Long before the followers of the one God came, that mound was here, marking out, and basking in, the flow. For thousands of years it has stood guard, an eternal testimony to knowledge almost lost. But there is something else awaiting you here, something special that no one before has paid much heed to. Have a look around.'

I did a quick scan of the churchyard. There was a collection of yews and tombstones - nothing unusual there. I felt the urge to walk to the east end of the church and on arrival had another look around. Then I saw it. To my right, about twenty yards away, was a large stone. I went over to take a closer look. It looked like a sarsen stone, like those at Avebury, and was about 4ft long, standing about 3ft tall.

'Well done. You have found the ancient one. The authors of your excellent book missed it, for the fence next to it has only recently been repaired and the undergrowth cleared as a consequence. You have found your first ley line mark stone. Congratulations!'

I bristled with pride as I surveyed *my stone,* and cleared some decaying plant stems from around the sides with my boots.

190

'But be mindful of what I told you before. When you find a 'new' stone, or suspect a ley alignment, do not let your ego take control. Be proud and pleased that you have been the instrument through which some of your spiritual heritage has been revealed, but do not think for a second that you would have found anything if the spirit of the place did not want it revealed. This is how a sacred stone can go unnoticed for centuries until someone comes along with new eyes to see. Love, humility and a different way of thinking opens the door of knowledge. Go on, dowse. Have fun!'

I picked up two flows with my dowsing rods, one coming from the mound, the other from the east end of the church. I then sat on my newly found stone brother, and could instantly feel the tingling thrill of planetary life-force flowing from the stone through my body.

'Now let us go into the church. There is much to see there too. It is good to frequent a church that stands on a ley, for it may have been built to Christianise a place that the local people already held as being holy. The Church was only too aware that such places were powerful conduits with which to connect with divinity.'

I stood at the porch, looking up at two gargoyles that returned my gaze from the top of the tower.

'Winged dragons and other creatures of mythology guard the leys. Look for them when you visit a church for they are clues that the site is on a sacred alignment.'

'But isn't an ancient site ruined by the erection of a church, such as here?'

'Well, many people would tell you so, especially those who hold more fundamentalist Pagan beliefs. They still blame the present Church for atrocities carried out by its misguided members hundreds of years ago. Every religion condemns that which it seeks to replace. The Church sought to convert here, so built this church on an existing sacred place. But I say this. Indeed recognise your Pagan heritage and honour those ancestors who died for their ideals and practices so that the old ways would be handed down. But do not become embroiled and embittered, for in doing so you are sending out negativity into the Cosmos, anger that spreads like a virus, to the extent that you will take it with you to ancient sacred sites. The past is done, and although you can look

back to learn from past 'mistakes', do so in a positive way, in a way that will help humanity move forward.'

'Sounds cool to me.'

'As to whether the erection of a Church, Abbey, temple, synagogue or mosque built on an ancient site is negative in the long run, depends on the intent of the original builders, as well as the design. Sites have indeed been irreparably damaged by a desire to destroy all vestiges of previous faiths. But in many cases, churches were built by wise men, such as the Templars, who knew that the power of their building would be greatly increased if they worked with the natural forces that flowed through the site and, accordingly, their architecture accesses and enhances the energies. Although much damage has been done through ignorance and a desire to control, there are also countless cathedrals, abbeys and lesser foundations that have actually had a beneficial effect on currents. St Michael's Mount in Cornwall is a fine example, as too Rosslyn Chapel, Chartres and Rennes-le-Chateaux. These and places like them were built with sacred geometry in mind, as well as paying heed to the position in the landscape.

'So Man enhanced what was already there, rather than destroying it.'

'Yes. In some cases a simple shrine or small stone circle was developed into something much grander, to procure a closer connection to divine forces – to get closer to their God – closer to me. A good example of this is how Stonehenge developed over many hundreds of years, from a simple enclosure of wooden posts, through to a simple stone circle, eventually to a much grander design. An evolution took place. Unfortunately, little heed is paid to natural forces when a new religious building is planned today, and damage to the Land results, especially in Britain, where the major energy flows are relatively close together.'

'OK. So what will I find inside this church?'

'Everything inside is a testimony to me for I am the same divinity they pray to, make no mistake. A rose by any other name... The Church has chiefly focused, however, on the male aspect of divinity, as that is the nature of Christianity. But take a closer look, for you will also find remnants of your Goddess.'

I opened the old wooden door, which creaked loudly, sending a reverberating echo throughout the interior. As I did a tour of the church and its features, I had a running commentary as I came across new features in the architecture.

'Symbols both transmit and reinforce a message. A picture really does contain a thousand words. Look at the Virgin Mary there, for instance.'

I stood before a beautiful stained glass depiction of Mary, who characteristically wore a blue dress.

'How can she be anyone but I? Make no mistake, Mary is the divine feminine, the Goddess, in disguise perhaps, but it is I. The divine mother gives the Church a feminine divinity to balance the male prophet. This is one of the reasons that the Catholic Church has grown, prospered, and dominated. Although there is a disparity between the role of men and women in the Church, energetically there is great balance in terms of symbolism and sacred geometry. The Solar Logos, the yang, male principle that is Jesus the Christ, is balanced perfectly by the lunar, yin, feminine energies of Mary, the Divine feminine principle. It is ironic indeed that an iconic image used to eradicate me from the hearts and minds of my people could well help ensure my survival in the consciousness of the masses.'

I continued around the church, pausing at a decorated block of stone.

'Take that dragon carving. It is an ancient symbol for the life-force of the Land, unseen forces to be both feared and respected. And take the scene of the Crucifixion before you. It is powerful, for it is meant to be. But older symbolism is present here also. The cross is an ancient sun symbol, which you saw on megaliths in Ireland, remember? The three women around the dying prophet: they are the three aspects of the turning year, the triple Goddess of myth. And that Norman font over there is simply my natural spring waters brought into the church. As such it is feminine symbolism, associated with water, childbirth and cleansing. And look high above you, at the face up there.'

I looked up to the beams in the roof and with a little squinting could make out a carved head with foliage emanating from its mouth.

'The Green Man, a universal ancient symbol of the fecundity of the Land, the Lord of the Forest, the spirit within

193

all of Nature. It is another example of an ancient symbol, beloved by the people and brought into the church. So you see that churches, in many cases, are local museums of ancient Pagan symbolism. Again, it is quite ironic that the use of these symbols in church architecture has ensured the survival of sacred Pagan icons.'

I was spellbound by the interpretation of these images, and suspected that most of the congregation of this church probably had little idea of the origins of their treasured icons either.

'Over here please, if you will. In every church or temple, mosque or ruined abbey, there is a power point. This is usually situated in or just in front of the high altar, or where it formerly stood in the case of ruins. Try dowsing for yourself and see what you find.'

I approached the altar with rod in hand. As I neared it, my rod began to spiral around clockwise, in an identical fashion to what had happened earlier at Wayland's Smithy. Could the same principles be operating in a church as in a four thousand-year-old chambered mound?

'Just like in the ancient chamber, this place is also the conduit, the point of power for connecting with the spirit of place, for contacting divinity, for contacting me. Whether it be built by Mayan, Roman, Egyptian, Christian or Pagan, in front of the altar is the place where the priest or priestess sought direct contact with their Divine. And the energy imprint remains, and in many cases the energy still flows. Now you can see – this church has in fact accommodated energies accompanying the St Michael Line, it hasn't destroyed them. Look around you at the hundreds of tons of natural stone used here, and especially at the solid buttresses and wide columns. All of these attract earth energies, just as if they were megaliths. The buttresses especially are rooted deep into the earth, just like standing stones.'

'I have Pagan friends who wouldn't be seen dead in a church. I think this may help.'

'Take them into an older church on a known ley line and show them the symbolism – they may recognise much of it - dragons, the green man and other mythological beasts. It may help defuse their negativity. The anger in people's hearts today concerning how wisewomen were treated by the Church in the past still fuels much negativity. This goes out across the cosmos as black energy. It is adding negative

energy to the Universe, as if they had torched our sisters themselves. Hate never heals, for only love can do that.'

'Sure thing! I will pass that on for sure. I will certainly look at churches in a new light in future. Thank you very much. What now, My Lady?'

'Well, I think the time has come to let you spread your wings, to do some dowsing and make more discoveries for yourself. Your route home will take you close to Avebury, a very powerful place as you have already experienced. Why not stop off and try your hand at more dowsing? Oh, and you may want to take in Winterbourne Monkton on the way. And perhaps before the next Full Moon you could try finding leys near where you live, for more stones surely lie in waiting, ready to be revealed. They are calling you.'

'Great. Just like Winnie the Pooh's honey pots!'

'Hmm. You could say that.'

Right on cue, my stomach let out a resounding growl – I was hungry!

'OK. But seriously, I think I must have lunch first, I'm famished - then I'll explore.'

'Next time the Silver Lady is ripe, I would like us to connect with the Natural beings of the Land, in particular trees, and their spirits, as well as their guardians.'

'Ah-ha, so you intend for me to become a Green Man?'

'In more ways than you think. I shall give you a clue to the next place we shall speak together: LOOK TO THE NEW TO RECEIVE THE OLD. I will leave you now, in a manner of speaking. But I am always with you, you know that. Now you can feel, with your rods and your heart, the pulse of my heartbeat, and you will readily perceive and receive the life-force wherever you are. Goodbye for now, my son.'

'Good bye, my Mother, and thank you.'

18. Strolling
with Mary and Michael

Traditional

And the vast form of Nature
like a serpent play'd before me.
(William Blake)

I stepped back outside into the cool October afternoon air, and was pleased to see that the sun was peeking through a clearing sky. *Look to the new to receive the old. What on Earth does that mean? Right then, Winterbourne Monkton it is.* Back in the car I found the village on my road map, and looked it up in *Sun and the Serpent*. It turned out (on page 114) that the church was the final port of call of the feminine, Mary current before it flowed south into the henge at Avebury, and that in its churchyard there was a megalith. *Cool!*

It was but a short journey west and I was soon rolling up at the church. A notice board proclaimed the church was dedicated to St Mary Magdalene, the heroine of *The Da Vinci Code*.

You don't say?

It also proclaimed that an annual flower festival took place there on July 22nd, to celebrate the saint's official festival. Hoicking my dowsing rods from my rucksack, I entered the churchyard and was almost immediately confronted by the 7ft long prone stone described by Miller and Broadhurst. It lay on the ground motionless and somewhat forlorn and I wondered what had transpired to topple this once proud megalith. The surface was pitted with numerous cup-shaped marks, which I thought might be why the stone was originally selected. I also noted that the stone was almost touching the east wall of the church and that the altar must be just feet away on the other side. I dowsed an energy line that flowed out from the wall, through the stone and off across the churchyard to a nearby yew tree. I went around to the entrance to the church and entered the porch with an air of expectation. As before, an old wooden door creaked as I entered. The air was stuffy and the church was dark and deserted. I found some switches and after some false starts the church burst into light.

Let there be light. And there was… and it is good.

The first thing that caught my eye was a powerful stained glass window depicting Mary Magdalene washing the feet of her Prophet, as described in the Bible. I had seen some debates in magazines and on TV that suggested that she wasn't the 'scarlet woman', the whore that she is painted as, but was in fact closer to Jesus, and may possibly have been a priestess of the Goddess. I looked at her depiction. Her sorrowful expression seemed to represent the subjugation of women over many centuries. I wondered what had been the relationship between them and whether *The Da Vinci Code* was more than fiction. Next up was the font. It was Norman in age, and although it was very worn, had some interesting embellishments. Rows of large chevrons decorated the stone basin and they reminded me of identical patterns at Fourknocks and in the Boyne Valley. Was there a common belief system connecting the Irish designs with the ones before me, some common knowledge of sacred geometry?

I then turned my attention to the area leading up to the altar. I stood to one side of the centre of the nave and focused on picking up the Mary current. I walked to the centre aisle and my dowsing rod turned strongly to the left. *I must be in the flow!* I followed where the rod was pointing, as it gently meandered, like a snake, towards the altar. 2ft from the altar the rods swung violently around on themselves and started spinning and I circled around with them, trying to keep up. Eventually the spiral got so small that I could turn no longer and concluded that I was at the centre of the energy node. That was just what I had dowsed at Wayland's Smithy and Ogbourne St Andrew, and demonstrated that some universal process was operating. I also noticed the feeling in my stomach, like fluttering butterflies. *Cool!*

My attention was then caught by the floor tiles, which were laid all around the altar. They were of attractive terracotta with floral designs. But something was different about the tile through which the energy was spiralling down. I got down on my hands and knees to make out the detail. And there they were – two tiny dragons in each corner of the tile, either side of a small design that could have been either a flower or a solar symbol. I got up and eagerly searched every other tile around the entire altar, even lifting up the altar skirt to examine beneath. There were no other dragons. The only tiles with tiny beasts were those marking out the energy node! *Funky!* I addressed the dragons directly.

'Hi, guys! How you doin'? I know why you're here, even if no one else does.'

I had a real rush of adrenaline at the thought that I had discovered something new. But then I remembered what the Goddess had said about finding things we consider 'new':

'Be proud and pleased… but do not think for a second that you would have found anything if the spirits of the place did not want it revealed to you.'

I addressed the tiny dragons again. 'OK, guys. Sorry, I got a bit carried away. This is all very new to me, OK? Thank you for revealing yourselves to me.'

I bowed ceremoniously, but not in jest, rather out of gratitude. Hmm, that felt good. I stood up and had the strangest sensation. It was as if the whole church, or some force within it, had breathed a sigh of relief that someone was once again appreciating the ancient encoded symbolism.

Outside there was another surprise. I did a circumnavigation of the church and came across a tree whose trunk was remarkably screwed up. And I don't mean stressed out, having a bad leaf day or anything like that. Its trunk had a spiralling growth, as if someone or something was twisting it into the ground like a giant corkscrew. I had read a book on dowsing published many years ago by Guy Underwood, a master dowser, in which he had noted how trees on flows or nodes of energy reflected this in the growth of their trunk. And there was one such example in front of me. Over the coming years I was to note how common twisted trees were at sacred sites.

It was now late afternoon and there was a distinct chill in the air, as the sun sank lower in the sky. I pushed on south to Avebury, scene of my magical visions in the recent past. But I was now going back with dowsing rods and *The Sun and the Serpent* in hand and a deep knowing that the holy temple of stones would surely be buzzing with the energy of the St Michael Line, enhanced by the Full Moon. I parked up at the Red Lion and crossed the road to the two huge megaliths known as The Cove. These were the remnants of what was formerly a sacred trinity of stones, aligned to receive the rays of the summer solstice sunrise. It was also the spot, according to Miller and Broadhurst, where the Michael and Mary flows converged, after several miles of separation. I stood just outside The Cove and asked to be shown where the two serpents came together, and I soon picked up the spot. It was around 15ft north of the stones and my rods crossed and stayed crossed as I went into the heart of The Cove. Here the energy was electric, with hairs standing up on the back of my neck and a tingling in my fingers.

All of a sudden I had a vibrating sensation in my trousers! Relax, it was my mobile phone! Although it was only a text trying to sell me a new deal on my call time, it made me think. From previous trips I was aware that in most parts of the henge and village I had had a very poor reception, with either no signal at all, or else a very weak one. I looked down at my mobile to see that I had three bars. *Cool. Now why is that?* I started to walk around both the inside and outside of the two giants stones of The Cove and noticed something remarkable. Outside The Cove my phone went back down to just one or two bars, whilst inside I had more reception. I had the urge to place my phone on the taller, southern stone of the pair and at one point – whoosh! A full signal! I took the phone off the stone and the signal dropped again. To me it seemed as if the energies of the stone where charging the phone up, or else the stone was itself serving as a giant aerial.

*Dowsing by mobile phone – now that **is** neat!*

Around the corner, I picked up the current again as it crossed the road, outside the old chapel that now housed the Tourist Information Centre. The energy went straight into the chapel, which I noticed was perfectly aligned with the flow. I bet no one went to sleep during services in that place! Passers by looked on inquisitively as I pranced up and down the road with my rods extended in front of me. Behind the chapel were a group of smaller stones and a big concrete pillar marking the former position of the Obelisk. This phallus-shaped giant had been over 20ft long and was the tallest stone we know to have stood at Avebury. The energies seemed attracted by the pillar before heading off in the direction of two gigantic megaliths on the other side of the field. Standing between these stones, imaginatively called stone No. 1 and No. 98 by archaeologists, was another magical experience. I could literally feel the twin flow of the joint Michael and Mary force pushing my stomach. It was as if I was standing midstream in a river, with the water up to my midriff. I was having problems standing still, so strong was the Full Moon flow. I sat down on the grass mid-stream and soaked it up like a sponge.

At the base of stone No. 1 there was an ancient niche, forming a definite, well-worn seat. A small group of foreign tourists were taking it in turns having their photos taken seated in the alcove and when they moved on I took my turn. Again, it was a profound experience, but this time I was filled with a feeling of great peace and balance. And this was despite the imposition of the traffic of the busy A4361 as it thundered up to Swindon to the North. But it did not bother me. The sounds of the vehicles, of nearby children playing, a distant drum beating, and birdsong, all seemed to fade away as I drifted away into prehistory. I got flashes of scenes of what had happened there thousands of years ago. I briefly glimpsed a great procession of people stretching off into the distance, hundreds walking towards the two big stones. In another instant I was outside myself and could see an old, sick-looking woman curled up on the stone seat, and a shaman-looking dude waving feathers over her head. A few seconds after, the scene flashed to a circle of people gathered around what looked like the body of a small child. She lay motionless on the ground in front of the stone as a shamanka beating a drum stood over her, chanting in a tongue I did not recognise.

'Excuse me!'

The visions were instantly snatched away. I opened my eyes to see a middle-aged woman, accompanied by two young children, who I supposed were her grandchildren.

'Erm, sorry to bother you, but could they sit in the seat, please, and have their photos taken?'

'Oh, of course,' I replied, 'sorry to hog it. I think I drifted off somewhere.'

'I think you did. Thank you.'

I vacated the hallowed seat, which was soon reoccupied by the younger pilgrims. More than a little spaced out, I wandered off back towards the centre of the village, my mind replaying the scenes I had witnessed. I reflected on the notion that I may have witnessed some sort of action replay, some ancestral memory imprinted at the locality. Perhaps the fact that I had been tuned into the energies had opened some sort of portal to these otherworldly realms. Or, and this really blew my mind, perhaps the visions I had seen were being played out in other dimensions *right there and then!* My years studying Eastern religions and the Human Potential Movement had convinced me that many other realities existed outside those we are normally privy to.

In the light of what I had experienced earlier that day, I decided to pay a visit to the church at Avebury before starting home. The air was even cooler and the sky had noticeably darkened as clouds gathered and the sun sank further. A quick inspection of the outside of the church revealed a megalith at the base of one of the buttresses, another sign that it was an ancient site prior to the coming of Christianity. Inside there were more treasures. A painting of St John showed him holding a chalice, out of which a snake reared its head. Was this a coded clue of the presence in the church of the serpentine energies of the earth? The legend goes that John was bitten by a snake but his faith saved him. But I wondered if the myth was hiding some deeper, esoteric secret. The chalice he held must surely represent the Grail, which I now held to be a sign of inner enlightenment, rather than the drinking vessel of the Last Supper.

The Norman font held further wonders. On one side was the image of a bishop having his toes nibbled by two dragons. Two dragons: I had seen these on the floor tile at Winterborne Monkton. Were these more clues that the Norman builders knew of the two currents that flow through Avebury? Back outside I noted gargoyles high up on the tower. They all sported wings and looking very dragon-like. Were these even more surreptitious messages encoded into the church by knowledgeable masons?

As I left Avebury I saw how the stones of the West Kennet Avenue meandered in an almost drunken way across the fields. The stone avenue was clearly following something, and the only something I could think of was the serpent-like earth energies of the Michael current, which flowed down the avenue. The stones meandered across the fields like the body of a gigantic snake, frozen on the landscape.

Over the next few weeks I was to go out on several trips to churches to check them out for telltale signs that something had been there before, as well as for evidence that they stood on ley lines. I wasn't to be disappointed, for in Dorset I found many such clues. At Toller Porcorum I located two megaliths at the entrance to the churchyard, and at Little Bredy I located an arc of megaliths on the north side of the church, as well as a large stone on the south by the gate. The church was also dedicated to St Michael! At the church at Milborne Port, on the Dorset–Somerset border, I dowsed two flows of energy crossing into the churchyard from the nearby river. They converged at a Victorian lamppost, on the top of which was carved a caduceus – two entwined serpents! On spotting this, a broad grin materialised across my face that lasted for several minutes. I followed the male current around the south side of the church where it entered through a door embellished with two dragons and a green man! On the other side of the church the feminine flow went through a buttress and on the inside focused on the font – water and childbirth: feminine symbolism!

But it was at the village of Stoke Trister, close to the A303 in South Somerset, that my mind was well and truly cudgelled. I had suspected an alignment that went across the Dorset-Somerset border, passing through that tiny hamlet. On arrival, I dowsed along the lane that ran by the church and an energy flow led me directly to a large stone just to the west of the churchyard wall, close to a rusty, overgrown gate. I dowsed a current that went from the stone, through the church porch, up the aisle, ending in a tight spiral in front of the altar. Underfoot I could feel some uneven ground under the carpet. It was the sort of carpet that was rolled out when the Queen comes, long and thin and not fixed to the floor beneath. I rolled it back and what I saw left me open-mouthed. It was an old, very worn slab of stone carved with various symbols, several of which were spiralling serpents, often in pairs, exactly marking the spot where my rod had spiralled around! *Wicked!* I pondered on who had made these symbols centuries ago, perhaps trusting that one day someone would come along and realise their true meaning.

'Thank you, whoever you were, your efforts were not in vain.'

At the nearby church of Cucklington, on the Somerset-Dorset border I found dragon-like gargoyles up the tower, more signs that perhaps a ley ran through the village. One of the stained glass windows, behind the high altar, caught my eye. It depicted Jesus, with Mary Magdalene and Elizabeth, mother of John the Baptist. Words from the last page of *The Da Vinci Code* came flooding back:

The quest for the Holy Grail is the quest to kneel before the bones of Mary Magdalene.
A journey to pray at the feet of the outcast one.

Controversy surrounded the alleged relationship between Mary Magdalene and Jesus, for it had been inferred that she was far more exalted and of higher status than we had been led to believe. Dan Brown and others had suggested that the Holy Grail was the bloodline that originated from their coupling. But I felt there might be even more to her than that. Did she also represent an aspect of the Goddess herself? In the scene before me, Mary Magdalene was also holding a chalice in her left hand and pointing to it with her right, as if she was telling Jesus something vital. Was he to drink from the Grail of Knowledge? Was she inferring that he was to attain the enlightenment that she already possessed?

All these revelations showed me that it wasn't just stone circles, megaliths and such like that attracted earth energies. Even when a cathedral, church or humble chapel was raised on an ancient site to appropriate the locality, the natural flow of earth energies would not be denied. Nature always found a way and, it seemed to me, would even take advantage of a Christian construction to enhance energies. The Templars and Masons knew of these flows of cosmic life-force and designed their churches and cathedrals accordingly. And the Templars had been devoted followers of Mary Magdalene.

19. Stones, Secateurs and Samhain

© P Knight

No one can investigate leys in the field for long, without being convinced that the way was planted with stones.
(Alfred Watkins, *The Old Straight Track*)

The next few weeks were spent poring over the OS maps that covered my native Dorset. I looked for the telltale alignments of ancient sites, hilltops and churches. I plotted what looked like several good candidates for genuine leys, but was always mindful to select for further inspection only those with six or more markers. Alfred Watkins and others had warned of chance alignments that would inevitably occur on any map. The more markers one had on a ley then the more likely it was, statistically, to be of a product of ancient wisdom, rather than modern imagination.

One of the most convincing of the leys I plotted (well it floated my boat!) ran from Stonehenge down through Dorset to the Nine Stones circle, near Winterbourne Abbas, and beyond. The Nine Stones was a typical Bronze Age circle of megaliths that unfortunately now stood within feet of the A35, one of the busiest routes in and out of the West Country. Nevertheless, the site was atmospheric, located at one corner of a large wood, and overshadowed by a huge beech tree, which formed an umbrella over the ancient stones. A few miles to the NNE of the circle, the ley crossed a bridge just north of a hamlet called Muckleford. Now I remembered from Watkins that where leys crossed rivers there often developed a ford or bridge to aid pilgrims. So, ten days before Samhain, I drove to the bridge on an afternoon blessed with a warm sun, which seemed to belong more to early September rather than mid-October. I stood on the old stone bridge under which the River Frome flowed vigorously, following autumnal rains a few days previous. I examined the south side of the bridge, and nearby banks, for any stones. No luck there. But on the north side, across the river, my attention was immediately drawn to a large thicket of nettles and brambles.

Now let me digress briefly to tell you of an important discovery I have made. Whenever I was shown 'new' stones, they were invariably incarcerated by a venomous cocktail of ivy, brambles and nettles! Alfred Watkins had not warned me of this. On many of my earlier outings (before purchasing my standard-issue gardening gloves) I would return home with hands that looked like pizza toppings, red and striated. Why brambles? Why nettles? Why not poppies, or sunflowers or other less aggressive adversaries? Perhaps dowser Guy Underwood offered some answers. At several ancient sites he found growths of brambles and ivy marking energy nodes, and other dowsers had noted growths of ivy on the Michael and Mary Line flows. So I guess everything was as it was meant to be.

Now, back to the bridge at Muckleford. After some trampling and pulling up of the offending undergrowth, to my delight I had exposed a prone stone that was all of 5ft long and 3ft across, just where the ancient ley crossed the river. I stood surveying my efforts with the pride of a new father in the maternity ward. I had brought my camera along and wanted to take a pic for my records, but I did not have a tape measure to show the scale. I decided to put my biro pen on the top of the megalith to give some idea of its dimensions. As I focused and prepared to click, out of the corner of my eye I detected a car approaching over the bridge. An aged gent with grey hair was driving, accompanied by his wife. I took a pace forward so as not to be run over, and carried on taking my shots. I heard the car slow right down as it passed behind me and could feel the gaze of its occupants. I wondered what they thought of the weirdo standing in the middle of nowhere taking a photo of a biro pen!

From Muckleford bridge the ley then proceeded to the Nine Stones via some earthworks and two tumuli, and carried on the other side, crossing a hill before going through another burial mound on White Hill and heading straight through a gap between two woods. But was there anything to be seen the other side of the woods? I noted that my line met the ancient ridgeway path that linked the Grey Mare Long Barrow and the Kingston Russell Stone Circle, so I thought it worthwhile to visit the spot. My ley passed very close to a field boundary so I had an accurate fix. It took just a few minutes to locate a very large stone that had fallen into a ditch. Again, I had to cut away brambles and some nettles, but to my relief the stone was mostly obscured by a mat of grass, which peeled away like a carpet, exposing the hidden stone beneath. It was about 5ft long and distinctly triangular, pointed at one end, whilst I took the thicker end as that which had originally been in the ground. I stood motionless, transfixed by the stone. How long had it been covered and forgotten? Another broad grin came over my face as a feeling of bliss swept through me. I was still mindful of the words of the Goddess. I was, after all, only uncovering that which had already been known of long ago. I named it the Goddess Stone, in her honour.

I felt good inside and knew I was doing something worthwhile. I dowsed the stone and found that it issued a flow of energy heading across the field in the direction of the Nine Stones, which stood about a mile distant, out of sight over the ridge. I later sat on the stone and sensed the energies thrill through my body until my head swam with the power of it all. I also thought about how I might be able to heal leys and the landscape. Could I positively influence sacred sites and the Land just by the power of thought and by simply sending my love along the flows to where it was needed? I recounted what the Goddess had said:

'By doing a ceremony or leaving crystals and other items, does your act benefit the place? If it is done out of pure love, out of genuine desire to help heal the site, the Land and ultimately the Planet, then healing is initiated.'

So I closed my eyes and visualised healing energy passing down the ley from where I sat. I imagined the Nine Stones receiving healing white light. The ancient megaliths glowed as the healing light filled them up to bursting. I then watched as streams of light shot out from every stone spreading like a spider's web out across the surrounding landscape. I was in a state of bliss as I felt at one with the Land. Sitting on the Goddess Stone, on that sunbathed October afternoon, I knew that the Land was receiving healing, and that I too was the recipient of therapeutic love from the Land. *If I can do this, then anyone can.* This is why this section of my diary has been included. The energies I felt and the vision I created to facilitate earth healing could be initiated by anyone with the humility and love to make the effort. And it seemed to me that the more we gave out, the more we would receive back:

'You and the Land are one and the same.'

Over the remainder of Autumn and into early Winter I sought out and found further stones not on any map or in any book. And every time I cleared a stone of vegetation, and meditated with it, the feeling was the same, that of a sigh of appreciation from the megalith. It was as if the stone could breathe once more, relieved of its choking constraints and exposed once more to the rays of the sun. I know from my own experience how down I get during the winter or during cloudy, sunless spells the British weather throws at us. I felt as if the forgotten stones had experienced something comparable, perhaps a version of SAD, only this time standing for *Stones Appreciate Discovery*.

It was soon a week before Samhain, the old Celtic New Year, better known now as Halloween. The moon was approaching new and on a particularly fine morning I was out again exploring Dorset. This time my quarry was the Hampton Hill Stone Circle, north of Abbotsbury. On the path up to the circle, I noticed two small stones half-obscured by an encroaching hedgerow. I cleared the stones, noting that they were both sarsens. The hill I was on was chalk, as revealed by the flints and chalk fragments in the fields. Watkins had said that ley mark stones were not of the local geology, so that ancient travellers could differentiate them from those cleared from nearby fields. Closer to the circle another stone, this time of limestone, sat neglected just inside a gate next to the track to the circle. On arriving at the stone circle itself, I was in for a shock. I could make out the tops of a few stones but brambles and ivy had consumed several others, somewhat similar to the way abandoned Egyptian temples are covered by the desert sands, or how Asian temples are consumed by jungle creepers. But by now I was armed to the teeth with my standard kit of secateurs, trowels, garden gloves and small shears that were stashed in my larger rucksack, and I set about the initial clearing of the circle.

It took around an hour to clear a small space around each stone, revealing about a dozen stones, ranging from 2-4ft long. (It would take two more visits in the future to clear the whole area around the circle, enabling a complete perambulation of the stones.) Walking around the circle was powerful and I was acutely aware of not being alone. Something, or someone, was watching my every move, I could feel it. A couple of times I even stopped to survey the landscape, but could see nothing, save for sheep and the odd soaring bird of prey in the distance. Inside me, however, I knew that whoever or whatever was witnessing my efforts was non-human. Perhaps it was the Elemental beings the Goddess had spoken of, or else the Spirits of the ancestors themselves, disturbed yet intrigued by my endeavours.

'OK. I know you are here. I hope I have your blessing to clear this sacred place of years of neglect. I come only to help heal the site and the Land. If you are pleased for me to carry on then please give me a sign, if you would, and I will continue.'

My words were carried off on the breeze, but I knew they had been heard. I stood motionless for several seconds before hearing a cry overhead. *It can't be!* I looked skyward to see a large buzzard circling overhead, and I mean directly overhead. It looked down at me and we connected. It cried out again and swooped down to around 10ft above my head before perching itself in a tree about 50ft away. The bird called out to me again. I acknowledged her greeting.

'Greetings again, my beautiful friend. It has been a while.' I bowed to the bird and then brought my eyes back to the stones, surveying each one in turn as I rotated at the circle's heart.

'I'll take that as a *yes* then. I shall continue. Thank you.'

After about another half an hour of clearing, I was getting tired. The brambles were almost impenetrable in places and by the end I had even exposed two stones I had not seen when I had begun. I packed up my tools and looked to my friend in the tree. She had remained still and silent throughout my clearing, but as I looked up she ascended to the skies once more. She made a rapid turn to my left, called out 'pee-you' and flew away in a dead straight line. As the bird got smaller and smaller, I could see she was making for the hill at Abbotsbury, which was crowned with St Catherine's Chapel. She was showing me something. Her flight was straight towards the chapel.

Straight flight. Straight line. Ley!

I swung around to face the opposite direction and found I could see the Hardy Monument tower, erected atop of a hill I knew to be crowned with Bronze Age tumuli. I stretched out arms in opposite directions and looked along them. The Hardy Monument, the stone circle and St Catherine's Chapel were in perfect alignment! This was my reward, a show of gratitude from the spirits of the place. Because I had acted with humility and selflessness, the stone circle had revealed an ancient secret to me.

However, I knew I had not actually discovered anything. How can one discover what's already there? Wasn't America there before Columbus happened along? The continent was also there before the Vikings left behind their carved stones. The Goddess had advocated that the more we treat the Land and its sacred sites with respect and reverence, the more will be presented for us for 'discovery'. After that, of course, it's down to each individual to spot the signs and follow the strands of synchronicity that may subsequently reveal secrets that had been forgotten for hundreds or thousands of years.

As I stood midst the Hampton Hill stones, looking in turn in opposite directions down the ley, something was kindled in me that was to last forever. I knew then that the landscape was replete with arcane knowledge, golden gems of wisdom woven into the geography, vestiges of times when people had a closer connection to the Landscape. As I surveyed the efforts of my stone clearing, I felt strongly that recovering *yesteryears* sacred sites *today* could help the generations of *tomorrow*. With his historian's hat on, Winston Churchill once said that the more we looked back, the better the future might be. Standing midst the stone circle, I could appreciate his sentiments.

I had one more stop that day. I had found a reference in a book to a megalith north of the village of Portesham, called the Moot Stone, and how the villagers of Kingston Russell and Portesham would meet there to discuss inter-parish business. The OS map of 1866 had shown the stone close by where I had parked previously for the Grey Mare and Her Colts Long Barrow. What interested me was that I had plotted a ley running from Broadmayne (meaning *Large Stone*), through the Hellstone Dolmen and other sites, which seemed to pass right through the position of the Moot Stone. Was the stone a prehistoric megalith that was used centuries later as a medieval gathering place? I rolled up at the spot, near the start of the track leading to Gorwell Farm, but could not see a stone. I inspected the hedgerows, which were dense, high and for the most part impenetrable, despite it being late October. Some ten minutes of probing, prodding and pushing my head into small gaps in the undergrowth revealed nothing, and I was just about to give in when I had a light bulb moment:

Let's dowse for it!

I eagerly retrieved my rods from the car and set about finding the lost stone. I stood in the nippy air and focused within on my quarry. I had walked but a few paces from the car when I picked up on a charge of energy. It led me towards a large mass of brambles and nettles some 20ft away, just to the left of the cattle grid that marked the entrance to Gorwell Farm. As I approached the entanglement, my rods started to turn in a spiralling motion and although the barbed vegetation soon barred my way, I held the rods over it as far as I could. The spiral got tighter and tighter – there was something hidden there! I got out the tools from the boot and set about clearing away years of neglect. Within seconds I could make out stone, and as I carried on, I slowly exposed more of it. I felt like Indiana Jones uncovering some exotic temple in a far-off jungle, and I was equally as excited!

It took about twenty minutes to reveal the full extent of the Moot Stone, for that's what it surely was, before I stood back to admire my efforts. The stone was a conglomeratic sarsen, around 7ft long, 4ft wide and about 2ft in depth. It was lying down and the shape was decidedly triangular, one end coming to a point, presumably the top of the stone when it had stood. I felt exhilarated and was aware of energy coming from the stone that seemed to express that it too was happy to once more feel the coastal breezes and the kiss of the sun on its ancient crystalline surface. It struck me that the British countryside must be littered with hundreds of lost stones, many of which, as Alfred Watkins had shown, still marked ley lines.

The end of October was marked by the festival of Samhain, nowadays degraded into the sordid festivities that have become Halloween, with American-style 'trick or treat' and all that. Traditionally, Samhain was the Celtic New Year, a time when the veil between this world and that of our ancestors was the thinnest. One could approach the spirits of our forebears, hence the association with ghouls and ghosties. I was wondering, however, if the so-called Celtic Fire Festivals (Samhain, Imbolc, Lammas and Beltaine) had a more ancient origin. I did not have to do too much research on the Net and in my archaeology books to realise that this was indeed the case. Ancient sites across Europe had alignments with sunrises and sunsets around these festivals, proving their antiquity. But were there any signs of these ancient practices in Dorset?

I obtained, again off the Net, the direction of where the sun rose and set for all the festivals and looked through the alignments of long barrows and stone circles across the county. I soon found several. Tumuli on skylines seemed a favourite, marking out festival sunrises or sunsets from other sacred places below. My ancestors were certainly positioning sites where they perceived sacred alignments in the geography. For instance, I found a group of three large megaliths lying in a field on the hillside above West Lulworth, by studying the old 1866 OS maps. The view from the stones was breathtaking, as a wide vista took in a large chunk of the Purbecks coastline going east from Lulworth Cove. But from the stones I noticed something weird. Three prominent headlands stood out before me - Arish Mell, Worbarrow Tout and St Alban's Head. But the amazing thing was that they were all in alignment, and from where I stood they aligned with sunrise on Samhain and Imbolc festivals, in early November and February respectively. Surely this alignment had something to do with why the stones were there.

At another sacred site, the old church at Whitcombe, south east of Dorchester, I found more examples of possible site evolution, i.e. that there had been something there prior to the church. Just before I entered the churchyard gate, I noticed a stone leaning against the outside of the wall. What's more, when I stood in the churchyard, I could see two groups of barrows on the skyline. My compass told me that they marked out the Midwinter and Samhain sunsets, when viewed from the church. If this wasn't enough, some work on the OS map showed that the church was in alignment with the Neolithic henge of Mount Pleasant, a megalith by the road to the west, the ruined stone circles at Littlemayne, and a tumulus on the crest of a hill further on SE. My whole being tingled with the excitement of it all.

Leys are for real!

For me, the takeover of Pagan sites by the Church was proven. I had the realisation that the history and prehistory I had been sold throughout my life was false. History was, after all, written by the victors, which in this case was the Church. Memories of prior Pagan spirituality had been almost completely eradicated – but not quite. People were now going back to sacred sites with 'new eyes', with dowsing rods, crystal pendulums and open hearts, finding what had really gone on in ancient times. There now existed proof of another past, a past where people were *part* of the Land and its energies. Even today, the Australian Aborigines say that they *belong* to the Land. As well as knowledge of alignments, both sacred and manmade, my ancestors had helped shape the spiritual heritage of my country, my Land. For I didn't give a toss who owned the land on which the stones lay. To me, it was my Land, the proprietress of my body and soul.

I wanted to mark Samhain, so I decided to return to one of my favourite ancient sites, one that held fond memories for me – Knowlton. The clocks had just 'gone back' an hour and sunrise was to be around 7.00am, which meant an early start. I arrived at the henge site around 6.30am; dawn was well under way and My Lady had painted streaks of red and purple upon the canvas of the sky. She hadn't learnt how to paint like that at evening art classes! She was a natural, one might say. I called out across the sacred site, my words carrying across the open fields:

'Good morning, My Lady.'

It was then that I had the feeling I was not alone. It was light enough for me to do a scan of the henge but I could not make anyone out. I approached the ruined church, as I had done before, but could see no one. I appeared to be alone. I threw my waterproof blanket to the ground and snuggled down in a corner where the east wall met the ruined porch. I could make out a rise on the skyline and knew instantly that this was where the sun would rise. The geography was, once again, portraying where the Sky God would make his appearance. I heard the occasional birdcall from across the fields and every now and again there were obtrusive headlights from passing vehicles along the nearby road.

Right on cue, just before 7.00am, the sun rose. A few thin clouds hovered over the glowing orb and caught its light. The scene was beautiful and seemed to be all mine!

'Good morning to you, My Lord.'

I closed my eyes to immerse myself in the sacred moment. The sun still illuminated my closed eyes for a while, so bright was its imprint on my retina. But this time it was different, for this time the image didn't fade. In fact, it got brighter, and brighter! It was not an optical phenomenon after all, but some independent light growing within my closed eyes. Yet it looked like the sun, and was right in front of me. The light increased in luminosity, and got steadily larger until it was as if the sun itself was just a few feet away from me. My inner vision was now filled with rainbow colours of such brilliance, and flames of gold and orange burst out of the core and leapt around the periphery of my inner vision. Then I realised what it could be. Could it be the spiritual essence of the sun, or at least its aura, interacting with my consciousness? Some eastern spirituality's believed that the Sun was the gateway to spiritual dimensions and that ethereal beings entered our solar system through this portal. My being was filled with energy too, and I felt as if I was being inflated. And then, in an instant, the image faded and my inner vision was dark once more.

I opened my eyes to see that the sun had been obscured by a thick cloud which had crept up whilst I was experiencing the vision. As the sun had been concealed, so too my vision of the sun's etheric/energetic body had vanished. I sat looking at the sunrise, which was still beautiful as the sun's rays shone out from behind the intruding clouds. The Goddess had impressed on me that everything was energy and that everything was connected to all else, and I knew that I had just experienced another vindication of her words. My body still buzzed with both the excitement and physical connection with the sun and I leant back against the flint-lined wall of the church – and just smiled. Anyone seeing me may have been excused for thinking I had been on a trip of some sort. In a way I had. Yet the trip I had experienced was life as it really was.

Before I left the henge, I stood between the two ancient yews that stand on the north bank. As at Avebury I could soon feel the flow of energy coming through the gap between them, as if the gnarled, wizened duo were channelling or siphoning the flow into the site. I had found that it took me several minutes to become attuned to such flows. I likened it to my body being a giant bath sponge. You put a sponge on the surface of your bath water and nothing seems to happen at first. But then the sponge gradually gets saturated with water until it fills to capacity. This is what seemed to happen with me. I start off feeling very little but gradually feel my stomach filling with energy, as if someone is blowing me up with a bicycle pump (don't ask where I've envisioned the pump going!). It reminded me of the lesson of the next Full Moon - connecting with trees. I had been finding more and more evidence that energies influenced vegetation, but also that the latter could also affect the flows of energy currents across the landscape. I looked forward with eager anticipation to the next conversation with the Goddess.

20. Ninth Moon – November: The New Forest Lesson – Spirit of the Green Man

© P Knight

*When one tries to rise above Nature,
one is liable to fall below it.*
(Sherlock Holmes)

I had been an ardent and unashamed tree-hugger for some time. When I was immersed big time into Buddhism, I had been taught to find a tree I felt a bond with and meditate beneath it, a practice symbolically mirroring the enlightenment of Siddhatta Gotama, who later became known as Buddha. In my efforts to clear my mind of distractions and find inner peace, I had also, unintentionally, sensed the power and love that emanated from trees when one sat beneath them. I was therefore intrigued by the Goddess's comments that I would be seeking out and connecting with trees and the spirit of the Green Man.

A little research into the foliated fellow revealed that the image had an ancient origin. The Greeks, Romans, Egyptians and the Celts all had Gods and Goddesses associated with the spirit of plants, forests and the fecundity of the Land. In Egypt, the male God Osiris was frequently shown with a green face, and Bacchus, the Roman god of wine and plants, was often depicted with a foliated head. The Church had merely taken over these icons, presumably to tell all and sundry that it was now the Christian God that blessed the fields and ensured the crops grew, and not Pagan deities. By bringing into churches an image that the illiterate peasantry would both recognise and relate to, the Church brought into its control all rituals and festivals connected with the Land, turning them into the hybrids now known as Easter, May Day, Lammas and the Harvest Festival.

On several of my excursions to sacred sites, I had noted large or unusual trees. At Glastonbury stood Gog and Magog, said to be the remnants of a Druid oak avenue that once ran up the slopes of the Tor. Apparently the Druids carried out their rituals in sacred groves, rather than in man-made temples. At Knowlton there were the two ancient yews on the henge bank, whilst at the Nine Stones, an umbrella of branches of the huge beech shrouded the Bronze Age circle. On my visits with the Goddess to both Wayland's Smithy and Ogbourne St Andrew there had been large trees in attendance. I wondered if perhaps this was because trees benefited from the earth energies that these sacred places attracted. Was there also, perhaps, some ancient tradition of planting and nurturing trees at such places? For I had found references to 'guardian trees' in a couple of dowsing books. I would ask the Goddess about these.

As the Full Moon approached, I pondered on the conundrum She had given me:

'Look to the new to receive the old.'

Beats me. New what? A newly erected stone circle? Several of these had been erected around the country in recent years. *Perhaps I'm off to New York or New Hampshire. Or how about New Zealand, My Lady? Now that's more like it!* But somehow I didn't think so. It had to be something to do with trees, so perhaps it was a wood, or a famous tree, or how about a forest? *New, hmm. Aha! Eureka! The New Forest. Yes, the New Forest.* That felt right. I was to go into the **New** Forest to receive more **Old** wisdom. *Perfect!*

I found that the area had a deep history of witchcraft and that covens still gathered there for rituals on special festival dates and full moons. I had made many trips to the area over several years, to walk in the forest and do some shopping in the funky shops in Burley, as well as to catch many a fine pub lunch. It was November, so at least the tourists would largely have gone, especially during weekdays, which was when the Full Moon was. *Perfect.* But where was it to be? Well, I intended to chill out again and be guided to wherever. However, the day before Full Moon, there I was, poring over the OS *New Forest* map, wondering

215

where the meeting place would be, and whether I could feel anything pulling me. But nothing. Even dowsing did not help.

OK, I give in. No forward planning this time.

Full Moon was around 11.00pm in the evening, but I set off around 5.15pm, just as it was almost dark. I had to skirt around the northern end of the Bournemouth conurbation, and got ensnarled in its rush hour traffic as a result. It was with some relief that I turned off the A31 and crossed a cattle grid that heralded my entrance into the Forest. The road to Burley was familiar to me, with its wide vistas of woods and open heathland. But night was falling and it took on a different atmosphere, ancient and broody. I passed ponies nibbling grass at the roadside, their eyes shining like diamonds in my headlights. It was good to see that they still roamed free, with few fences to bar their way, at least not along that stretch. The road then meandered through woods, around some twisting turns before finally arriving at Burley. This small hamlet was famous for its association with witches and hoards of tourists brought welcome income to this otherwise sleepy corner of rural England. I passed several shops with names that mirrored the folklore, such as *A Coven of Witches* and the *Sorcerer's Apprentice,* filled to the gunnels with witchy and other myth and magic paraphernalia. Then, just past the pub, I saw a sign for the church, going off to the left, and felt inclined to stop off there.

I felt sure that it would be locked at such a late hour, but, to my astonishment, it was not. I was disappointed that the church was 'modern', but inside I was to come face to face with images that were poignant and profound. A stained glass window dated AD2000 depicted planet Earth being held and supported by several hands, of various colours and ages. It seemed relevant, for the window demonstrated that we should nurture and love the planet. Moving further along the church, I came across another window, this time depicting St George slaying a dragon. But it was a window to the left of the altar that left me spellbound; such was its beauty and power. It was a stained glass depiction of Mary, bedecked in blue and white and holding a white lily. The style was Art Nouveau, incorporating very sinuous, organic lines. But the portrayal was unusual, for Mary was looking directly into my eyes and, more than this, she was gazing directly into my soul. Her honesty and purity pierced my consciousness and I stood mesmerized as I returned her entrancing stare. More than ever I knew that Mary was indeed the Goddess, the Divine Feminine who had survived, through the Christian Myth, as Virgin and Holy Mother.

'Hello, Holy Mother… for I know it is you, my Divine Mother, my Goddess.'

I might well have imagined it, but I thought I saw a very slight smile on her lips, as if she were pleased by the recognition of her true nature. The Goddess had gone underground, in a manner of speaking, but I knew her for real now. As at Ogbourne St Andrew, the old ways had unwittingly endured by means of the new. *Excellent!* As I walked back towards the door, I spotted another window depicting three women, said to be Faith, Hope and Charity. I wondered if it were more ancient symbolism, encoded within the stained glass. Perhaps the Goddess would have the answer.

My instinct said to retrace my route back to the village, turn left at the pub and head out in an easterly direction. I had the map on the seat beside me but did not give it more than the occasional glance, for it was my sixth sense that was in the driving seat. Before long I came a place where five roads met. I pulled up briefly to survey the situation. The last of the blue had long disappeared from the sky and the Moon was up to my left. She was resplendent in a clear sky and I could make out the first bright stars of the evening through my windscreen.

I felt impelled to carry straight on but almost immediately I encountered a gate that barred my way. I parked up and got out to inspect the obstacle. The gate was locked, although the tarred road continued beyond, before disappearing into the night. A glance at the map in my headlights showed I was at an isolated place called Clay Hill, and that the closed road was still a public right of way on foot.

'Oh well, here goes.'

I donned my waterproof coat and trousers and packed a torch, gloves, the map and some water in my small rucksack. When I extinguished the car lights, I realised how dark it was, and initially I couldn't make out any landscape features at all. But gradually my eyes got accustomed, and I began to discern hills, tree lines and the lights of distant cottages. The moon shone in the east and after a few minutes more, I could see that it was casting an eerie light over the Land, transforming it into a realm of ancient myth.

'Good evening, Lady of the Night.' I bowed with reverence to the Night Queen, and headed off across an ashen landscape.

The walking was good initially, along a tarred road littered with fallen leaves. But before long the road was replaced by a well-defined dirt track, which continued due east, dimly lit by the moon which shone directly in front of me. I could hear distant owl hoots and the occasional horse whinny, as well as the distant hum of traffic. After about ten minutes, I became aware that the rumble and racket was getting unpleasantly louder and realised I was heading directly towards a main road, which I took to be the A35. Sure enough, within a few minutes I was standing just fifty yards from the road, which was still busy despite it being about 7.30pm. As I watched this ugly transgression snake insidiously across the Land, I wished I had been Moses, and that I could have magically opened up a chasm, through which I could have crossed. I felt I had to cross the road, so I went for it, urged on by a dark wood that beckoned from the other side. I negotiated the road during a brief respite from blinding headlights and promptly stepped over a stile that accompanied a bridleway sign.

I carried on with a quick step in an effort to get back into the quiet of the forest. The moon was still directly in front of me and she seemed to be calling me onward. The track was faintly illuminated by her light, but the woods to my right were pitch black. I kept scanning the areas either side of the path and soon came to a gate to my right, which marked the public right of way into the woods. However, I did not feel inclined to go through it – not yet!

So I ignored the gate and continued along the earthen track, but soon becoming aware of a shadowy 'something' a few yards ahead, to the left of the track. As I got closer I could see it was a tree, about 7-8ft tall, surrounded by a low, wooden fence. Closer inspection showed that the tree appeared dead, and that what I had taken for living tree growth were in fact large clumps of ivy. I shone my torch at the lower parts of the trunk and could see that it was hollowed out, revealing it's age. Next to the tree was a smaller companion, also within the fence. Although it was bare of leaves, fallen ones scattered around its base betrayed its species. It was a young oak, which I surmised might have been deliberately planted beside its older brother. But why did a fence surround them? It seemed to imply that they were being protected, perhaps because of some local myth or historical significance. I took out my map and examined it with my torch. After retracing my steps, I was able to see where I was. And on the map, there was the tree, marked by the words *Naked Man*.

My research beforehand had revealed a reference to *The Naked Man*, mentioned in 18th Century records as the Wilverley Oak, used for hanging highwaymen. It was an ancient tree of which legends told of covens meeting on the Full Moon. I promptly looked around me, and stood still and silent. Nothing. No one. *Good! But why have I come here?* Perhaps the answer would be revealed later. In the meantime I stood by the tree, bathed in the moon's healing light.

I had stood there for several minutes when the silence was interrupted by the resounding **CRACK** of a branch being broken nearby, making me jump out of my skin! I turned, but could see nothing in the shadows from whence the sound had come. I was not alone. I raised my torch, pointing it down the track, towards the gate I had passed. I switched it on and was met by two small brilliant reflections – they were eyes! Then I could make out fainter reflections, those of magnificent antlers. It was a fallow deer, and more precisely it was a fully mature buck. And what's more, it looked exactly like the one I had encountered on Dartmoor. But surely it couldn't be. *No way!* One stag looked pretty much like another, didn't it? But inside I just knew it was the very same that had come to me under the August moon.

This is nuts! How can this be!

I took a couple of slow steps towards him. He did not move, nor did he avert his gaze. Every now and again the lights of his eyes would go out momentarily as he blinked, but he never took his eyes off me. I continued my slow, measured approach. When I got to around 60ft from him I stopped, as I could now clearly make out his entire form; I wanted to appreciate the magical encounter in case he suddenly bolted. Then my breath was really taken away. One of the points on his left antler had been broken off, and he also had a small nick in his right ear. It *was* the same stag, no doubt about it! He was my totem. My flash of recognition seemed to be the cue for the beast to raise his head skywards and issue a loud bellow that echoed across the Forest.

I replied in soft, non-threatening tones.

'Hello again, my friend.'

He appeared to respond, by rolling his head from side to side, his antlers moving in great swathes.

He then repeated his fanfare with equal volume, before turning to his right and disappearing into the darkness of the adjacent wood. He was beckoning me to follow him; I had been summoned, and I would follow. I went over to where he had vanished into the wood and flashed my torch, illuminating the gate that I had passed a short time before. Next to it was a gap in the fence, through which I presumed the stag had gone. I could make out a path heading into the woods and an inspection of the mud revealed the stag's fresh hoof prints. I closed the gate behind me and gingerly followed the path into the wood, which soon closed in on me, blotting out the moonlight. At times my feet trudged through heaps of fallen leaves and my torch caught a myriad shades of brown, red and orange. I carried on for around five minutes, stumbling every now and again on unobserved tree roots that had seemingly lain in ambush. Whenever I showed any indecision as to which way to go, the stag would call out, unseen somewhere in front of me, as if to reassure me I was heading in the right direction. My torch had also started flickering, and I figured that I had better save my batteries should I need it later. I stood still for a few moments until my eyes were accustomed more to the darkness before carrying on. It was with some relief that I made out moonlight, flooding down into a clearing ahead. I stepped into the dell and stood motionless for a while, happy to be immersed once more in the moon's rays. Then I sensed her presence. I knew the Goddess was with me.

'Good evening, my son. You are well?'

'Good evening to you too, My Lady, and yes, I am extremely well, thank you.'

'Good. That is good. Well done for finding this hallowed place.'

'Well, it was my stag friend who guided me really.'

'And do you think for a second that you and he are not one? He is your totem and therefore is part of you. He can feel what you feel. He knows when you need help and reassurance. He also appears to remind you of the qualities of the stag, for he epitomizes the male spirit of the Land, Cernunnos, the Horned One, Herne the Hunter. The antlers are shaman's symbols of connections to higher forms of attunement, as well as heightened perceptions, for they grow behind the eyes. Each year they are shed and grow back larger, symbolising for you the shedding of the old, and new inner growth. A deer's way is also a combination of both wisdom and innocence. Remember when I said it was a return to innocence that you sought?'

'Yes, I do remember. I am bowled over with the thought that the same deer I met on Dartmoor is here in the New Forest. Now I can

220

quite believe that Sirius, my totem wolf, could be anywhere and everywhere, for she is spirit. But the deer?'

'Oh dear, if you'll excuse the pun, I thought we had been over all this. You are separating the physical and the spirit again. They are one and the same. They are interconnected. They are proactive with each other. They ARE each other. One cannot have one world without the other – they co-exist side-by-side. Do not return to the duality delusion, for it is just a chimera. The spirit of your stag brother is well advanced and knows that both time and space are illusory and can, to a certain extent, be transcended. Time is but an illusion, remember? In fact, your horned friend is already back on Dartmoor. He is, let me see, standing just below Hounds Tor if I'm not mistaken, which of course I can never be!'

'OK. I'm sorry. But this world of physicality is so plausible and convincing, and every now and again I forget who I really am.'

'Do not fret, for you and I are both on this wondrous adventure together, and I also need human forgetfulness so that I can experience a million ways of remembering, each of which will be new. Remembering equals growth, for you and for me.'

'Thank you. Well, I made it. What's going down tonight? Hey, and what about *The Naked Man* then, and the covens and so on?'

'Yes, it is indeed a revered and sacred place. But more of that later. For there is an old friend I wish you to meet. He is already here in the clearing. Have you not noticed him?'

I spun around surveying the clearing, and the trees on the periphery that were catching the moon's beams. I could not make out anything but trees.

'You are merely looking again, not seeing... SEE!'

I focused again around the northern side of the clearing, where the moon was illuminating the nearest trees. There was something strange about the trunk of one of the larger trees that caught my attention, so I went over for a closer inspection. Yes, there was a face in the bark of the tree! The features were so huge that I had not made them out before. There were two large, deep-set eyes with large eyebrows, a bulbous nose and a mouth, formed by a large split in the trunk.

'Now I see it!'

'What do you see?'

221

'I see that face over there. I've seen lots of these in the past and have had great fun spotting features like this when out walking or in my car, features that resemble something. My friends have said a few times that I'm out of *my* tree. They're called simulacra, aren't they? It's amazing what the human imagination can conjure up, isn't it? This one reminds me of the Ent in *Lord of the Rings*. This isn't the type that throws boulders at Orcs, is it?'

'Ah, so you see such forms as mere figments of your imagination, do you - just amusing coincidences?'

'Er… well, yes. But I've got a funny feeling you're gonna tell me there's more to it than that. Right?'

'A fool sees not the same tree that a wise man sees. Perhaps for Ent you could say Entity. Please be seated on the ground, facing our ancient oak brother.'

I sat down, cross-legged on the leaf-littered forest floor.

'Good, now close your eyes… relax… and open your mind and your heart to that which may astound you. Now go deeper. Connect with the tree. Feel the energy passing between you along the web of life... feel! … SEE!'

I soon went down into a very deep state of being, as I connected with both the earth beneath and my inner calm place. I had done this practice many times in the past, but never in the dead of night, in a forest clearing under the Full Moon, and under the auspices of the Earth Mother! As at Avebury, I soon felt the pulse, the buzz of earth energies as they flowed up my spine and filled my head with power and light. Then, in my mind's eye, I could make out the gnarled features of the oak, but the clarity was well in excess of any visions I had had before. It was as if I my eyes were open, for I could make out every tiny detail of the knotted and twisted trunk and every branch and twig that emanated from it. The scene was played out in grey hues, perfectly mirroring the moonlit physical world outside.

'Welcome, human.'

The words boomed into my ears and I winced with surprise. The voice that filled my head was a deep male baritone, old and authoritative, and not too dissimilar to the Ents of Tolkien. The words had issued from the 'mouth' I had seen in the oak, which was now animated, as too were the eyes, which looked down on me, as if searching my very soul. I felt nervous and it took all my self-control to keep my eyes shut.

'I am Mugna, King of the Duir. The Great Mother has asked me to converse with you about the ways of trees and the

222

forests. It has been many years since such things were openly said to humankind. Not since the times of the great bards, times of Druids, Merlin and Taliesin, has there been such oration. The word Druid comes from 'duir', the ancient name of the oak, such was their loving relationship to us trees. Both Odin and Buddha sat under and within our branches to receive deep wisdom. But there have been long hard times since humankind danced to my glory around campfire and maypole, and jumped my fires at Beltaine. It was the trees that first gave Mankind the idea of erecting stones, for they mirror us, resting fast within the earth whilst reaching upwards to the sky. When the trees were enchanted, there was hope for the trees, but in the last two thousand years, things have changed, and changed for the worse. I have witnessed the untold suffering of my brethren, as millions have sacrificed themselves for humankind.'

'Sacrificed?'

'Yes, sacrificed. Every tree that has been felled for shelter has made a sacrifice to the Goddess for the development of humankind; every fire lit with kindling likewise, as too every murder in the name of progress, such as the clearing of forests for new roads and buildings. Much we have given, and still give. Once there was balance. When trees were felled, time was then given for woods and forests to recover, to renew. But humankind has bred too quickly for the trees to match, and as a consequence, we have been almost wiped out. From being respected and held as sacred, trees have been reduced to a commodity to be used and abused. Even the spirits of the mighty ones were reduced to decoration in the churches of the newcomers, as the Green Man, in an effort to convert those who held us dear in their hearts.'

'You paint a bad picture of Mankind. I'm not saying I disagree, but, with respect, is it as bad as you make out? I still see loads of woods and trees around in towns and in the countryside.'

'This may well appear so, but the number of my brothers and sisters left standing is but a fraction of what once was, and a great percentage of these are young. And a critical threshold is approaching. You have taken and taken from us, and in return we have given and still give the oxygen you need to survive. But you are fast approaching a time when we cannot supply what the planet needs, there are simply not going to be enough of us to support life as you know it. As

your wise sage Gandhi once said: 'The earth has enough for every man's need, but not for every man's greed.' Those words now ring true. It is a sad, sad business indeed.'

'I am sorry. I did not understand. Forgive me.'

'Do not worry about it, young sir. Few do understand the plight that could befall the planet if things do not change. And it is not just the number of trees left, but also the age of them. As ancient trees are felled, with them goes ancestral memory, which can no longer be accessed by humans, animals or Otherworldly beings. The huge sacred groves, the abode of my ancient cousins, are now very few in number, too few to maintain the flow of healthy energies, or to sustain important facets of the wisdom of the Land.'

'What happens when an ancient tree dies?'

'In the normal state of things, its spirit will flourish again in its offspring. As with humankind the spirit lives on after physical death. But with fewer middle-aged and elder trees to hold the energy, spirit and ancient wisdom, there is an imbalance. Imagine, if you will, your world populated only by the very old and the very young, with no teenagers or adults. How can the knowledge of life be passed from the elderly to young infants? It cannot. The young do not have the capacity to receive the complexities of knowledge that the elders possess.'

'I see. I also see large coniferous plantations being planted and fewer woods of large deciduous trees. Is this an imbalance?'

'Of course it is. It is not natural. It is an imbalance again. My conifer brothers and sisters only possess tiny leaves that give off only a small percentage of oxygen compared to my broad-leaved kin. Walk through a pine plantation. It supports but a fraction of animals and birds compared to that of a wood of oak, beech or ash. More disparity where once there was harmony.'

'What is it you wish me to pass on to people?'

'Tell them these things, and make sure they heed these words well. Firstly, there is spirit residing in every tree, a life-force that nurtures not only its immediate environment, such as supporting wildlife, but also stretching out across the Land, for large trees invigorate and energise the landscape for miles around. Also, you must reduce the amount of trees being felled considerably and the amount of carbons you are producing. We are trying our best to adapt to changing

224

climates, but we cannot possibly give the world the oxygen it now craves, nor absorb all the pollutants you are generating. It is now imperative that there is a cessation of the felling of my brothers and sisters in the great rain forests. These great gatherings of ancient souls are literally the lungs of the Great Mother. Do you wish to asphyxiate your mother? Man must again learn to respect and honour all animals and plants, and realise that they have an equal right to be here. We are all part of the great hoop of life, and nothing stands higher or lower than anything else. In a sacred circle, all are equal.'

'OK. I will tell them all of this.'

'Also tell humankind that the wisdom held within trees is the acumen of the planetary spirit. Landscape myths and memory are encapsulated within a tree's soul, and the loss of this from the Land would be a terrible blow to everything that lives on it, including humankind. Trees give humans much more than firewood, shelter and food, for we hold within us the spirit of the Land itself. We are holders of what has gone before, including the nobler aspects of humankind, memories of an age when people lived in accord with the processes of Nature. Cut us down and you lose part of yourselves, just as surely as if you were to cut off a limb. In addition to this, due to our upright growth and the heights we attain, trees channel energies from the cosmos, focusing them here on earth. Infant trees cannot do this so efficiently, another reason why it is not sufficient in itself to repopulate the world with young trees. Tree planting must be coupled with a cessation of the felling of my ancient elder brothers and sisters.'

'I feel so sad and so ashamed at what we have done. Do you feel the pain at what has been done to your brethren?'

'Yes, I do. I have spirit, a physical body, an aura and feelings just as you, small brother. My heart weeps when I think of the old friends I have lost. As I said, nothing dies, for spirit is immortal, but the old ones have past onto realms where they can no long dwell on the physical plane, nor can they communicate with me as they did. I have lost many, many dear friends, right across the world. And it did not matter how far away they once were. I once had centuries of intellectual conversation with an old redwood in America. Until he was cut down to make way for a freeway... hmm.'

His voice changed to one of sorrowful mourning.

'The day he was felled, we felt his loss right around the planet. I never heard from him again from that day on. Mmm... my old heart is sad indeed. I often feel as if my own days are number'd. My sap does not rise as it once did.'

The tale was heart-rending and I could feel myself welling up.

'But do not despair, for all is not lost. The Great Mother is working through you and you have a noble heart. I would lastly like to send out an invitation to all humankind to come and spend time with us, meditate with us, dream with us, talk to us, laugh with us, cry with us. Just come and befriend us once more. When you hug a tree and exchange emotions, a ripple of love and hope travels through the Land and healing takes place. We are more similar than you might think. By keeping your feet firmly on the ground you can nevertheless aspire to reach for the skies. You too can keep grounded by your physical and spiritual connection to the earth, whilst reaching up to the cosmos. Trees are the ultimate expression of living in harmony with the planet. Even when you go into the churches of the Solar prophet, seek out the Green Man, for it is I that will return your gaze. Now then, reverberations along the Web tell me you must leave now, but I will be here whenever you need to spend time with an old, craggy fuddy-duddy. Blessings, little sir.'

'Blessings to you too, Mugna, King of the Duir… and thank you.'

The image faded from my mind's eye and once again I sensed the smells of the forest. I had not noticed how the air had chilled or how cold my nose and hands were. I instinctively got up and went over to the giant oak. I clambered over exposed roots and put my arms around its gnarled girth. My heart filled with the energy of my ancient friend, and a tear rolled onto his wizened bark.

'Come, my son…' the Goddess softy interceded, *'… some people are gathering nearby and await you. It is the time of the ripened moon.'*

With great reluctance, I relinquished my tree-hug and stepped back into the centre of the dell, and looked skyward at the moon.

'Is there really hope, my Mother, for the trees and humankind?'

'There is always hope. Mugna's words and your presence here this night are proof of that. Come, retrace you steps to the Naked Man. But be mindful not to use your torch when you approach the edge of the woods. Be quiet and simply observe what you see.'

226

21. The Coven and the Dragon Tree

© P Knight

He is father. Even more, God is mother,
who does not want to harm us.
(Pope John Paul I, Rome blessing, 1978.)

I wended my way back through the wood, only deviating slightly from the original track as I negotiated my way through denser sections of undergrowth. As I approached the gate at the edge I became aware of voices. They were not far off to my right, coming from the direction of *The Naked Man,* and sounded as if several people were involved in conversation. I skirted the edge of the wood, staying in the shadows, taking care to tread softly on the crisp leaf-fall. About 100ft from the gathering I stopped. In the moonlight I counted twenty people, most of whom were quite sensibly attired in warm coats, scarves and gloves - temperatures were plummeting, and I could now see my breath. My curiosity held me spellbound as they suddenly broke ranks to form, with palpable organisation, a circle enclosing *The Naked Man*. They held hands and I realised if their numbers had been less they would not have been able to completely encircle the fence that enclosed the tree. It was a striking sight, twenty souls unified in a common cause around the sacred tree. I had no doubt that folklore concerning covens meeting here *in the past* needed updating, for there before me was a group of people holding hands under the Full Moon.

I stood in the shadows, maintaining my clandestine observation, feeling somewhat guilty for being an onlooker to a ritual that was not meant for the uninitiated and uninvited.

'But you are meant to witness this, or else you would not be.'

'I know,' I whispered back.

I could not catch all the words of the ceremony that ensued, as people took turns in saying short mantras and invocations. But I gathered that they had started by casting the circle, and had then honoured the four cardinal directions, dedicating them variously to air, fire, water and air. A figure in the centre then raised his or her arms, pointing what looked like a long staff moonward. Attached to the end was a huge quartz crystal, which periodically flashed as it caught the moonlight. The ensemble then circled the tree, still holding hands, first clockwise, and then the other way. They stood still again and the central figure, who wore a long black cloak, shouted up to the moon with a woman's voice:

'Diana, we greet thee. We honour thee. We honour thy cycles and your ripeness this night, and thank thee for your illuminating radiance. On this sacred night at this sacrosanct tree we ask that thy blessings and healing light be bestowed on those here present in this hallowed circle. We stand here as one group soul to send out healing to our Mother, the Land, and to all Mankind, wherever it be needed. May your healing light bless the planet with curative and beneficial energy. May the Land be forever bathed in your light and your divine love. So mote it be!'

To which the whole circle echoed a resounding, 'So mote it be!'

'Ditto' I echoed, softly.

'Ditto, indeed,' added the Goddess.

A few words were said by the other members of the circle in turn, which seemed to be individual words of healing and prayers, only a few of which I caught. *Well, this is hardly a group of naked witches prancing around in a circle before cavorting into the woods for a depraved orgy, is it?* But seriously, it was encouraging to see such a group who were clearly Pagan in persuasion sending out healing to the planet with seemingly no ulterior motive, such as gratuitous sex, and apparently with no obvious need to sacrifice either a chicken or a virgin! I knew I could talk to these people, for they spoke the language of the Goddess, like Diana and Ken's group at Stonehenge. However, I still felt like an interloper. How could I approach them without the risk of ruining the sanctity of the moment, and breaking the combined energy of the circle?

But then events transpired that took any decision of whether or not to join the group out of my hands, as the central figure turned to face my direction. She was looking straight at me, even though I must surely have been invisible to her, totally unilluminated in the shadows.

'We have a guest this night', she called out, 'an honoured guest who has been guided here by the Goddess. Come, my friend, show yourself. Do not be afraid, for we share your love for her. Come, please.'

She's calling out to me. She knows I'm here!

Stepping out of the shadows, the moonlight hit me and my body cast sharp, deep shadows to my left. I walked slowly towards the circle and noticed as I did so that the ones with their back to me were looking over their shoulders in an effort to witness my approach. A few feet from the gathering, two of their number separated and held their hands out to me. I took hold and joined the circle.

I could now make out the central woman more clearly. She wore a hooded cloak, much of which obscured her face, but she was in her mid-forties, I would guess, and her features and figure were lean and sharp. Her eyes glistened in the moonlight, matching the brilliance of the large yet elegant quartz crystal attached to the end of her staff.

'Welcome, my friend. My name is Cerridwen and we have been expecting you. The Great Mother came to me in a dream several days ago and told me of your quest. You are privileged indeed and we honour what you are doing for the planet and Mankind.' She bowed slightly in my direction before addressing the whole group.

'This is the man I told you may come this night, should the Goddess deem it so.'

With those words, exclamations of welcome, approval and acceptance echoed around the clearing.

'Please stay with us, to honour the Moon and this night,' she requested.

'I would be honoured to, thank you', I replied, returning Cerridwen's bow.

I spent the next twenty minutes or so trying to follow and repeat various group chants and invocations, as well as listening to individual contributions of prayers and poetry. At last I felt part of a movement that was helping heal the planet. I wondered what my dear departed father would think if he were to see me with this band of merry souls, around a dead tree under the Full Moon.

'Do not worry. Your father approves and is proud of you.'

Tears filled my eyes at the Goddess's words, which only I had heard. I looked up to the starry heavens and knew Dad was watching. I whispered to the stars:

'OK, Dad. Thank you… love you.'

Eventually a blessing of the Elementals of the four directions was enacted and the circle closed. Various items, which had lain on the ground within the circle, such as antlers, candles, feathers, crystals and a dagger, were carefully and reverentially wrapped in black and purple velvet and placed in a small wooden casket. The mood then changed, as wine and bread magically materialised from concealed bags and pockets. I was told that on previous gatherings they often had to form a circle *inside* the fence because of insufficient numbers, as I had suspected. They used the tree as a focus because it stood on a sacred place and rumour had it that the famous New Forest white witch, the late Sybil Leek, had officiated rites there. I exchanged experiences with several of the others as a close bond was forged between us. It turned out that several of them had had incredible experiences at sacred sites, seeing visions, feeling the love and presence of the Goddess, whilst others had exchanged love and energies with trees. Several patted me on the back in a congratulatory manner, as if they understood exactly the nature of my quest. In fact, I thought it strange that no one asked me details of my encounters with the Goddess, only asking general questions such as where I had been, and when, before exchanging their own experiences. It was as if they appreciated that what had been given to me by My Lady had been just for me only, for the time being at least. Their deep respect for the Goddess's plan was sufficient to override curiosity.

After a while, with the temperature continuing to drop towards freezing, we said our goodbyes and I exchanged telephone numbers with some of the group, including Cerridwen. They invited me to further Full Moon gatherings but also made it clear that they appreciated that I may be otherwise engaged over the next few, as I had further encounters with the Goddess. They departed in several cars, which had been parked further down the road, presumably so as not to draw attention to the gathering. As the last car disappeared into the night, I crossed the road, retracing my steps back across the open heath towards my car.

The moon was brilliant now, high in the sky on the borders of Cancer and Gemini, and my body cast stark, black shadows before me. Sirius, the Dog Star, was almost due south, with Orion's belt pointing to it. Every now and again I would look to my left to view the brilliant star, remembering my totem that bore the same name. Despite the brilliance of the lunar orb, I could still make out hundreds of stars, such was the clarity of the air. The Goddess and I struck up our final conversation of the night.

'You know, My lady, one of those guys was a banker, another a traffic warden and Cerridwen manages a charity shop. They are just run-of-the mill-people.'

'With respect, aren't you yourself such a person?'

'Yes, exactly, and that's the point, isn't it? Tonight there wasn't a Goth, hippy or spliff in sight, not that there's anything wrong with any of that. But we need to change the heart of society, don't we, and that can be best achieved by people who live at the heart of communities, not just those at the extremities. Now I *really* do believe there is hope for the planet.'

'As I said before, there is always hope. The night has been a good one, another recovered piece in the jigsaw of planetary healing, and another step towards the salvation of Mankind. I will cease our conversation now, as you need to concentrate on negotiating the uneven and frosty ground before you. But I say this to you: try to spend as much time as you can with trees. It will help you connect to me whenever you doubt, need reassurance, or need to recharge your physical and spiritual batteries. And in view of this I would like you, if you would, to look up an old tree friend of mine.'

'Oh, yes? Who's that then – an old ash or a yew?'

'Well, actually, he's a dragon.'

'A dragon?'

'But he's also a Duir brother, a mighty ancient oak. He stands proud on a spirit line that goes all the way to Stonehenge. He resembles a dragon and symbolises those fiery forces that still breath fire across the Land. He stands not far from Knowlton, at Woodlands. He needs your help.'

'I will find him and do what I can. Oh, by the way, can you give me a clue where our next meeting will be, and what the lesson will be about?'

'Hmm. Let me see. OK. It is winter now and I know you feel the need to travel abroad and...'

'Yes!'

'... I thought you'd be pleased. You have earned it. The next discourse will be about honouring the ancestors and connecting to ancestral memory. And where better to do this than where dwells Mané Lud and Le Grand Menhir Brisé, a place where our stone brothers have assembled in large numbers? I bid you farewell now.'

'Good night, my Mother. Oh, and by the way, I recognised you in the window at Burley. You looked beautiful.'

'Why, thank you. Yes, we did good work there... Good night, my son.'

During the drive home, my mind and heart raced with anticipation, for I felt sure I was off to Brittany for the next Full Moon. I recognised one of the places she had mentioned as being around the south coast, near Carnac. My research into ancient sites had revealed the region to be rich in megaliths and dolmens of a similar age and design to their British counterparts. I also understood that the greatest numerical concentration of such monuments in Europe was in Brittany, so I was really excited. I had never been to the area, and hoped it would be warmer than anywhere She might have chosen in Britain. *Thanks, My Lady!*

In the meanwhile, I had been given clues by which I could help someone in distress, a dragon no less. Over the next few days, I tried to find out where I was meant to go. She had said,

'... he's also a Duir brother, an oak... on a spirit line that goes to Stonehenge. He resembles a dragon... not far from Knowlton, at Woodlands.'

I knew Knowlton well enough but how close was *'not far'*, and in which direction? The spirit line was presumably a ley alignment, so I put myself to work to see if I could find any leys that passed through or close to Woodlands, a small village on Cranborne Chase. But after some initial attempts I could find nothing that went through the church of Woodlands. So I decided to broaden my brief. It could, after all, be in the *parish* of that name, which covered a much wider area. On the third day, just as I was about to give in, something clicked. I had already plotted several leys associated with Knowlton's Neolithic henges, which radiated out like the spokes of a wheel. One of these ran east-west, passing through Hod Hill, Long Crichel Church, Knowlton to the Verwood megalith and onward to tumuli to the east. Part of this line ran through the northern part of Woodlands parish. I knew from previous experience that interesting things could often be found where two leys crossed. So I honed in on this line to see if I could find any others that intersected it going north to Stonehenge. There was just one! An alignment ran up from the Purbecks, via some tumuli, a crossroads, hill summits and an old chapel at Woodlands, through a stone on an old OS map to the north, through Wilton and on to Stonehenge. Just north of Woodlands this line and the one from Knowlton intersected. *Bingo!*

I marked the spot with a tiny circle on my OS map and sat staring at it for a while. But before the hour was up, I was off. The chilled air cut into my face as I arrived and alighted from my car. Leaves were scattered along the lane in which I had parked. I was standing at a T- junction and, amazingly, one road was east-west, the other north-south, both exactly mirroring the two leys that converged at that point. But what was it that had drawn me there, if indeed it were the right place? Well, whether it was the correct place to find the oak or not, I knew from experience that I was there for a good reason, no matter what. I was not prepared, however, for what greeted me as I turned away from the junction. On the east side of the road stood a huge tree, overhanging the road. And more than this, the whole tree resembled a huge creature rising from beneath the earth. It had a deep-set hollow eye, gaping mouth, a goatee beard, and even a snout. I had found the dragon!

I approached, and soon saw that it *was* an oak. Its leaves had nearly all fallen off, and were scattered in heaps around the base of the trunk. One side of the tree was completely hollowed out and explained the top heavy lean over the road. Something caught my eye at the foot of the trunk. I cleared away ivy and leaves to reveal a stone plaque! On it was a description of the *Remedy Oak*, as it was described, and how Edward VI had come to the locality, *'… to touch the King's evil'*. It was a place of ancient healing, on leys to both Stonehenge and Knowlton, and the tree resembled a dragon! What more could one ask for? I was ecstatic at the revelation and managed to find a space where ivy had not grown and hugged the tree with my most heartfelt embrace.

But my euphoria was short-lived, however, as an inspection of the mighty oak saw that it appeared to be in trouble. For one, it was being held up by a gigantic solid steel cable that was fastened to the tree at one end and into the ground some yards to the east. Some sort of rescue operation had taken place to keep the tree upright, presumably because of its historic folklore. Secondly, virtually the whole of the lower half of the tree, and much of the upper, was covered with thick growths of ivy, some strands of which were four inches thick. It felt as if the tree, already old and weak, was being choked to death by the parasitic ivy.

I looked up to the face that loomed above me. *Not if I can help it!* I got my shears, secateurs and heavy-duty gloves from the car and returned to the tree. But I first wanted to know if I really was meant to be here to clear the tree of its freeloading assailants.

'Well, my ancient friend, would you like to breathe more easily? Should I clear this ivy from you?'

'Yes sir, if you would be so kind.'

The words resounded very softly around my head, in a deep, elderly male voice, but as clearly as those I had heard from the Goddess and the tree spirit Mugna.

'OK, then. Let's get to it!'

The work was hard but the coldness of the afternoon helped. In fact, at one stage, I was reduced to wearing just a shirt, discarding both my coat and jumper. I cut, pulled, ripped and sliced my way through filament after filament, strand after strand of the entangled, suffocating growth. I exposed sections of bark that had not seen the light of day for many years, and I could almost feel the tree take in deep breaths as I cleared the lowest part of the invading menace. At full stretch I could only reach up to about 8ft from the ground, but I figured that if I was to completely clear everything below this, including digging up as many ivy and bramble roots I could find, then everything above must surely wither in time. After about an hour, my work was done. It was as if the tree had had a shave, and although it still needed a haircut above, I felt I had done enough. I stood back and admired my efforts, just as a cold rain began to fall. I bowed to the liberated oak dragon and vowed to return before long to ensure the ivy had indeed died off.

Mugna, the Oak King, had said that to heal trees and spend time with them was beneficial to both the Land and ourselves. I could sense that the overground energies passing this way would surely be in better stead now. The dragon could again weave his magic and breathe his fiery breath across the Land, unrestrained by the throttling mass that had restricted him. As I headed back to the dryness of my car, I turned to face the tree and felt a rush of love and beautiful energy passed between us. The mighty oak dragon was connecting with me, and I with him, and a smile spread across both our lips. I knew then that dragons still lived, if we knew where to look. He breathed fire into my heart that day,

234

and the healing that resulted passed down the ley to Stonehenge, the temple on the plain, and even beyond that.

Mugna had confirmed to me that green man carvings represented the Christianisation of the old tree spirits and the Lord of the Forest, the Celtic Cernunnos. As I visited churches I would make a point of looking for these vestiges of the old ways. I found them all around Dorset, Somerset, Wiltshire, indeed everywhere I went. There did not seem to be any geographical favouritism, but rather had a universal distribution. In some places, such as in the cathedrals of Exeter and Winchester, I found dozens of them, many painted in green, brown and gold. Another striking example was in the choir area of Christchurch Priory, where a figure completely covered from top to toe in foliage wielded a club, not unlike the Cerne Giant.

At less grandiose churches, especially in rural areas, I found the green man in obscure corners, high up in rafters, or elevated high on church towers. At Mappowder, a small village in central Dorset, a green man carved in stone was particularly potent as it was large, made of stone, and easy to inspect just behind the pulpit. This and others displayed the secret lore of the stonemasons. And every time I found a new green man, my thoughts drifted back to that night in the New Forest, when the Oak King spoke to me. I often wondered if green man carvings were made as a result of rural folk actually conversing with tree spirits centuries ago, times when people still visited sacred groves to meet and revere tree spirits, thanking them for the bounty given to them by the Land.

22. Tenth Moon – December: Carnac, France Lesson - Connecting with Ancestors

© P Knight

Ancestors provide a vital connection to the Divine,
to the Source of all life.
(From *Spinning the Wheel of Ana,* Kathy Jones)

I was brimming with excitement at the prospect of going to Brittany. During my previous research, Brittany had kept cropping up, and in particular the area around Carnac, on the south coast. Thousands of megaliths, called menhirs, had survived Man and the elements, including the tallest, longest and heaviest standing stones in Europe! It was the densest population of prehistoric megaliths in the world, according to some, and many were arranged in rows and avenues that marched across the Land for miles. The prospect was exhilarating – thousands of ancient stones, as well as readily accessible tombs, many enriched with carvings, similar in design to those of Ireland. In fact the more I compared the Irish and Breton Neolithic sites, the more I appreciated just how much they had in common, from the point of view of design, carvings, alignments, grave goods, and the fact that many of the French sites had also been Christianised. I was sure that the area would be alive with major flows of earth energy but did not know how to begin to plot any alignments, as there were so many stones, tumuli, rows, churches and other relevant features on my 1:25 000 maps.

Some work had been done by researchers such as Alexander Thom, who had advocated several astronomical alignments in the area, some of which involved the gigantic prone Le Grand Menhir Brisé (meaning *The Big Broken Megalith*). Others had suggested further alignments relating to solar and lunar events, but nothing much had been published concerning dowsing or leys. The sheer number of ancient stone sites suggested that the area around Carnac was as important as Stonehenge or Avebury in its day. This was the prehistoric Glastonbury, the ancient Jerusalem, the centre of the Neolithic ceremonial world. I was bowled over by the scale and size of the monuments, as photos showed people being dwarfed by megaliths reaching 20ft tall. It was the first time that the Goddess had despatched me to mainland Europe, and she seemed to have picked arguably the best area in terms of quantity and size of megaliths. *I can't wait!*

My route to Brittany was via a flight to Rennes, the nearest direct flight airport to Carnac, and I touched down around noon. By that time I was feeling a little apprehensive as to whether my French would hold up, as it had been years since I had been in France, and prior to that had only done French 0-level at school - aged sixteen! *Oh well, in for a penny in for a Euro!* However, after my initial attempts at *merci* and *bonjour*, I felt a bit more at ease. I passed through customs without being stopped, but again displayed the guilt that many of us seem to exude, even when we have nothing to hide! Weird.

I picked up my hire car and was soon on my way southwest along the N24, a route that would eventually take me to Carnac via Vannes and Ploërmel. I had to adapt to the steering wheel being on the wrong side, and driving on the right was also a bit strange, but as everyone else seemed to know which side to drive on, I followed them. The journey was reminiscent of Ireland, with long stretches of open road, despite it being the start of the Christmas holiday. I arrived in Carnac around 3.00pm, under cloudy, drizzly skies, and the out-of-season streets were strangely deserted, as if some western gunfight were about to take place. From where I parked the car, I safely negotiated crossing the road to the hotel, with no sign of Clint Eastwood or any tobacco-chewing Mexicans. At reception, I spoke a little French and the receptionist spoke some English, so it all worked out fine. My room was adequate with a nice view across the Carnac rooftops, to the vast expanse of the Gulf of Morbihan beyond.

I soon had my Michelin maps laid out on the bed as I looked for clues to where I would meet Her Ladyship. It was the day before Full Moon, so I needed some inspiration. The map was festooned with all manner of stone avenues, menhirs, tombs and the like, hundreds of them within a few square miles of where I sat. 'Needle in a haystack' came to mind, but I knew that I would find the right place and would not be daunted by the prospect, as I had been in Ireland. It was raining and consequently was already getting quite dark by 3.30pm. I had a quick trot around town only to find, as it was outside the tourist season, that most of the shops were closed. I couldn't even find a restaurant or café that was open. Fortunately, just down the road from the hotel, there was a pizza take-away. I consumed a *grande pizza végétarien* in my hotel room, before organising a rough itinerary for the following day. I turned in for an early night around 10.30pm.

I awoke around 7.30am to birdsong, and the light streaming through my window invited me out on to the balcony.

'Bonjour, Brittany!'

No one answered, but I knew the megaliths had heard me. They were waiting for me, that much I was sure of. The rain had stopped, but it was still overcast, with a distinct chill.

*Oh, well, it **is** December after all, and as long as it stays dry, that'll do me!*

After breakfast I set off, maps and guidebooks on the passenger seat, out into the wild grey yonder of Brittany. My first stops were the magnificent Mènec, Kermario and Kerlescan megalithic alignments. Although regarded as separate stone rows, I could see instantly that they must originally have formed one complex, comprising hundreds of stones marching across the Brittany landscape. They resembled somewhat the legions of Terracotta Warriors in China, or perhaps herds of migrating wildebeest. Up to a dozen rows of stones, some over 10ft tall, ran parallel across fields and through woods. I could see that they were not straight, but sinuous, as if following something. To me there was only one answer – they were marking out the serpent-like currents of earth energies that flowed across the Land. I intended to check this out with my dowsing rods, but a shock awaited me at my initial stops. The rows were all fenced off - I could not believe it. I frustratingly peered over chest-high fencing, and knew that this was not how we were meant to interact with the stones. A notice board, thankfully in English and French, said that the restricted access was to hold back erosion of the sites, but as I looked around me I could see no one else around on this damp, cold day and wondered why the fields were not open at least 'out of season.' Stonehenge came to mind, and my mind jostled with the pros and cons of restricting access to sacred places.

Even from outside the megalithic fields were impressive, with literally hundreds of huge ancient sentinels disappearing into the distance. They really did remind me of photos I had seen of the Chinese warriors: row upon row of impressive figures, each unique. I took some photos and did a little dowsing on my side of the fence at Mènec village, where I was able to look along the axis of the rows. My dowsing rods confirmed that the stone rows were channelling energies, sometimes with a male feel, at other times with a more feminine vibration. But I wanted to get amongst the stones. My map pinpointed a smaller site called *Petit Mènec Alignement*, which stood in woods at the eastern extremity of the alignments. I would see if I could gain access to my stone brothers and sisters there. Rain was threatening, and small drops impacted on my windscreen as I arrived at a small wooded lay-by, opposite which stood a wooden sign pronouncing *Petit Mènec.* I followed the arrow and immediately entered enchanted woodland, through which ran several long rows of megaliths.

The woodland floor was carpeted with a myriad of fallen, golden leaves and the stones rose out of these like antediluvian creatures lifted from some ancient myth. Over 150 stones marched through a sinuous clearing, stretching out into the distance, inviting me to follow. I was able to walk among these ancient stones to my heart's content, pausing occasionally to take in the magical unfolding scenes that constantly changed before my eyes. I sat against a couple of stones that had drawn me to them, and closing my eyes became aware of energies spiralling around them that were making me tingle and shimmy. At times I felt that I was not alone, that invisible eyes were observing my every move. Every now and again I would spontaneously smile in the direction of some tree or megalith, from which I sensed I was being observed. An exchange of love passed between the place and my being, and a bubble of ecstasy grew within. One particular stone took my eye, because it so resembled the features of some woodland elf or goblin. It was only about 4ft high, but called me nonetheless. I stood in front of the megalith and greeted it:

'Bonjour, my stone brother. Tell me, where am I to meet Our Lady on this Full Moon? Do you know? Can you tell me?'

The stone did not answer verbally, but I still felt it had something to say, so I circled around it, looking for a sign or clue. Then I spotted something. The top of the stone comprised an almost horizontal ledge, which was around eye level to me. On it there lay two twigs, which had presumably fallen from overhanging pine trees. One twig was sort of Y-shaped, and across it lay the other. Together they were undoubtedly forming the letter *K*. I gave a smile, for I knew it meant something. *K - now what is that then?* I returned to the other side of the stone and looked into the 'eye' of the stone face before me.

'Thank you, my friend. Thank you - and Au Revoir!'

I bowed my head to the stone, and headed back to the car.

K... K... K... what does it mean... K what?

Back inside, I got out my guidebook, Aubrey Burl's essential *Megalithic Brittany*. In the Carnac section there were several places beginning with K, in fact TOO MANY! *Hmm. I wonder which one it is?* I looked out of the car, smiling to myself, suspecting that the Goddess was also amused by my efforts.

'OK, then, M' Lady, I'll dowse for it.'

I got out of the car and unfolded my map on the bonnet. I retrieved my tiger's eye pendulum from its pouch and held it over the map. I had got increasingly confident with my ability to dowse over previous months. Following energy lines across the Land, and seeing my pendulum spin excitedly over megaliths, had reinforced to me the existence of an unseen vitality and spiritual essence in the Land.

'OK. Please show me where I am to meet *Madame Gaia* this evening - for *zee tête-à-tête!*'

I concentrated hard on the issue in hand, repeating my request over and over again. I slowly moved the pendulum over the map, suspending it about two inches above. I held it over the Locmariaquer Peninsular, which I knew was home to several major sites, such as Le Grand Brisé, Le Table Des Marchands and Les Pierres-Plats, places already on my *'must see'* list. But the pendulum did not swing at all over these. I came west across the River Crach and my pendulum swept over the alignments and their associated menhirs. Again nothing. I then held it over the famous Tumulus St-Michel, the ancient passage grave with the church on top. But again, there was no movement from the pendulum. I continued over the map in an easterly direction and

240

noticed that my crystal passed over several places beginning with *K*, such as Kermario, Kermaux, Kerluir and Kerousse. Next I altered direction and moved my pendulum north, and almost immediately it began to swing in a small circle. I continued a fraction further and the pendulum went berserk. Within seconds it was swinging in a wide arc, gathering speed until eventually it took all I had to keep hold of the chain!

'OK. I get the point. Let's see then!'

With those words the pendulum ceased swinging and came to rest, motionless save for a slight wobble from the breeze. I put my finger on the map immediately below the point of the crystal. There was the word 'tumulus', and next to it 'Kercado Chât'.

Voilà!

Burl's guide described Kercado as one of the most important Neolithic passage graves in Brittany, and one of the oldest with datable finds going back to 4675 BC, making it the oldest man-made monument I had visited to date. On the underside of the capstone, and on some of the uprights, there were carvings, as well as a surrounding stone circle and a crowning megalith on top of the mound. It looked a fantastic place, yet was not one of the most famous. The Goddess had chosen this place for reasons that would no doubt become clear before the night was through. I hastily gathered up my belongings and jumped back into my car.

'Nice one, M' Lady. Nice one.'

Full Moon was around 7.15pm, well after dark at that time of year, so I had a few hours to kill before I needed to go to Kercado, which was only about ten minutes drive to the west. I decided to take in a couple of the more spectacular menhirs near Carnac whilst it was still light. The first was Le Gèant du Manio, west of Kerlescan, reached via a lovely wooded walk. It was quite literally a 20ft high penis! It stood huge and erect in a forest clearing, next to a trapezoidal megalithic enclosure a few yards to the north. The sheer scale of the stone made me stand back and stare in awe as to the technique of its erection (excuse the pun!) and its purpose. Burl stated that the stone possibly had astronomical alignments with others in the area, and its sheer size would have ensured it would have been visible for miles around, prior to the encroachment of the trees that now encircled it. I gave the stone a huge hug, even though my outstretched arms only went around a quarter of its girth.

Next stop was the menhir near the D186 road, opposite the turning to Kerlegad (No. 181 in Burl's guide). A couple of minutes' walk along a partially overgrown path skirting a wood brought me to the megalith. It stood 9ft tall and was remarkable for the fact that leaning against it, and growing around the top of the stone, was a pine tree. The tree leaned into the stone as if attracted by some unseen magnetism, and perhaps it was. The tree and the megalith seemed happy bedfellows, standing together, seemingly forgotten, less than a mile away from the famous alignments that drew thousands of visitors. From that stone, according to Burl, one would have formerly seen the winter solstice sun rising over the Manio megalith, the one I had just visited. It must have been an impressive sight all those thousands of years ago, seeing the giant phallus silhouetted against the sun on the shortest day.

And so to Kercado and what I hoped would be my next rendezvous with the Lady. It was approaching sunset, although cloud cover ruined any hope of seeing it. Dusk was imminent as I drove my car up the long, straight drive that led to Château Kercado. The estate was heavily wooded and trees totally encircled the designated parking area. A wooden sign directed me to the tumulus. I bundled a couple of nightlights, a lighter, my dowsing rod, my torch, digital camera and a plastic sheet into my rucksack, and set off. I could see the fine Château through an arch, but it was marked *Privé – Entrée Interdite*, which I took to mean, 'no entry, mate!' This bothered me not as I wasn't going that way, and I soon arrived at a small shed-like structure, totally open on one side, through which I was directed. Inside was a table on which were spread sheets of paper, which turned out to be short guides to the site, in various languages. I found the English account and took a digital photo of it for later reference. The info was fascinating, telling how the tumulus was restored in 1925 and confirming its age at 4,500 BC to 4,800 BC. Hmm, that was old, even by the standards of the ancient sites I had visited in Britain and Ireland. It went on to describe the main chamber as comprising eight menhirs and *'a great table'*, presumably the capstone. It told of the unearthing of 147 beads of *'a sea-green precious stone from the neck of a chieftain'*, indicating a high status burial.

I left the hut and to my horror was immediately accosted by a Coca-Cola vending machine! *Is nothing sacred?* Leaving that intrusion behind, I was directed through a stone arch and into a beautifully mysterious area, bordered by woods, which led to another ancient arch, next to which very old stone steps ascended a high wall. The whole scene was magical in the fading light and I took a snap with my camera before passing through the arch. And there finally, immediately in front of me, was the Kercado tumulus. Surrounded on all sides by a thick wood, it stood in a magnificent setting. The mound looked complete, and was enclosed by the stone circle Burl had mentioned. I could see the lone megalith on top, which seemed to be standing guard, like a Grail Knight guarding the holy chalice at some secret locality. The clearing was covered in fallen leaves, and the air was chilled and damp, a truly primeval and timeless scene. I looked around, but I was on my own - no locals, no tourists, no pilgrims to disturb the sanctity of the moment. It was dead calm and it seemed as if the trees themselves were waiting for my next move.

I approached the ancient mound in the failing light. To my left was an outlying stone, about fifty metres from the entrance, but I bypassed it, clambering to the top of the mound to stand next to the single, phallus-shaped megalith that stood proudly at the summit. I took my pendulum from its pouch and held it a few inches above the top of the stone. Immediately it began to swing in a clock-wise motion and within seconds was frantically whizzing around in such a wide arc that I had to tighten my grip on the chain.

'Well, My Lady, the Full Moon has got this placed all charged up, that's for sure.'

I retraced my steps back down the side of the mound to the forest floor and took a few paces to my right until I stood in front of the entrance. The lintel over the opening was low, about shoulder height on me, comprising a huge solid block of granite. Either side were walls of smaller stones, reminiscent of Newgrange and some of the Cotswold Neolithic passage mounds I had visited in the summer. I peered into the entrance. It was jet-black inside, receiving hardly any illumination as the light continued to fade.

'Bonsoir, my son. Come in, for I have been waiting for you.'
'Bonsoir to you too, My Lady.'

I took the torch out of my backpack and with one click the passage in front of me burst into life. I crouched down and started down the ancient tunnel, keeping my head low. I shuffled along foetal-like for about ten yards before the central chamber opened up. As I shone the light around, ancient carvings revealed themselves, most appearing to be squares and grid-like patterns. After a few sweeps of the ceiling I located the axe carving on the underside of the huge capstone. I stood up and ran my fingers over the feature. I found it incredible that someone had created it over 6,000 years ago.

'Incredible, indeed. Men and women have come to this place for many millennia, seeking my council, to hear my words, to receive healing. Your archaeologists have proven that this is almost the oldest Neolithic monument in Europe. They have also satisfied themselves that this place was in continual use for many centuries. It is a special place, and in fact stands on the highest natural point of the Carnac area.'

I began to notice that my stomach was filling up with energy, and my fingers were tingling as they touched cold stone.

'The place feels alive. It's buzzing with energy, I can feel it.'

I lit two nightlights and settled down on my plastic sheet, leaning back against ancient stone.

'The place surely is alive. But then everything is, isn't it? This is an ancestral place where your distant forebears gathered at Full Moon, on nights like tonight, to venerate me and to contact their ancestors.'

'Contact their ancestors? You mean *really* meet them, in the flesh so to speak?'

'No, of course not. When a soul is separated from flesh, as at physical death, then it cannot go back to that body, save for very rare circumstances when a consciousness is sufficiently advanced. Even the Bible says, 'From dust thou art made, and unto dust shall thou return', meaning that nothing physical survives, that all is transient. By meeting the ancestors, I mean to converse with their spirits for guidance, solace, healing, and sometimes simply out of love for departed ones. This is the purpose of tonight's meeting. I wish people to appreciate their ancestors, the debt they owe them, and for the wisdom they still have to offer you. Their bodies may have returned to the Land, but their souls are free and for a while they can be contacted. This is still the basis of shamanism across the world, as it was in the past. For millennia, wise men and women have sought contact with those whom had gone before, to engender healing, to attain knowledge, and for honouring departed kinsfolk. Proof that the builders of ancient places believed their ancestors lived on is provided by the grave goods they buried with the departed. These were left for the deceased to use in their new life in the Otherworld, much the same as the Egyptians did.'

'I see. Tell me, in coming to places like this, can I potentially contact those who previously visited this place, and were perhaps even interred here?'

'Oh, certainly, and much more than that. Any place of ancestral power, from churchyard to tumulus, from passage grave to mausoleum, is a bridge to ancestral realms. And it is not just a matter of contacting those whom either were interred in, or made use of, a sacred place such as this. This holy monument, for instance, has been and still is, a conduit, a crossing point, for a shaman to contact other souls that may never have been here physically. Shamans can draw to them untold souls, ancestors and totems from elsewhere in the Universe, for they have the skills, techniques, focus and power to procure this.'

'Yes, but I'm no shaman.'

'It is true that you are less empowered at this moment in time. You are also restricted by the wishes of those you seek to contact, regarding the purpose for which contact is sought, and whether it is beneficial for a connection to be made. In most cases it is not. Many souls will have moved on, have new agendas, or actually feel it more loving and beneficial not to reply when they are called. Although these souls do not see the highest picture of the Universe, as I do, they nevertheless stand on a higher viewpoint than you.'

'So what is this debt we owe our ancestors, both individually and as a species?'

'All the sacred places you have visited, and will visit in the coming full moons, were built by your ancestors. Perhaps it would help if you regarded them not so much as your ancestors, but rather your relatives. You are related to all humans, through your DNA, and so you yourself are a relative, a descendant, of the people who erected this mound thousands of years ago. Stonehenge, Avebury, Newgrange, the Pyramids and all the other sacred places around the world owe their construction and survival to the faith and ingenuity of your distant relatives. Do you not owe them much?'

'Oui, Madame, I do indeed.'

'And this comes down to an individual level too. Your own parents, grandparents and great grandparents, whom you remember, all helped create your body and mind. And I speak not only of physical levels. For all your relatives made

decisions and actions on a soul level to enable you to be born and for your life to point in certain directions, with particular agendas. Your spirit too conspired with all of your relatives, deceased and living, to construct the beautiful body and mind that is you. Do you not owe them much?'

'I sure do.'

'Also be mindful that to honour your ancestors is also to honour yourself.'

'Myself? How come?'

'Are you so sure that you have not been this way before? Have you not been to a sacred place for the first time and had the strong feeling that you had been there before? Well, there is a very good reason for this.'

'You mean I may have been there in a past life?'

'Yes. So when you go to such a place, and honour the ancestors, your ancestors, you may well be honouring your own spirit essence that lived and died there thousands of years ago. To honour the memory of your ancestors, and what they achieved, is also to honour yourself, in the same way as to honour and nurture the Land is to honour and nurture yourself. You can affect the Land by letting the Land influence you. You will be amazed in the years to come how Universal laws have worked through seemingly unrelated events in your life. The spirit of the Land never stops watching you. The eyes of truth are never closed.'

'I already am amazed. You know, recently I've been thinking more and more about my father, especially as January gets nearer, the first anniversary of his death.'

'Correction, if I may. January will be the first anniversary of his PHYSICAL death.'

'I guess. But I do miss him. Yet I have recently dared to believe that I may yet contact him, or that he may contact me, perhaps at somewhere like this.'

'I cannot and will not intervene between individual souls, be they in spirit or on the Earth Plane. Although they are part of me, like the corpuscles and atoms of your body are to you, they possess their own will, their own agendas. It could be that contact with the spirit of your father may not serve either of you, or else just one of you, in which case it would not take place. Perhaps a change of attitude is required. Your society sees death as an ending, some great disaster, something which happens without planning or purpose. But realise this,

no soul enters nor leaves this physical plane by accident, despite what sensationalists may tell you. I know all. I am all. So therefore I cannot make mistakes. Everything happens for good reason, and ultimately that reason is for me to once again know myself in the form of pure love. Individual souls are part of the whole, are affected by the whole, and in turn influence the whole. In this context, how can anything happen that is not meant to?'

'It doesn't always appear that way though, does it, especially when disasters occur?'

'The death of a very young child, the demise of people in a plane crash, or through disease or starvation, all seem to strike savagely without forethought or reason. But believe me, there is reason and purpose for every single atom that spins in the Universe. Have faith, for this is surely so. Grieve for the fact that you miss your father, for that is a testament of your love for him, but grieve not because he is dead, for he is not.'

'So is my father watching over me? Can you tell me this much at least?'

'But of course he is. And he may continue to do so for some time yet. This is one of the rationales behind people undertaking pilgrimage to their ancestral graves or similar epitaphs, as well as spending time at places their loved ones appreciated or held as sacred. Honour also their birthday, and the anniversary of their passing from their physical body. Both of these are holy days, marking the sacred genesis and glorious completion of their latest incarnation. Both are worthy of celebration.'

I welled up with these words, as images of my father danced in and out of my head. Through misting eyes I could see the ancient carvings animated by the flickering lights. I suddenly felt a shiver of cold air sweep across my body and I zipped up my fleece in response.

'Feeling cold, my messenger? There is a reason for this. You have visitors.'

'Er, visitors?'

'The ancestors of this place wish to make themselves known to you. You are honoured. Come, my son, ready yourself. Dry your eyes… sit back against the carved stone behind you, for you will be in contact with ancient symbols

that will open your inner eye... when you are ready, please close your eyes.'

I did as I was asked. I looked behind me to confirm that the stone I was to lean against was indeed etched with geometrical patterns. I turned and settled back against the ancient images. Closing my eyes, my inner vision saw only pitch darkness initially, a void even the nightlights could not penetrate. But all that soon changed. I began to become aware of faint swirling patterns in my mind's eye, which gradually increased in brightness. After about thirty seconds, they were as bright as torches. Spirals, concentric circles, serpent-like images, shimmering squares and triangles, all danced before me. I recognised many from Newgrange and other ancient sites and realised from where my ancestors had got their inspiration - messages from the Gods, from the ancestors. It was a pyrotechnic display without equal, as images bright enough to make me wince danced in and out of my inner vision.

Then I was aware that other images were mixed in with the dancing lights, faint at first, but then brighter and more lucid. They were human faces! A whole procession took turns in approaching me before fading at the last moment, to be replaced by another, and then another. Some were old, some bearded, some male, others female, mostly elders but occasionally a child. I felt love unbounded from all of them, and some even smiled at me. One grey-bearded elder paused momentarily, long enough for him to nod to me. Some wore ancient clothes, such as hoods made of skins, whilst others wore feathers in their hair. One or two had woad paint on their faces, including zigzag motifs, whilst one elder woman had a spiral tattooed on her forehead.

I have no idea how long the ancestral procession lasted, but it ended abruptly. I was suddenly in darkness and once again felt the chilled December air whistle through my hair. I also noticed that my heart was racing at quite a pace, pulsing in my ears.

'You see, your ancestors are never far away, and localities such as this are sacred liminal places, where worlds merge. The seen and the unseen converge here, as they can at any site of ancestral power. And be aware also that a place such as this has a guardian.'

'A guardian?'

'Yes. And I do not mean a knight in shining armour sporting a sword, like in a Grail myth. No, for guardians are spiritual beings who have chosen to look after the energies of a place, and very often they will be the essence of an

ancestor that had a close connection with a locality when they were in physicality. These can be contacted so you may let them know your purpose, by means of meditation and visualisation, or sometimes through simply asking. Much knowledge will be forthcoming if you convince a guardian of your love and good intentions for the ancestors and the Land. Be mindful that a guardian can block, as well as allow, the flow of wisdom. Many people go to ancient places with the intention of obtaining personal power for purely selfish, ego-driven means. Have no fear, for a guardian will not permit deeper truths to be known to such people. It is those with a purity of heart that will be rewarded.'

'I see. I have certainly felt the presence of 'something' before, a feeling that I was not alone. But tell me, My Lady, why did I not see my father just then? I was hoping he would appear.'

'I know you were. But he may well contact you directly if, and when, the time is right. Do not fret. He loves you still and watches you. He is so, so proud of you. Let that be enough for now. This ancient place was not sacred to him in any of his former lives, so why would he appear here? He does not have any psychic or energetic links to this site. The others you have just witnessed possess such a connection. You must seek out your father's special places, or else energetically create a special, sacred place where you may, if there is good purpose, connect more lucidly. Come, open your eyes.'

I did so and was greeted by a wondrous sight. Looking back along the passage to the outside world, I could see that a faint but definite light now illuminated the ground outside the entrance. The Full Moon had risen!

'Go and look! It has cleared and is a fine night for mice and men. Experience! Appreciate!'

I hastily gathered up my belongings, blew out the nightlights and made my way back along the passage to the entrance of the mound. I rose to my feet on reaching the outside and stared up at the moon, which was shining through leafless trees, accompanied by scudding white-horse clouds. It was indeed beautiful. The moonlight was catching the outlying megalith and the black shadow cast by the stone reached out towards me along the leaf-strewn forest floor. It was emotive - the place, the energy, the moon, the ancestors - and me to witness it all. I greeted the shining orb with outstretched arms and an open heart.

'Bonsoir, La Lune.'

I stood in the clearing, next to the ancient mound, for several minutes, absorbing the healing light, before the Goddess gently spoke.

'And what of your father, your own beloved ancestor? What of him?'

'I now know what I must do with his ashes. I have hung onto them in an effort to cling on to him in some loving, yet twisted, way. But I now know that he lives, and is with me, so I must return his physical remains to you, My Lady, I must return his body to the Land. And I know where. It is time for me to bid him 'au revoir' until next we meet. I will give him back to you at an ancient sacred site, a place of the ancestors.'

'This is good. Closure is the phrase, I believe. Yet it is never really closure, for your love for him and his love for you will ensure that you will never be truly separated. One day your souls will merge again, as they have in the past. Be patient. In the meantime, spread the word about having respect for your ancestors, ancient and recent, and about visiting their sacred places, to revere and cherish your memories of them. You owe so much to your forebears, yet be mindful that they are watching you and are indebted to you also for preserving both their memories and their sacred places. By remembering where you have come from you will enrich your world today, and the world you will create for yourself tomorrow.'

'The ancestors are still here, aren't they? They never left, did they? How can they leave? For that would mean your soul, Mother, would also leave. And you can never leave for you are everything, everywhere. The souls of the ancestors, every single one of them, are in your soul – in the Land.'

'You have it, my son, yes, you have it! Nothing truly dies. It is all a matter of changes in vibration, rather than decay into oblivion. As you stand here, you are both living human being and ancestor, for you have been this way many times. And one day, someone will honour you as his or her departed ancestor. And when they do, you will feel their love for you, as strong as if you were standing face to face with them. Love never, ever dies. If it ever did, then so would I - so would the Universe. Love transcends time. Love truly is the binding force that holds everything together and drives the Cosmos. I am love and, as a consequence, so must you be.'

250

'I am love. That's it, isn't it? Love really is the bottom line of all things - of life, death, rebirth, gravity, humanity, Planet Earth, evolution… everything.'

'Oui, mon fils – trés bien!'

The air was now turning icy. The clouds had mostly cleared and several brilliant stars shone above the treetops. Orion and Sirius had risen in the east and above them the moon's wizened face gazed down. The moon was in Cancer, just to the left of Castor and Pollux, the bright twins of Gemini. The clearing, the mound and yours truly were all bathed in the beautiful brilliance of the Lady of the Night.

'It is perfect, just perfect.'

'It always is! On this night the Lady of the Skies will be at her highest of the whole year. Walk gently under her radiant light. I will leave you now, or rather our conversation will cease. Go lay your father's ashes to rest. You know where and will know how. Go honour your ancestors and yourself and, consequently, you will honour me. What more could I ask of you? We shall next meet at a temple on a Rose Line, where fiction meets reality, and a hundred green faces bare witness. We will then speak of Grails and how people can again embrace me through the two Marys. Bon Nuit.'

'Merci beaucoup, My Lady. Au Revoir.'

I turned to face the pitch-blackness of the passage and bowed my head.

'And merci to you too, mes ancêtres.'

Despite the brilliance of the moon, I could barely make out the arch, the threshold between the woods and the Château, through which I had passed earlier. It stood beneath denser undergrowth, and eerie shadows hung motionless in the still of the night. Yet, passing beneath it, I felt no fear as I made my way back down the short flight of stone steps, past the vending machine and out through the entrance. My hire car reflected the moon's silver rays and shone in the darkness like a huge glow-worm. I looked back for one last time before getting in. The air was distinctly cold now and the windscreen was dusted with a thin layer of frost. I had not noticed how cold it had become. Perhaps it was my preoccupation with the unfolding events inside Kercado, or perhaps it had been the powerful energies, that had kept me immune from M'Lady's chilled kiss. It must have been down to freezing but I hadn't noticed. Her breath was now wintry and that of my own could be seen dancing in the moonlight.

It was still only 8.30pm, and the night was yet young, as they say. On my way back to Carnac, I drove along the road that followed the stone alignments and was compelled to stop the car and once again step out into the night. The rows of gigantic stones were like a herd of migrating dinosaurs or, better still, creatures of an alien race. A low mist concealed their feet, and their tops rose up like whales emerging from a coastal fog. It was as if they had been petrified by some foul means. Scottie had not beamed them up in time perhaps. The moonlight picked out anthropomorphic features on many of the stones, some so real that they might suddenly spring to life, as if released from a magic spell by the kiss of Prince Charming. But as I watched, they continued their moon-bathed slumber, silent and motionless - no Scottie, no rescuing prince on a noble steed. Yet the ancient brothers seemed content, even meditative, basking in the healing light of the Queen of the Night. They possessed such power and majesty in their immobility. For quite a while we stood together, the stones and I, until the cold once again clawed at my skin. They had no such problems. As the Goddess had promised, the moon was very high in the sky, and would rise still higher as midnight approached. The shadows cast by my stone brothers were shortening all the time, yet nothing could detract from the stark contrast between the illuminated stone and the pitch-blackness of the shadows in their wake.

I bid them all a fond adieu, my words echoing over increasingly misty fields.

'Bon nuit, mes frères. Bon nuit.'

23. Madeleine, Prêtres and Prejudice

© P Knight

Jesus was the original feminist. He intended for the future of His Church to be in the hands of Mary Magdalene.
(Sir Leigh Teabing, in *The Da Vinci Code*)

I awoke next morning feeling both light-headed and exhilarated. It was still getting light when I showered, and the sun was barely up as I sat down to breakfast. From my table I could see out across Carnac, which was waking under a sky that was heavy with a shrouding mist that blended with a featureless sky. I had already stood on my balcony, and been lashed by a slight, yet fiercely cold wind that had arisen during the night - winter was beginning to bite. But I had another day in Brittany before my flight home and intended to make the most of it.

Since I had seen ancient carvings on my trip to Ireland, I had been both fascinated and intrigued by them. Spirals, grids and serpents had leapt out of rocks and into my mind, insistently invading my thoughts, inviting me to speculate as to their meaning. The Goddess said they could aid contact with the spirit world, so I wanted to visit some localities local to Carnac that still possessed these enigmatic images in situ. Could I interact with the ancient symbols? Would they again open up my consciousness?

First stop was the Neolithic passage grave of Les Pierres-Plat, on the Locmariaquer Peninsular, some miles east of Carnac. This angled *'allée coudée'* had no less than thirteen decorated uprights, according to Aubrey Burl's guide, and he should know. Signs directed me to a car park, and I was soon on a promenade that held back a beach of sand and shingle, sprinkled with beautiful tiny white shells. The sea was moody, complementing a grey sky and misty horizon. The coastal breeze was cold and I saw no reason to dally out in the elements, even though it was a scene of stark beauty. I scanned the beach in all directions - it was totally deserted. This was hardly surprising really as the weather was chilly and it was low season. Once again, I welcomed the privacy.

Just yards from this beach stood a tall, lean megalith, which was slightly taller than myself. Like a petrified sentry, it guarded the entrance to the Les Pierres-Plat passage grave. I could see flat slabs of stone beyond, marking out the course of the passages below ground, and I discerned a change in direction about half way along. Approaching the entrance I paused, focusing on any beings, spirits or ancestors that might be present. I assured them of my sincerity and of the nature of my visit. I felt that they had heard my statement of intent and were OK with me going in. I peered into the shadows, which were jet black, despite it being broad daylight; the small entrance allowed in very little light from the outside world. I switched on my torch, which illuminated several stones either side of me. I had to crouch down, as the entrance lintel was much too low for me to otherwise enter. I scampered into the darkness of the passage, and was reduced to a half-crawling, half-kneeling stance. Many of the stones glistened with tracks of rainwater and the floor was awash with small puddles, which soon saturated the knees of my trousers. Almost immediately I noticed carvings. They were faint but definite, appearing as tiny dots surrounded by a border, resembling a shield, not unlike Egyptian cartouches. A little further in, the passage turned 45° to the left and more carvings soon became apparent. This time they were far more elaborate. More borders contained crescents, discs and circles, some resembling breasts, whilst others were like eyes, peering trance-like from ancient stone.

One of the most spectacular images was an upright megalith with the depiction of a leaf on the left side, and next to it what could only be a 15-inch erect penis! The two demonstrated to me a clear association between fertility and the fecundity of the Land. There in front of me was the male principle, the yang element of Nature that ensured the balance of life on Earth. I looked at the carved phallus not just out of admiration of the quality of the depiction, but also out of envy of its size! I don't know if it was through some weird sense of wishful thinking or what, but I sensed that the stone was the one I should focus on. I sat cross-legged on the floor facing the carved stone, the latter of which was illuminated by my torch, locked permanently 'on'. I focused my attention on the leaf and the accompanying phallus, in an attempt to let the images seep into my mind, into my very psyche. I was by now becoming cold and damp and the wetness on the floor did not help. I adjusted my waterproof coat so that my derrière rested on it, affording protection against the chamber's moist carpet.

Several minutes passed, and several more followed. I continued to focus clearly on the symbols, blotting out all other intrusive thoughts. After a while it became difficult to keep my eyes in focus, an effect I had experienced in the past whilst looking up at the Full Moon. I decided to let my eyes go, to let them go out of focus and see where it led me, if anywhere! From then on, the images fluctuated between that of sharp focus and blurred abstracts.

Then suddenly my head began to throb with a really bad headache. At first I wondered if it was a result of my eyesight being out of control, but then I realised that there was a rhythm to the surges of unpleasantness. It was as if someone were pounding a steady drum beat, regular and almost hypnotic. Hypnotic, yes, perhaps that was the desired effect. I went with it and let myself go down still further into the images. Then things began to change, as the images came into sharp focus and started to expand. They were either coming towards me, or else I was being projected into them! They soon filled my vision and the leaf became animated and started to shimmer, as if it was being blown by a gentle breeze. It now appeared suspended right before my eyes, inches away, and was glowing with scintillating, oscillating gold and silver threads of light. Then the leaf turned bright green, only then to change to slightly darker shades, as if it where emerging and growing on the branch of a tree. My attention was then drawn to the phallus to the right of the leaf. That too was now sheathed in golden light and was throbbing. After a few moments there was an ejaculation of brilliant orbs of light, which burst upwards and cascaded down before my eyes.

The male principle is fertilising the Land.

And then, in just a few seconds, the images faded and retreated into the surface of the ancient stone. All was as before - and my headache had gone. I sat there, motionless, staring at the carvings before me. All was still and silent, save for the cries of seagulls and the sound of waves breaking on the shore. My experience opened up immense possibilities for interacting with ancient carved images. Although I was no shaman, and had probably only scratched the surface of potential experiences, it had been incredible. What interaction had taken place with these carvings thousands of years ago? For ancient rituals, my ancestors may have been under the influence of hallucinogenic plants, may have been drumming or dancing for hours, or deprived themselves of food and sleep, and other practices that would have helped them contact other realms. Nevertheless, I felt very privileged to have had my experience and was keen for more interaction with these enigmatic ancestral symbols. I pondered on the immense potential of the stored knowledge encoded into these images at hundreds of sacred sites across the world. The cryptic verses of *The Da Vinci Code* had nothing on these beauties!

After the short journey half way up the Locmariaquer Peninsula, my next ports of call were the neighbouring monuments of Le Table des Marchands and Le Grand Menhir Brisé. They stood yards from each other within the confines of a tourist complex, complete with visitor centre and shop - thankfully on a smaller scale than at Newgrange. Out of season opening times were very restrictive, so I arrived about noon, in plenty of time. I paid my €4.00 entrance fee and had a quick look around the bookshop. The walls were lined with large, spectacular images of carvings taken from inside Le Table des Marchands passage grave, which I would soon enter.

Emerging from the heated visitor centre into the cold December Brittany air was a shock, and made me realise just how chilled it was. I followed a gravel path, which passed the depleted Er Grah Tumulus, and continued around to the passage grave, which rose impressively from the lawned enclosure. It was grass-covered and domed, like a turtle stranded on a beach. Standing outside Le Table des Marchands, I was impressed immediately by its similarity to some of the Irish tombs. The portal was formed by two uprights, straddled by a huge horizontal granite megalith. Either side of the entrance were retaining walls of smaller stones, defining a crescental forecourt, reminiscent of Newgrange. I looked around and once again found I was on my own. Few people were venturing out on such a cold winter's day – only mad dogs and English men go out in the *solei froid de midi!*

With torch in hand I entered the passage. I only had to stoop slightly as the whole construction was on a much grander scale than that of Les Pierres-Plat. The passage was higher, and wider and the feeling was one of more communal gatherings, as opposed to Kercado and Les Pierres-Plat, which seemed to have been for more personal shamanic use. The guidebooks said that an important feature of Le Table des Marchands was a carved hafted axe on the underside of the giant 40 ton capstone, similar to the one at Kercado. Once inside the granite chamber, my torch soon found the feature, which was large and finely executed. I reached up and ran my fingers gently over the intricate ancient glyph, and contact with it made my fingertips tingle. Nearby was what looked like a shepherd's crook, some of which appeared to have been broken off. These carvings were spectacular enough, but the pièce de résistance was the ancient artwork carved on a huge stone at the back of the chamber. This stone was about 7ft tall and about the same across, and stood dimly illuminated by the light that permeated from the outside world. The slab was covered, almost from top to bottom, with what were described as 'shepherds' crooks'. I counted around fifty of them, each about a foot high. Near the base of the stone was a different symbol, which looked to me like a solar disk. Although the official exclamation was that they were crooks, they looked to me like stalks of wheat, the tops of which were bending in one direction, as if swaying in a gentle summer breeze. The sun glyph below certainly suggested a connection between the ripening 'stalks' and the Sun God.

I was in half a mind to focus on the symbols as I had earlier at Les Pierres-Plat, but noises from outside the chamber told me I was no longer alone. I turned towards the entrance to find a whole gaggle of chattering *enfants*, presumably on some educational trip. Some of the children came immediately into the passage but turned abruptly and went back out when summoned by one of the teachers.

'Oh, well,' I addressed the symbols, '… it was not meant to be.'

I gathered my things, and bowed to the sun symbol before making my way back outside. I came out into a veritable scrum of children, of both sexes, aged between about 9 and 13. They all twittered away simultaneously and so rapidly that my pidgin French could not keep up.

I waded through the throng and headed off towards the daddy of all European megaliths, Le Grand Menhir Brisé, which lay broken in four huge fragments a hundred yards away. Even from that distance it looked immense, yet as I approached, the full scale of the monument took my breath away. The gigantic phallic monolith originally measured over 60ft in length. If it ever had been erect (so to speak!) it would have dwarfed all other European standing stones by some margin. According to the works of Julian Cope and Aubrey Burl, some controversy still surrounded the fallen colossus, as to whether it was ever raised or, as some argue, whether it collapsed and fragmented under its own weight. If my ancestors had indeed managed the incredible feat of its erection (!) then the colossus would have been observable from many miles away. In fact, surveyor Alexander Thom suggested several astronomical alignments with neighbouring megaliths. I stood within a few yards of the fallen giant and felt a real sadness emanating from its broken heart. It seemed as if the Land itself had been deprived of its manhood, cruelly cut down in some desecrating act of landscape castration.

'Man, you were one big son of a gun, weren't you my friend? Who did this to you then, hey?'

I then had the urge to get a dowsing rod from my rucksack and see what energies I could pick up around the collapsed giant. Most of the school party had gone into the body of Le Table des Marchands, and a welcomed hush descended over the cold field that enclosed the two monuments. First I went around to the broader, flat-bottomed end and immediately picked up a very strong current of energy that flowed straight into its base. I went around to the other end and picked it up again, finding that it flowed into the other fallen fragment a few feet away. This happened again - all the prone fragments had a powerful current of life-force flowing the entire length, from base to tip, despite the physical separation of each fragment. Despite the destruction, the energies would not be denied. But something was gnawing away inside my head. It reminded me of something I had seen very recently. Then it dawned on me – the carved phallus on the stone at Les Pierres-Plat, the image I had interacted with earlier that morning. That was also an erect phallus – a mini version of the huge one before me. What's more, the two sites were only about a mile from each other, with low intervening ground. Surely the huge willy before me would have been visible from the seaside passage grave. I had seen a vision of energy shooting from the top of the carving, and now I had dowsed Divine energy flowing out of the tip of the Le Grand Menhir Brisé. It was as if the act of human

258

ejaculation was being energetically repeated on a grander scale. The Goddess had said that processes present in the microcosm of Man, both physically and spiritually, could be found throughout Nature. *As above, so below!*

It was soon time for me to think about heading back towards Rennes, where my flight awaited in about four hours. But there was one final place I wished to see in Southern Brittany. The publication of *The Da Vinci Code* had made me aware of the many chapels and churches dedicated to Mary Magdalene. Why were so many places, especially Catholic, devoted to the so-called 'fallen woman' of the New Testament? Dan Brown, and before him Lynne Picknett, had suggested that she was more than a sinner saved from damnation, but was in fact Jesus' wife, and that she even bore a child after his death. Perhaps she was indeed a wise woman, even a priestess, who had given Jesus advice on matters regarding the Divine Feminine, moon magic and herbs. Her inclusion into the inner sanctum of the disciples also gave the group a balance of yin and yang. Why shouldn't Jesus have married anyway, for surely he would have been more respected by the populace as a mature married family man, better than if he had remained a single dude? As a Jew, he would normally have been married by his late twenties or early thirties.

The reason I have shared these thoughts with you is that on my Brittany map, some miles NE of Carnac, I had seen a Neolithic dolmen called Dolmen de la Madeleine, which translated as *Magdalene's Dolmen*. And what's more, just a few hundred metres to the south stood Chapelle de la Madeleine. I was intrigued. Was it another example of site evolution, whereby a Pagan site had later been Christianised? And if so, were there any links with the Knights Templar who, according to Dan Brown and many alternative writers, had revered Mary Magdalene as the carrier of Jesus' offspring, and whose body they later hid? In true Robert Langdon style, I sped off on my own mini-quest for Mary Magdalene, unfortunately minus the gorgeous Sophie Neveu.

Oh, well, you can't win 'em all!

'Watch out Opus Dei, here I come - Yee ha!'

I made my way north and then east out of Carnac, passing for the last time the megalithic avenues that accompany the D196.

'Au revoir, old friends.'

Then it was north along the D186, before turning off right to the hamlet of Kerguéarec. I passed through the sleepy village and turned north into increasingly rural and desolate countryside. I noticed a lonely wayside cross on my left, just before a church came into view in front of me. I soon pulled up by the side of the road, directly in front of Chapelle de la Madeleine.

The scene was straight out of the film of Dan Brown's book and he couldn't have written it better. The chapel was isolated, the nearest farm being about a mile to the north. It was surrounded by open fields and across these blew a chilling wind. I could see the dolmen in the field a few hundred yards to the north, the capstone of which appeared to have collapsed. The skies were overcast and leaden, and fallen leaves danced around my feet as I entered the churchyard.

The chapel was small, built of brown stone, and had a simple roof, with a thin spire rising from it at the western end, from which, curiously, hung a bell. The fallen leaves had originated from an encirclement of tall trees that enclosed the churchyard. They rose from the earth into grey skies, like the thin fingers of a fairytale witch. I walked across to a notice board that stood to my right. Perhaps it would give me some information, some clues. But my first discovery was made a few yards before I reached it. There, by the side of the road next to the car park entrance, was a large prone stone. *How old are you then?* Had it lain there since before the church had been built? I could make out more large stones incorporated into an adjacent stonewall.

The notice board itself was full of useful information, with dates, events and such. But unfortunately for me, it was all in French! Now although I had been getting by on my pidgin French, I still did not know enough of the language to stuff a small croissant.

Oh, well, here goes. If Robert Langdon can translate thousand-year-old encryptions, then I can surely cope with a small notice board in the backwaters of Brittany.

I took out the small French dictionary from my rucksack, which I felt I would need. *Now, let's see.* I scanned the script before me in an effort to string together words I could decipher, or recognised. I soon made out parts that seemed relevant, such as *'... léproserie mediévales'*, which told me of medieval leper houses, and the mention of, *'... un éstablissement de moines rouges'* intrigued me. A few flicks through my French dictionary revealed that the original chapel was founded by *'Red Monks'*, which I knew from my research on the Grail legends was a name sometimes given to the Knights Templar.

'Voilà!'

It got even more interesting a little further down: A passage referred to, *'... moines hospitaliers de Saint Jean de Jerusalem'.* Here the Knight's Hospitallers, the sister sect of the Templars, had built a hospital or sanctuary for *'... l'époque des Croisades'.* In other words, Crusaders who had contracted leprosy were brought here for either healing or palliative care. So I had a connection with *two* orders that had built many foundations on sacred energy sites across Europe. *Wow!* Further on down, the text related how some sacred stones had been taken from there to Carnac, and also how a well had magical, curative properties. So, in one locality, I had found a Mary Magdalene chapel, a healing well, megaliths, links with the Templars and the Hospitallers - and a Neolithic dolmen to boot!

I looked around and scanned the churchyard for the sacred well. Just to the east of the chapel was an altar which looked distinctly modern in appearance, but to the right of that, tucked away in a corner of the enclosure, was a small roofed stone structure, just a few feet high. As I made my way to it I skirted a round enclosure, defined by a low stonewall. I remembered how the Templars used to gather in round chapels and wondered if ancient gatherings were once held here too, or perhaps still were! Entrée down to the waters of the well was via a short flight of stone steps, but access was now restricted by an iron grille. I could see, however, that it was still fed by water, on which floated suspended leaves and twigs. Although half-forgotten, I could feel the sanctity of the place, and knew that the healing waters were probably why the chapel was built there in the first place. Even prior to that, perhaps the dolmen had been erected close to the water source, which would have originally been a natural spring.

I was disappointed to find that the door to the chapel was locked. So I decided to visit the nearby dolmen and pay my respects to the ancestors. I was surprised to see that a faint, yet definite path had been worn across the field from the church to the dolmen. But as I approached the ancient stones, I was overcome with a feeling of sadness, as if the very stones themselves were crying out. Half a dozen megaliths at various angles were desperately trying to support the huge capstone, which had partially collapsed and leaned at a very acute angle. It was somewhat reminiscent of scenes from the film *Titanic*, moments before the ship slid beneath the sea. The stones were partially overgrown with brambles, and lumps of concrete and broken bricks were strewn around. I gave the nearest standing stone a big hug and sent it healing love. I stashed some of the litter, including two Coke cans, into my rucksack.

I was soon conscious that it was time for me to move on – a flight awaited me at Rennes. As I turned back towards the chapel, however, I could make out two figures, in dark apparel, standing by the modern altar in the churchyard. By the time I had reached the edge of the field it was clear that they were priests. I once again amused myself with thoughts of Silas and Opus Dei – *Oh no, they're on to me!* I would have to walk past them and I rehearsed my greeting: *Now let's see: 'Bonjour, mes Pères.' That should do.*

They had been aware of my approach and both replied to my greeting almost simultaneously:

'Bonjour, mon fils.'

Both wore long, black garments and priest collars. One was grey-haired, in his mid-fifties, whilst the other was about twenty, whom I took to be a novice.

The elder priest approached me and offered his hand.

'Bienvenu a la Chapelle Sainte de Notre Dame.'

I shook his hand but my puzzled expression must have given the game away, for I had only grasped a little of what he had said.

'The Holy Father', added the younger priest, '… said, *Welcome to the Holy Chapel of Our Lady.*'

We all smiled as one and my relief that he could speak English was palpable.

'You are English?' the younger man enquired.

'Indeed. And my French is very poor, I am afraid.'

'Oh, zat is OK, my son,' said the elder priest, again to my relief. *They both speak English!*

'I am trying hard to learn,' I continued, ' for I love the language and your country.'

The older man held his arms aloft and looked around at the surrounding scenery. 'Oui. It is, how you zay, irrésistible – magnifique!'

Then his eyes focused on mine. 'Tell me, my son, what brings you to Le Chapelle Madeleine on such a cold day, out of season? We do not get many, er, touristes Anglais here zis time of year.'

His voice held a hint of suspicion and I suddenly felt as if I was being subtly interrogated. I paused momentarily before answering; *How much should I tell him?* Would he appreciate *The Da Vinci Code* stuff, the Templars, ley lines, dowsing and the rest? I certainly thought it best not to go down the road of visions of the ancestors, ejaculating carvings or conversations with the Earth Mother!

'Oh, I visit ancient sacred sites, er, mégalithes. And of course Brittany has many of these. And I also visit chapels and churches that I believe replaced former ancient Pagan places.'

'Mais, oui,' the elder priest replied, '… we are, how you say, fortunate to have such a rich heritage. One can trace also the évolution, er, the transition, from the barbaric, heathen times to zee coming of Our Sauveur Jésus Christe.'

I felt I had to be careful. The young priest did in fact have blonde hair, and visions of Silas, the Opus Dei psychopath, came flooding back!

'With respect, Father, I see signs all around me that the builders of the ancient megaliths were intelligent, and knew astronomy and had a complex religion that was very well-connected with the Land. They respected the Land in a way that cultures since have not.'

The elder priest surveyed me intently, before replying.

'That may well be the case, but I zee no point in looking into zings that have been replaced by a higher truth. Zose were dark times that, how you zay, preceded and prepared us for the coming of the One God. Don't you agree, mon fils?'

His eyes were now intense and he had stepped closer to me, eager for my reply. 'Silas' stood a few feet behind and to his left, and I had visions of him suddenly producing a knife or gun from beneath his long gown, should I fail to give a satisfactory reply to my inquisitor.

'With regret, Father, I am afraid that I cannot totally share your beliefs. I believe that looking back at how our distant ancestors related to and lived on the Land can help us out of this mess today. The Bible gave Man dominion over the Earth, permission to abuse and pillage natural resources. Ancient people lived closer to the Land, respecting it, living in close harmony with natural cycles. Later religions, including Christianity, encouraged the plunder of the natural resources of her body.'

Woops! As soon as the word *her* had crossed my lips, I knew I might be in trouble. But had he spotted it? The hell he had!

'You say *'her'*. Do you also believe that the land is *la femme*, a woman?'

Oh well, just say it how you see it.

'Well, I do believe that there is both the Divine Masculine and the Divine Feminine in the Universe. All ancient religions, including

263

early Islam, Hinduism and Christianity, revered equally the divine masculine and the divine feminine. The balance of yin and yang, male and female, is essential for life to survive on Earth. And I see everything on Earth as a physical expression of Divine thought.'

He was eager and instant in his retort.

'But surely, my son, God created everything in the Universe. The gods and goddesses of ancient times were merely the interpretation of God's creations by *personnes primitifs*, sorry, how you say, simple people. Now we know better.'

I looked at the chapel over his shoulder, gathering my thoughts for the reply. He followed the direction of my gaze and then turned back to me.

'Ah, my son, perhaps I see the reason for your visit. This was a Templar place, and has a dédecace to Marie Madeleine or, how you say, Mary Magdalene. I gather many people have been visiting places such as this following *The Da Vinci Code* book and zee movie. It has made me much smile since all this came out. Tell me, what do you think of the book and the hérétique ideas about the blood lines and of Marie Madeleine being the wife of Our Sauveur Jésus?'

Oh well, in for a penny in for a Euro. Go for it!

'I think that the bottom line is this, Father. Whether Mary Magdalene married Jesus and had a baby or not, and whether a bloodline survives to this day or not, isn't the point. The real issue is whether the church believed it to be true and suppressed the information. Did they deliberately falsify records and make subsequent editions of the Bible with the view of both reducing Mary Magdalene to a fallen woman, and hiding the fact that Jesus had been married? Marriage would have relegated him, no matter how gifted and wonderful he undoubtedly was, to a mere human being. Marriage and having offspring are very human activities after all. And what's more, despite new gospels being found in the desert, the Church refuses to incorporate these into the Bible, or even recognise them as having equal authority to Biblical texts.'

The elder priest replied with a louder, harsher voice.

'Oui, I understand you. But what you are saying is that the whole Catholic Church is founded on a lie. Can you see the damage that would do if people start believing this garbage? You are implying that the holy fathers who put together the Holy Book are liars, and every Pope since for that matter. Sacré Bleu! How can you expect people to believe in such zings? That would threaten their faith?'

'It is indeed a big issue, Father,' I continued, 'but don't you have faith that Catholic people can make up their own minds? Is their faith already so poor that you fear they will be pushed over the edge and renounce their religion? Whether these theories turn out to be true or not, the suppression of alternative ideas and healthy debate is surely a worse sin than the content of such debate? Surely, Father, truth will prevail. If your beliefs are true, then God will reveal it. Surely there is a difference between faith and blind faith. Which would the Church rather have?'

He eyed me quizzically. I had not implied that *The Da Vinci Code* theories were true, but had just argued that the debate should take place. It seemed to have taken the wind out of his sails.

'You are a man of some wisdom, my son. For you did not really answer my question yet have spoken words I can respect to a certain degree. The Church will always encourage healthy debate, after all. We have been guilty in the past, perhaps, of appearing secretive, and conspiracy theory makers have had plenty to, how you say, sink their teeth into...'

'Then, Father,' I interrupted, '*The Da Vinci Code* could ultimately end up as a blessing for the Church. People may well look into such things and, by rejecting them, reaffirm their faith. I hear that Christian places such as Rosslyn, the Vatican, St Sulpice, Rennes Le Château and the Temple Church in London have benefited from increased numbers of visitors, with much needed income as a result. And more people are enquiring about the real practices of Opus Dei. So everyone benefits.'

'Yes, but it is making money based on a falsehood, as far as I am concerned.'

I replied quickly. 'Yes, I suppose it is. But haven't people been accusing the Church of having done similar things for centuries?'

'No. There is a difference. And it is this. The Bible is true and should be taken literally. It is the word of God. There are no lies. This is the difference between the Holy Scriptures and Monsieur Brown's fable – the Bible is the word of God, while *The Da Vinci Code* is the work of a man, pure fantasy... it is a novel. Voilà!'

Words from *The Da Vinci Code* came flooding into my head: *'So dark the con of Man.'* My knee-jerk reaction was to come back with something like, 'Christianity kicked off with a good novel too, mate', but somehow I resisted – just! I decided to attempt to diffuse the situation.

'But surely, Father, the Bible was written by very mortal men, men such as you and I. Men who had a belief in something they could not actually prove, but who felt it to be true. This is what Dan Brown has done. He has put out into the common arena the *possibility* that a book written by men, the Bible, may not be 100% accurate. That is all. All men, no matter how well intentioned, are influenced by both dogma and their peers. You can hardly say that the Bible was written by men who were unbiased.'

'This is true, my son. But, at the end of the day, the Bible is a holy book on which millions base their lives. *The Da Vinci Code* will never, ever replace that.'

'It's not meant to, Father, and never was. It's just a story. Sometimes simple but moving stories inspire people to look at the world and themselves differently, and can even change the world – as I am sure you can appreciate.'

The mood changed and we shared a smile, having reached an unvoiced agreement to disagree.

He looked at the darkening skies and then at his wristwatch.

'Well, it has been interesting to talk with you, to get the view of someone who has obviously been influenced by such notions. But I must leave you now. I will pray for you and those like you. We are all children of God after all.'

'Indeed, Father.'

We exchanged a handshake and a feeling of mutual respect passed between us. He turned away, heading off towards his car.

'Au Revoir! Come, Jean-Pierre… Allez y!'

'Au Revoir to you too, Father', I called after him.

He was already several yards distant when the young priest passed me. He slowed down momentarily and whispered into my left ear as he passed:

'I am going to read Monsieur Brown's book!'

The smile we exchanged bridged the chasm that separated our belief systems.

We are all children of the Goddess after all.

24. Returning my Father to the Land

© P Knight

When it's your time to go, to die, you can't do anything about it. It's meant to be.

(Ernest Knight, 1926-2005)

Two other events occupied my thoughts during December – Christmas and the Winter Solstice. Now on the surface they seem like two totally unconnected events. The former is the time of the year well loved by children, a time of Santa Claus and reindeers, stockings, office parties and presents under the tree. The latter is only truly appreciated by those on the Pagan fringes of society. They know it as an ancient mid-winter festival, celebrating the time when days are shortest and the sun is at its lowest in the sky. This ancient festival was chosen by early Christians to celebrate the birth of their Saviour partly because it would hijack the old midwinter festivities. People were already partying at that time of year, so the Church would let them carry on, but in the name of the new God. Shrewd move, guys!

For the mid-winter solstice I went up to the southern terminal of the Dorset Cursus, a six-mile long Neolithic processional way that straddles Cranborne Chase. Two long barrows were self-aligned with the sunrise on the shortest day and nearby I stood on the terminal mound of the cursus. The morning was crisp, frost crunched under my feet, the sky was perfectly clear, and a thin crescent moon hung low in the southeast. Just before 8.00am the sun rose over the distant skyline, in perfect alignment with the two ancient mounds. I knew as I stood there, alone and cold, that thousands of years ago my ancestors had likewise stood at the same spot, to witness the rebirth of the Sky God, following the longest night. The sun was reborn out of the tummy of the Goddess before my eyes and all seemed well in the Cosmos. I was now more aware of the ever-changing cycles of the Land, and that the Goddess never slept, even in the dead of winter.

I have a son in his twenties in Devon and a 10-year-old daughter in Dorset, from two different former relationships and tried as best I could to spread myself around, to distribute and exchange Christmas gifts and generally have a good time. They had both become aware that I had been travelling around more than before, but just put it down to me having more money than sense following my redundancy, or else I was at the onset of some mid-life crisis. Either way, I did not feel inclined to fill them in too much at that stage. Part of me still thought I would wake up one morning to realise that it really had all been just a dream. But I hoped not!

Just before Christmas I also visited my mother in Birmingham. She was in her 80's, still sprightly and quick on her feet although not able to care for herself since my father passed away. She lived in a fantastic rest home in Birmingham, run by kind and dedicated people. My visits to her always reminded me, with some sadness, of my father, who had died quite recently. He was never really into Christmas, bemoaning it as too commercialised, although he did partake in the free seasonal drinks offered to him by his club! But to me, Christmas would never ever be the same without him. His ashes were still in a casket in my bedroom, as I had not felt inclined to spread them anywhere. But I always knew I would find a place that would feel just right, as my distant ancestors had with their kin thousands of years ago. They had chosen with great care the places of interment for their beloved ones. The Goddess had spoken to me about revering my ancestors, and I had been to several places rich in ancestral memory. Was the place I had in mind suitable for my father?

So Christmas came and went and was good all told - presents under glittery trees, and more than a little mead being consumed, or the modern equivalent to be honest. But my mind was constantly preoccupied by a time that was soon to come – the laying to rest of my father's ashes.

It was soon New Year and by then I knew exactly where I was going – Avebury. My lessons from the Goddess about ancestors, and my visions of them, had helped me connect with my father and my memories of him. For the first time I really grasped how much I owed my recent ancestors, including my great-grandparents, grandparents, and, of course, my mother and father. My departed father seemed closer to me than ever and I felt a reassurance from him that my project with the Goddess was indeed noble.

Ever since his cremation his ashes had rested under my PC desk, confined unceremoniously to a plastic receptacle. I had held on to some part of him, I guess, not wanting to finally let go, for in doing so would have been an acknowledgement of the permanency of his demise. But following the events of Brittany, I felt almost compelled to release his ashes back to the Land, back to Her. His soul was truly free, and so also his bodily remains. I did not need to cling on to him any more.

I spent New Year's Eve with some friends, exchanging notes about trips we had been on. I told them much of my exploits in Brittany, but not everything. My exchange with the priests at Chapelle de la Madeleine sparked off a furore of debate, much of it focused on trashing the Church. But I could not see the point. I took no comfort in attacking those who I saw as victims. I left the gathering not long after midnight.

I arose on New Year's Day around 7.00am, and despite the reduced sleep felt fresh and focused. I opened the curtains to find the sun shining brightly in a clear blue sky. *Great!* After the cold and rain of Brittany I was uplifted and knew that January 1st was going to be good. I had chosen that day to scatter my father's ashes, because it was symbolically a passing from the old to the new, a liminal time, a passage from the past to the future. It just seemed right.

I arrived at Avebury about 11.30am, and found quite a number of people milling around the stones and the village. Although it was Sunday, there was not the usual scrum that the Sabbath often generated, especially during the summer or bank holidays. The sun was brilliant, and although it was approaching the south, was nevertheless low in the sky. There was not a single cloud, and the air was cool, yet not cold. It was glorious!

I placed the casket containing my father's ashes into my rucksack and made a slow circumnavigation of the henge, passing every remaining stone of the outer ring. I wanted one last walk alone with my Dad. As a child, he had taken me on many walks, whilst mother cooked the Sunday roast. I loved our times alone together and worshipped him, as most sons do their father.

'Well, Dad, I wanted to have this last walk with you, to show you these stones, which you never saw whilst you were alive. I wanted to share them with you now, on this our last walk together.'

On my way back to the car, I spotted Morris Dancers doing a New Year's Day gig outside the Red Lion. They were encircled by a small gathering, which I joined. They waved their hankies and crashed their sticks and jingled their bells like it was Christmas Eve. And all the time I was watching them I really felt as if my father was looking over my shoulder. Before long the performance was over and the ensemble made their way into the pub, no doubt for a well-deserved pint or two.

That was cool, Dad, wasn't it? Come on, let's go.

We set off down the West Kennet stone avenue, my father and I, and the sun warmed my face as well as my heart. I stopped every now and again to show him some of the faces in the megaliths, for I knew he was watching. I wondered how many people had processed down the same route over millennia long past, on their way to West Kennet long barrow, perhaps to bury their own dead. To my left I could see ancient mounds on the skyline, many surrounded and partially concealed by tall trees, as if they had secrets to hide.

'See those mounds, Dad? I wonder if you and I were once laid to rest in any of those. Makes you think, doesn't it?'

I cut across the hill and, with Silbury Hill rising majestically to my right, continued on towards the long barrow, which I could now see silhouetted on the sky line ahead.

'Oh, Dad, I wish we could have walked here together. This place is so sacred to me. That's why I've brought you here. There are a lot worse places, eh?'

I crossed the main road and followed the path across the fields, over the small bridge that crosses the Kennet, before starting the gentle ascent up to the long barrow.

'This is our last journey, Dad... well, in this life anyhow. I hope I have chosen the right place for you. I hope you approve. Do you?'

The next instant I heard a sound from overhead that I immediately recognised. It was the cry of a buzzard – and not any old buzzard either. Yes, it was unmistakable. It hovered over my head about 100ft up, and seemed to move off when it was sure I had seen it. It flew on in front of me, marking my way, before circling the elongated mound of West Kennet, which stood out on the skyline.

'OK, I get the message. Thanks, my old friend.'

At that, the bird made a final circle before heading off in a westerly direction. My eyes followed the bird until it was a dot, and felt sure it would not be the last time our paths would cross.

The last few hundred yards to the long barrow were emotional. I could feel myself welling up and I stumbled a couple of times on unseen obstacles. Then I remembered what the Goddess had said about my totem animals, that they could be summoned when needed. I had met Sirius the wolf on Dartmoor and now I really needed her. I stopped on the path and turned slowly around, surveying my world, and called out across the landscape.

'Sirius. Sirius, my wise friend, I need you now. I need your courage. Please honour me with your presence.'

Slowly rotating, I surveyed the rolling hills before me; Silbury Hill, lines of trees and distant barrows passed before my eyes. All was still. There was no wind, and no people that I could see. The only sound was the dull background rumble of traffic passing along the road below. I heard no howl. There was no wolf.

I turned to face the long mound again and resumed my mournful, trudging ascent. But I soon became aware of something brushing up against my right hand. At first I thought it was tall grass, but then saw that the field was barren. Then I surmised that it might be an insect buzzing around me. *But it's the middle of winter!* I stopped but could see nothing that would have warranted such a feeling. And then the sensation happened again. It felt like, yes, just like fur! A few steps later I realised what it was, that my invocation had been answered – Sirius was walking beside me! She was unseen, yet she was there, I could feel her. I outstretched my hand and could feel my fingers pass through her fur. Although I could not see Sirius, I knew she was accompanying me up to the place of ancestors.

'Thank you, Sirius. Thank you so much. I needed to do this on my own, with no other people I mean, but I appreciate your presence, and can feel your love and strength. I'm sure Dad does too. OK, guys, let's do it!' Together, we continued the ascent.

At the top I stood outside the chambered mound, where huge ancient sarsen stones towered above me. I looked around and, once again, I seemed to have the place to myself. The sun, although low in the early afternoon sky, was warming my face, and the breeze was but a tickle on my checks. I lined myself up with the central blocking stone, which displayed a huge one-metre-long gash, surely symbolic of the vulva of the Earth Mother. I immediately sensed the flow of energy through my body, and my stomach soon seemed as if it would burst. I was standing mid-flow in the Mary current of the St Michael Line, the famous ley that ran from Cornwall, through Glastonbury and Avebury, and onward to East Anglia. I closed my eyes and soaked up the planetary power and love. My hands were hanging by my side and every now and again I felt the unseen but attendant Sirius brush against them, as if to reassure me. After several minutes it felt right to commence what I was there to do.

Right, here goes.

I clambered around the side of entrance stones and entered the belly of the chambered tomb. It took a few moments to get accustomed to the dimness, despite the presence of a small glass skylight in the roof of the main chamber. I walked along the passage, surveying briefly the four antechambers on the way – they were empty. It seemed that only the ancestors were in residence, and I was grateful for that.

'Thank you, Mother.'

From my rucksack I produced a small church candle and placed it on the ground in the centre of the womb-like chamber. I lit it and leaned back against one of the stones that comprised the chamber walls, as I had done in Brittany. Then I retrieved the purple urn that contained my father's mortal remains and placed them on the ground in front of me.

'Well, Dad, this is it.'

I knew that my words were not wasted. He was listening.

'I feel privileged to have had you as my Dad. You were truly my friend. I cannot honestly remember having a single argument with you in the whole of my adult life. You let me get on with my life, whilst always watching from the wings. You were always there for me when I needed support, financial or otherwise, and did not judge me when I made mistakes or things did not work out - you just quietly supported me. You were always there for me.'

Tears rolled down my face as I succumbed to the moment.

'You did not show your emotions readily, but I guess men of your generation were not encouraged to, were they? But you showed your love for me in plain talking and a supportive way that was you, Dad. And for all your seemingly hard working class exterior, I know you did at times feel pain inside, such as the time I saw tears in your eyes at the deathbed of your own mother. Dad, I can honestly say to you that I have no regrets whatsoever in having had you as my father. Dad, I'll miss you. I already am.'

I then took out from my pocket a copy of *The Prophet*, that masterful work by artist and mystic Kahlil Gibran. A friend had recommended this beautifully poetic book years ago in the infancy of my spiritual path. And within its hallowed and well-thumbed pages were the perfect passages. The prophet Almustaffa had been asked about death. What he replied was timeless wisdom. My words echoed around the ancient womb as I read it aloud:

'You would know the secret of death.

But how shall you find it unless you seek it in the heart of life?

If you would indeed behold the spirit of death, open your heart wide unto the body of life.

For life and death are one, even as the river and sea are one.

In the depth of your hopes and desires lies your silent knowledge of the beyond;

And like seeds dreaming beneath the snow your heart dreams of spring.

Trust the dreams, for in them is hidden the gate to eternity.

For what is it to die but to stand naked in the wind and melt into the sun?

And what is to cease breathing but to free the breath from its restless tides, that it may rise and expand and seek God unencumbered?

Only when you drink from the river of silence shall you indeed sing.

And when you have reached the mountain top, then you shall begin to climb.

And when the earth shall claim your limbs, then you shall truly dance.'

I then flicked forward and read out the final words of the book:

'A little while, a moment of rest upon the wind, and another woman shall bear me.'

Returning the book to my pocket with one hand, I wiped the tears from my eyes as best I could with the other and rose to my feet, hugging the urn. The top unscrewed easily and revealed a slip of paper with my father's details on. This I kissed before placing it in my pocket. I then proceeded to scatter the ashes over the floor of the main chamber. Being mid-winter, the ground was damp and dark, and the pale ashes were clearly visible as they hit the ground. The finer particles bounced and settled a few inches from impact. I sprinkled the ashes around the main chamber, along the passage, and then deposited a little in each of the four antechambers. By the time I had arrived back at the entrance the urn was but half full, but that had been my intention. I wanted to spread some on the outside of the mound, so that my father would quite literally return to the soil - enriching it, becoming one with it.

I surveyed the surrounding landscape as I stood atop the ancient mound. The place still belonged only to Dad, Sirius, the Ancestors and myself. I walked slowly up and down the mound, letting small amounts of ash fall onto the grass. Every now and then a stronger breeze would carry ash almost horizontally and it would disappear into the distance. My dad was being blown by the winds of the Goddess. His soul was indeed soaring.

When the urn was almost empty, the pangs of pain and sorry really hit home. I collected the last grains and held them in my cupped hands.

'Good bye, Dad…I miss you… I love you… I always will…'

With these words I tossed the last fistful up into the air and they were carried away into the arms of the Goddess.

'A little while, a moment of rest upon the wind, and another woman shall bear you.'

It was done. And it felt so, so right. The place would be more sacred to me now than it ever could have been. I now had a place to come and honour not just my distant ancestors, but also my own immediate ancestor, my father. The grasses and flowers that would grow there would contain part of my father within them. The heart of the mound itself contained my father's ashes too, just as they had contained the remains of other departed loved ones, thousands of years ago. And more than this, from then on whenever I stood on the St Michael Line, at any point between Cornwall and the East Coast, I would be connected to this place, connected to my father. Yes, it felt right.

I climbed down from the mound and started to make my way down the hill. I halted when I sensed something wet on my hand. Closer inspection revealed that the back of my hand was moist, as if it had been licked, which of course it had been.

'Thank you, Sirius.'

With that a stronger breeze brushed past me before all was still once more. Sirius had gone. I turned around to face the long barrow, now silhouetted on the skyline.

'Happy New Year, Dad.'

25. Eleventh Moon – January: Rosslyn Chapel Lesson – The Grail and Mary Magdalene

© P Knight

I saw a Chapel all of gold
That none did dare to enter in.
I saw a Serpent rise between
the white pillars of the door,
Down the golden hinges tore.
(William Blake)

Well, it was January - a new year, a new cycle. And something very unusual was to happen – two full moons in the same calendar month. Apparently, this came around every few years due to the fact that the moon's cycle is around 28 days. It stood to reason that occasionally we would get two full moons, or new moons for that matter, in the same month.

So both the eleventh and twelfth lessons from the Goddess were to be conveyed to me in January, one near the start of the month, the other on the last day. But where was it all to take place? Abroad again? I hoped so. Or were the two places going to be nearer to home? The Goddess herself had already given me clues on the last Full Moon:

'Until we meet next time at the temple on the Rose Line, where fiction meets reality.'

Now I knew from my research, and from *The Da Vinci Code* of course, that a Rose Line was a term for a solar meridian, a line of Longitude. The main one in Brown's book crossed Paris, represented on the ground by plaques, and included St-Sulpice. This had been the world's Prime Meridian until 1884, when it was transferred to Greenwich. Was I going to Paris in just two days? Was it to be at the Louvre, where Langdon found Mary Magdalene's tomb resting under the two pyramids? But Dan Brown's hero also went to Rosslyn Chapel, near Edinburgh. Langdon and Neveu realised that the physical remains of Mary Magdalene had once lain at Rosslyn, only to have been subsequently removed. Known as the *Cathedral of Codes*, the chapel had long been associated with the Knights Templar. Some researchers claimed that the original spelling of Rosslyn, i.e. Roslin, came from *Rose Line*, or Line of the Rose, meaning the Holy Blood Line. Others said it was named from the meridian on which it stood, which also passed close to Glastonbury. Brown stated that, 'The line is associated with King Arthur and thought by many to be a central pillar in Britain's sacred geometry.' Other authors have cited another *Rose Line*, which places Rosslyn in alignment with Edinburgh, Scone Palace, and Balmoral. And yet another had Rosslyn on a different *Rose Line* altogether! Was it really a matter of which book you read, or did the holy chapel in fact stand on *several* sacred alignments?

Well now, which is it to be? Paris or Rosslyn?

The Goddess had also said we would meet, *'... **where a hundred green faces bear witness.'** Aha!* That was what did it for me, for this afforded the answer to the riddle. In more than one book I had read that the architecture of Rosslyn displayed over a hundred Green Man carvings, symbols of pre-Christian origin.

Rosslyn it is then!

Needless to say, I re-read the last few chapters of *The Da Vinci Code*, which included Rosslyn, to remind myself of what happened to the heroes there. I also went on the Net, and with over 449,000 hits when you put *'Da Vinci Code Rosslyn'* into Google, I found a plethora of info. The official Rosslyn Chapel website told me how they expected over 140,000 visitors in the year to come, four times the number of just a few years ago! The website now received over 30,000 hits every week!

There, I told the French priest everyone would benefit!

But time was ticking by and it was now a race to get up there by the Full Moon. I searched the Net, only to be disappointed to find that there was either no service to Edinburgh (the nearest airport to Rosslyn) or else seats were all booked. I must admit that I did sense something of a panic, as if Silas himself were homing in on me! But finally, I got the flight I needed, on the day I wanted and from Southampton Airport, only an hour and a half from my home. The day return would afford me about eight hours in Edinburgh, more than enough time to get to the chapel and have a good look around. But I also had to find the place where the Goddess could communicate with me and I feared Rosslyn would be overrun by tourists, all milling around clutching copies of Dan Brown's book. It was January, however, and a cold, wet one at that, so I hoped I would not encounter the tourist scrum I feared.

The drive to the airport was uneventful and the flight similarly so. It was showery and the occasional unannounced buffeting of the plane reminded me of how small and vulnerable we are compared to the raw power of Nature. I landed in a cold and damp Edinburgh and could not get into a taxi quick enough. The journey to Rosslyn took about twenty minutes, avoiding Edinburgh's traffic by taking the ring road.

I asked to be dropped off in the centre of Rosslyn village, as I wanted to approach the chapel by foot, to get a feel for the place. The taxi sped off, and I stood at a crossroads that had pubs on two corners and a sign showing me that Rosslyn Chapel was down the lane opposite. The January air seemed considerably colder than that of Southampton, so I zipped up my waterproofs and pulled my collar up around my neck.

The lane soon descended, passing a car park, and then a wooden sign informing me that *Da Vinci manure* was for sale from a farm nearby – for 50p a bag. (I laughed out loud, getting a few looks from passing visitors.) *Give me a break. Whatever next? After the Last Supper Mints? Or how about Dan Brownies!* I then passed a peculiar cottage that was painted bright orange, which resembled a huge tangerine on an LSD trip! A plaque announced that it had formerly been a pub and dated from 1660. Presumably the cottage had not been that colour in those days! Perhaps the present owner had shares in a certain mobile phone network!

Next to the cottage was the chapel, which I could make out over a wall. I had seen what I took to be a factory roof from the top of the lane but now realised that it was a protective covering, which completely shrouded the entire chapel, as if it were about to be

277

consumed by some giant metallic shark. After passing through the entrance building, via the inevitable gift shop, I stood just yards from the chapel entrance. Scaffolding, giant blocks of concrete, awnings and planks covered the outside of the hallowed building like an insidious cancer. The faces of gargoyles peered out from behind, as if screaming out their last death throes across Rosslyn Glen below. My guidebook said that the sheath was a necessary evil, to enable the monument to dry out for restoration work, and to shelter it from further acid rain erosion.

I climbed steps up to a walkway that had been afforded by the scaffolding, offering me the opportunity to appreciate the skills of the masons. Despite the ugly intrusion, the beauty and intricacy of the masons' handiwork shone through. The Green Man, dragons, griffins, roses and all manner of heads showed why restoration and emergency measures were now vital. Some of the more severely worn features, now almost indiscernible, clung on to the masonry like melting snow in a thaw. Despite the erosion, however, there was no concealing the loving art of the mason, whose work was impressive even after hundreds of years.

Climbing back down the makeshift steps to ground level, I made my way to the main entrance. Either side of the door, large banners had been erected. One read,

FROM ROME, THE NURSE OF SCIENCE AND ARTS
LO! ARCHITECTURE ALL HER POWER IMPARTS
STEALS FROM EACH TEMPLE EVERY TEMPTING FORM
AND ROBS ST PETER'S, ROSLIN TO ADORN
James Alves, The Banks of Esk, 1800

The other was equally poetic and praiseworthy:

LIKE MANY FRENCH CATHEDRALS,
THE CHAPEL HAS BEEN A BIBLE IN STONE.
IT MIGHT QUITE AS PICTURESQUELY
AND FAR MORE TRULY BE DESCRIBED
AS WOODS BURSTING INTO SONG.
Ian C Hannah, 1934

Another sign informed me that, even out of season, there were hourly tours around the chapel. The next one was in half an hour, so I hoped for some relative quiet in the meantime.

Several fellow pilgrims had preceded me inside, but as I approached the doorway I was fleetingly alone, with no other souls in sight. I crossed the threshold and paused beneath the arched stonework. Energy hit my stomach like a bolt of lightning, briefly taking my breath away, causing me to wobble momentarily. My experiences with the Goddess over ten months had not just opened up my mind, but also my sensitivities to unseen forces at sacred sites. As I stood there I could quite readily feel the flow of energies as they passed through my body. It was as if the chapel were full to bursting point, like a balloon about to pop, and energy was rushing out through the door. It was the strongest flow of energies I had experienced in a church, and I was certain that the impending Full Moon, now only two hours away, had much to do with the effect I was feeling.

Walking around the inside of the chapel was an experience I shall never forget. Almost every piece of masonry was covered with exquisite carvings, from the green man to dragons, from angels to delicately sculpted foliage. Initially, I followed the official guidebook, to familiarise myself with the layout. I located the Apprentice Pillar with attendant dragons around its base, the Mason's Pillar with its intricate stone foliage, and the incredible green man that hung over the Lady Chapel. His features were so life-like - I felt sure he would spring to life at any moment. Every way I turned there were sculptures of beasts, biblical scenes and horned creatures, and the whole of the ceiling was covered with flowers and stars. It was breathtaking. What's more, the whole of the chapel's interior was very sympathetically and atmospherically lit - dark corners were interspersed with thoughtfully positioned spotlighting, bringing out the best of the masons' art.

After around twenty minutes of jaw-dropping meandering, I sat down on one of the pews and closed my eyes to simply feel. I could sense the power of the locality, which must have been chosen with great care, possibly on the site of a more ancient sacred place. In the darkness of my closed eyes I could see occasional pulses of energy, shimmering colours that periodically flashed by in sinuous flows and pulsating ripples.

This place is alive!

All the time whilst inside the chapel, around half a dozen others had been in there with me, all of whom seemed equally in awe. I detected French and Italian accents, as well as those of two Americans. I was so glad that I had not come in season, for

Rosslyn, like Stonehenge, was fast becoming a victim of its own magnificence.

I opened my eyes and stared up to the ceiling, which was decorated with exquisite five-pointed stars. The famous cryptic verse from *The Da Vinci Code* came flooding into my mind:

> **The Holy Grail 'neath ancient Roslin waits**
> **The blade and chalice guarding o'er Her gates**
> **Adorned in masters' loving art, She lies**
> **She rests at last beneath the starry skies**

This would indeed have been a fitting resting place for the Grail, be it holy vessel or the tomb of the Magdalene. The spirit of the Divine Feminine seeped from every block of stone, from every lovingly crafted image. I whispered upward towards the star-spangled heavens.

'Where are you, my Mother? Is this the place?'

There was no reply, save for a man's voice announcing that a tour was about to begin and that anyone wishing to join it should assemble outside. *Outside!* I looked around to find that I was suddenly alone in the chapel. Now how often would that have happened since Dan Brown's book had hit the headlines?

This has to be it.

'Are you here, Mother?'

'Of course!'

'Oh, thank goodness!'

'One always ought to thank goodness. Come, quickly, down the steps to the oldest part of Rosslyn. The guide will show his party around the outside first, and then come inside. We may have but fifteen minutes undisturbed.'

I passed by the Apprentice Pillar and gazed down the flight of stone steps that led down to the crypt, or sacristy. As I descended I recalled the identical descent made by Langdon and Neveu in the movie. They had descended into a small side-room, and then down into a cellar where they discovered that Sophie was the living descendant of Mary Magdalene and Jesus. At the foot of my descent there was a rectangular room, bare of furniture or monuments save for a stone slab next to the wall, low down to my left. The walls were bare, and in terms of architecture the contrast with the chapel above could hardly have been more pronounced. It reminded me, strangely enough, of the differences between the King's Chamber of the Great Pyramid, which was devoid of any decoration, and other Egyptian tombs and temples I had visited, in which almost every inch of stone had been adorned with intricate symbolism. I crossed the room and saw that the larger of the two stone monuments bore inscriptions, revealing that it was the tombstone of a 13th Century Templar Knight.

'Of yes, they were in this area, and their ghosts roam many an old castle and deserted wood around these parts. The chapel's architecture is a magical blend of Pagan, Middle Eastern and Christian symbolism, inspired by, but of course not crafted by, the original Templars. It is a place where myth and reality blend, and subsist hand-in-hand. It is a sacred and powerful portal to the realms of Spirit, whatever one's spiritual persuasion. It is one of those places that can give the pilgrim whatever they desire, regardless of creed, colour or religion.'

The room was cold and a shiver swept through my body. On the walls near the tombstone, I saw Rosslyn's famous collection of Mason's Marks, a whole anthology of symbols that, according to my guidebook, had been left by the builders of the chapel. I could make out five-pointed stars, triangles, pyramids, swastikas, runes, crosses, all manner of glyphs.

'Some have tried to read all sorts of coded messages into these symbols, but I have to inform them that they are simply the marks left by proud masons, their calling cards if you wish. It is true that some of the symbols are also icons of sacred geometry, remnants of times when the old ways, the alchemical ways, were still honoured, times when folk knew that a sacred symbol possessed a power and an energy in itself. That is the link that these marks have to the past, not any hidden code.'

'OK. I guess some people get carried away every time they see a group of letters or symbols that cannot be explained.'

'All too often! These symbols are vestiges of an age of mystery and magic, but the assemblage here is not in itself mysterious. Come, let us get down to the lesson at hand, and why you have come to this hallowed place.'

I crouched down against the wall below the Masons' Marks, only inches from the Templar tombstone. It felt good there, despite the coldness of the ancient stone slabs.

'Much has been put out into the public domain recently concerning Mary Magdalene, holy bloodlines, Merovingians, the Grail, cover-ups, conspiracies, and so on and so forth.'

'Wow, you can say that again. People are getting a lot of mileage and making a lot of money on the shoulders of Dan Brown and dear old Mary Magdalene.'

'There is, of course, nothing wrong with generating money, per se. But I am concerned that too much information is going around the world that is totally false. I am constantly amused at how researchers get on the right track in uncovering another essential piece of your spiritual history, through often painstaking and exemplary research, only to then take things too far. Many writers have come to realise that the more outlandish their theories are, the more books they sell. But this does the whole subject a disservice, and, in fact, defeats the whole point of the exercise. I will not name any names, for the majority of the authors are genuine in their beliefs and are still to be credited for getting history re-written, or at least looked at afresh.'

'I guess this is one reason why we are at Rosslyn, right?'

'Exactly, my son. This is truly a blessed place, built on earlier sacred ground that was, as still is, the focus for powerful energies. My life-force thrills through the chapel, and my energy pulses through its masonry, as you have felt. But a chalice called the Grail was never here. The original Templars could not have visited the chapel. And Mary Magdalene was never entombed here - not here anyway!'

'Hang on. What do you mean, *not here anyway!* You imply that she is entombed somewhere else.'

'Of course, she is. She is in my body. And there my dearly beloved daughter will remain. The part of me that was briefly the Magdalene is now within my spirit once more. But her story is gradually being revealed, and rightly so, for she was a wise and powerful woman, a worthy role model for today's seekers of Truth, especially women.'

'So, please tell me. Is the Holy Grail either the bloodline or the mortal remains of Mary Magdalene? What is the Grail?'

'What is the Grail? I am afraid some may feel my answer to your question might be somewhat ambiguous. But let's have a look at some of the main contenders that have been put forward in recent years, for there have been many:

1) The Grail was the chalice used at the Last Supper.

2) The Grail is a bloodline that goes back to Jesus and Mary Magdalene, the 'receptacle' or chalice actually being her womb.

3) The Grail is the body/tomb of Mary Magdalene, hidden in some secret locality.

4) The Grail is a metaphor for personal enlightenment and Truth.

5) The Grail is a furtherance of the ancient myth of the Cauldron of Annwn, with its powers of regeneration, as spoken of by Taliesin.

You asked the question as if there were a definitive answer, as if one of the possibilities were 'true' whilst the other four were not, as if one were 'real', whilst the others were 'myth'. But surely, over the last few months, have you not had to rethink what is true and what is false, what is real and what is illusion? Your beliefs determine what your future will bring. And your beliefs about the past likewise affect history.'

'You mean that differing beliefs create varying versions of history? This does my head in. Surely history, the past, has gone and is set in stone. How can we change it?'

'You can change history because it does not exist as a finite entity. History is an intellectual device to organise previous events, in the hope of giving order to the present. Don't forget, history was written by people who were not there, usually a long time after events, and is largely based on the earlier views of others who were not there either! Liken your relationship to the past to that of a tree. The top branches are the most recent growth, whilst the roots under the earth can be seen as your past, out of view beneath the soil. Water and nutrients are absorbed through the root system and nourish the whole tree, from bottom up. But there is another flow, as solar energy is absorbed by the leaves along with CO_2. Here, nutrients are flowing from the top down, and this flow too affects the vitality of the tree. The uppermost chain of events can affect the oldest and deepest parts of the tree, those farthest from the new growth.'

'So are you saying that there can be many histories, depending on any number of diverse views.'

'Oh, it is this and more. The past only lives in the present. And now is always the point of power, the only time in Divine creativity. It is not history that keeps past events alive – it is how you perceive them NOW. Time is simply an eternal unfoldment as Now moves on from Now to another Now, remember? There is no past, present and future, only now, only ever now.'

'I still cannot get my head around stuff like this. But I guess what you're saying is that all five of the options about the Grail are true. Some people, cynics, are gonna love this, saying that you are fudging the issue, and are not giving a definitive answer.'

'That they may. But how can I give you ought else, for there IS no definitive answer. Please try to understand that it is not the destination that is the key, but the journey. You have heard this before, I am sure, but it IS deeply laced with truth. Whilst people argue about what is 'true', regarding where and what the destination is, they are not in the now. They are missing the point. It is the SEARCH for the chalice used at the Last Supper that is important. It is the sheer POSSIBILITY that Jesus and Mary Magdalene may have produced the child Sarah, and that a bloodline MAY have survived that is significant. It is the POSSIBILITY that the tomb of Mary Magdalene may lie hidden somewhere that is important. This leads to the possibility that the Grail is a metaphor for personal enlightenment and Truth. For this surely is the sum of the others.'

I looked down at the tomb of the Knight beside me. I wondered if he knew the answer.

'I said many months ago that my prime focus was to create until I can create no more, that I might know myself. The gathering of new experiences is what the universe is all about. The Grail is in all of you, in the form of your personal exploration of the cosmos, whether on a 'conscious' level or otherwise. You are living the Grail Journey as an individual, as a species, and as a planet. My Grail is to know myself so how can yours be anything less? To Arthurian followers, it is the Grail cup they seek. To some people it is catching a live specimen of the Loch Ness Monster or a Yeti. To others it is finding the ruined temples of Atlantis at the bottom of the ocean, or that they will witness an alien spacecraft landing on the lawns of the White House or on Glastonbury Tor. People are reaching out for things constantly, and whether or not they find their goal is immaterial.

'So myth and reality can be one and the same.'

'But, of course. For thousands of years shamanic and alchemical practitioners have proven that there is no difference between myth and reality. The shaman passes with ease from one state to the other. This is because it is an illusion to suppose that they are separate. Science is turning

myth into reality on a daily basis. Theories initially regarded as 'alternative' are later accepted as being 'real' and pass into mainstream thought. And more than this, events taking place today may likewise pass into myth. Chinese whispers, exaggeration, embellishment of an original event, all create tomorrow's folklore and legend. Did Jesus really turn water to wine? Did Moses really divide the waters of the Red Sea? Did the Madonna really appear at Lourdes? The bottom line is — does it matter?'

'But some of these weird theories, or any idea for that matter, may send us down the wrong road, couldn't they?'

'There are no wrong roads. Every highway marks out your journey, our journey. There are no cul-de-sacs, because in going down each apparent dead end, you still partake a sacred journey. The fact that you go down any road means it must be necessary, because you and I need to travel that road. If I didn't need to manifest an event, it would not happen, could not happen, remember?'

'You know, the thought that Mary Magdalene was a wise woman, a priestess and the wife of Jesus, really appeals to me. I feel a real affinity with this mysterious lady. She seems to represent the rawer, more sexual and risqué aspect of my psyche.'

'The woman that was Mary Magdalene was indeed a wise, advanced soul, with a deep connection to the Land, and one with whom Jesus took council. That was how their mutual attraction began, through reciprocated respect, for they were equally advanced spiritually and intellectually. She was not a 'fallen woman' at all. The 'seven demons' reportedly cast out of her was merely a memory of Jesus healing and balancing her seven chakras. The religion that became Christianity could just as easily have been built around her, if jealousy and the male ego had not intervened. It was because her persona was so powerful that the Church feared her. In Book of Revelations 19:7 you can read that '... the marriage of the Lamb is come, and his wife hath made herself ready for him.' It would seem that Jesus is permitted to take a wife some time in the future, but not in the past!'

'Funky. Some could see that passage as proof that he will return and reunite with Mary Magdalene. But I wonder if some Pagans may feel uneasy with the fact that you're saying that

Biblical events actually took place. Many choose to see Christianity as being based on a myth, and a book of fiction.'

'Much of the Bible is creative writing, this is true, and old Pagan myths were retold and reinvented with good intention to give the new religion substance. But Pagans must also ask themselves if the words contained within the Mabinogion, Le Morte D'Arthur, the Gnostic Gospels, the Brigattivita, the Torah or the writings of Taliesin are 100% factual records. Myths have been used to get messages across to the masses since time immemorial. The organised religions have merely retold established and often ancient creation myths, miracle stories, heroic quests and the like to get their own agendas across. All religions have done it - because the strategy works! You could in fact treat the Bible in a similar manner to that of any work of myth or legend: Ask not if the myths are historically sound, but rather are they spiritually true.'

'And what about the Templars? Some people say they were blood-thirsty soldiers, whilst others revere them as a spiritual cult upholding high ideals. Some people today model themselves on the Templars, not to mention King Arthur.'

'In the initial organisation and foundation of any religious cult, there are those who follow the high ideals of the founder, whilst there are those who would take advantage of their position for personal gain. It has always been so and still happens today. All I say is that you can be discerning. More than anything, The Da Vinci Code has made people sit up and think, as you admirably advocated to the priest in Brittany, to question if what they had been told of the past was totally truthful. Whether you are Pagan, Christian, Muslim, Jew, Buddhist, Taoist or whoever, always seek to find the pure kernel that founded your belief system. Find your own truth. Certainly take council from your elders, be they rabbi, priest or Druid, but make up your own mind. Or rather, I should say make up your own heart. What feels right? What does not? Do not be afraid to question those in authority. If they are sincere and truthful, they will value and respect your examination and will speak to you from their own hearts. Remember at all times what the evolution of this planet, this Universe, is all about. I seek to know myself, and I will not do this if everyone thinks, lives and acts identically. You are not robots. You are imbued with my will to find, to explore, to quest, to experience, to LIVE!'

'But with that in mind, is it OK then to follow conspiracy theories when they beckon us? Sometimes people get a 'gut feeling', when an outlandish theory comes out, that it contains at least a germ of truth. Surely we are doing what you say – to question everything?'

'You are absolutely correct. Whatever pulls you, go with it. But be mindful that your healthy enquiries do not turn into imprisoning scepticism. I can tell you now that there are those souls experiencing lower vibrations seeking to distract you from the light, from higher love. In many cases, it is the conspiracy theory that is the conspiracy! Ironic, isn't it? You may think that exposés of cover-ups and corruptions are liberating you from control of some kind. In some cases, rarely, this may be true and great growth and healing results. But it is a sad testimony to the human condition that most so-called conspiracy theory revelations are themselves the very means of slowing your march towards pure love. Tell me, what do you feel when you read about the Illuminati, or hoaxed moon landings, or the New World Order, or that you are being controlled by Aliens or Royal Reptiles? What effect does that have on you? Does it make you feel happier? Does the exposure of an alleged cover-up make you feel elated and free?'

'No, it doesn't. In fact, I often feel more depressed and helpless.'

'Of course, you do. In most cases, it has a negative effect. You feel controlled – you feel lost and fearful. And at that point you really have lost - and fear has won. I say to you, be aware, be watchful, be informed, be discriminating, but do not incarcerate yourself in a mental prison of mistrust and cynicism, a prison of your own making. We are all returning to pure love and pure light – why linger on the side shows?'

'I really believe that the Church has been withholding information about their early days, about Mary Magdalene and all the blood-line stuff. Should it affect a Christian's faith?'

'If the debate causes Christians to look within and question their faith and the sincerity of their hierarchy, then all well and good. To question is to exercise your freewill, the very freewill the Church says I gave you. How can anyone deny your enquiring about such a fundamental issue as your faith? In any case, most will perhaps realise that you cannot blame today's Church for the mistakes made by well-intentioned but misguided souls centuries ago. Let's all move on. Let the truths come out. People will respect honesty from today's

Vatican, even if it admits it made mistakes in the past. Move on and focus on what really matters, and that is the now, and the future you are creating as a result. Ultimately, there will only be one spiritual path, that of the Land, with the realisation that everything has consciousness. This is the only way I can see humankind ultimately surviving. Without a close connection to Nature the future is going to be very eventful, to say the least. At one time, all nations and peoples of the world revered me, nurturing Nature, and held me as sacred. It may be that you will return to this again, but this time out of necessity. I, the Goddess, has been worshipped for centuries as Mary, Mother of Jesus, without people knowing it, but now is the time for people to revere and respect me as the Land itself, rather than through icons, no matter how holy.'

'When I sense you near me, My Lady, and hear your words, I feel as if I have found my Grail.'

'Thank you. Such a statement honours me. But, without wishing to shake you up, I must tell you that you have taken but the first few steps on your Quest. Despite all you have witnessed and learnt in recent months, you cannot even begin to imagine the magic and wonder of the journeys that potentially await you. You have not found your Grail, not just yet. I know this because I am yet to find mine. But be assured, for you are now inextricably moving toward it.'

I could hear voices coming from upstairs, and knew that the guide had entered the chapel, with his attentive, shuffling public. I stood and turned to face the etched Masonic symbols on the wall.

'Whatever you or anyone else regards the Grail to be, it is valid. Follow your personal calling. You can search for that cup, or that bloodline or seek that lost tomb for the "treasure" that beckons you. But you should always be mindful that you are more likely to find what you seek within yourselves, than you ever will without.'

'I understand.'

I could hear footsteps behind me - people were descending into the crypt.

'They are approaching, my Mother.'

'Later this month, proceed to the temple of Knights in the City of the Dragon. You will see visions of the past and of possible futures, from the all-seeing preceptor, at sunset and moonrise. Goodbye for now, my son.'

'Farewell to you too, my Mother.'

Passing people on the stairs, I retraced my steps back up to the chapel, which was now bustling. Many were huddled around the guide, who was enlightening them regarding the interior artwork. I made my way through the throng to the exit, where I turned, taking in the chapel's grandeur and beauty for one last time. Outside the cold January wind assaulted my body, and I zipped up my coat and put on my gloves. The skies were darkening, and I knew that the sun was sinking, heralding the end of another short January day. Looking up, I could see only clouds, and wondered if I would actually get to see the Full Moon at all that night.

But I need not have worried, for just after take off, as we lifted above the grey clouds of Edinburgh, the moon came into view through my window, resplendent in the north-east, already high in the sky. And there it stayed, guiding me home throughout most of the flight. Occasionally her light would reflect off clouds below, giving them the appearance of an illuminated mist, suspended over some mythical lake. It seemed as if Excalibur itself would rise from unseen waters.

All the way back, my eyes were transfixed by the moon's splendour, but my thoughts were already occupied by the closing conundrum the Goddess had left me. Where was I to meet her later that month, the month of two full moons? It seemed incredible that before the end of the month the moon's face would shrink to nothing, and then grow again to full. And before then I needed to find out where my penultimate lesson would take place. But I knew the answer would come, as the answers to all life's questions do – we just have to believe it.

26. Finding Mary

© P Knight

*All that is born, all that is created, all the elements of
nature are interwoven and united with each other.*
(From *The Gospel of Mary Magdalene*)

January was notable for cold sunny days and freezing nights. I
reacquainted myself with the winter stars, such as Orion, Gemini
and, most magically, Sirius, the brightest star. Every time I gazed
at its brilliance in the inky firmament, I was reminded of my totem
Sirius, the spirit wolf I had met on Dartmoor and who had been at
my side at West Kennet. Some mornings I arose early to see the
moon in the dawn sky, growing smaller by the day until it
eventually became invisible as it passed between Planet Earth
and the Solar Father. A few days later it reappeared in the dusk
sky, a thin crescent near the planet Venus, the Goddess of Love.
It seemed appropriate that the three brightest objects in the
January night sky - the Moon, Venus and Sirius - had all played
such a part in my life during the past year: for every month I found
myself at some sacred place for the Full Moon; Venus was
symbolic of the love the Goddess was showing Mankind, in an
effort to guide us all to a more spiritual, earth-honouring life; and
Sirius, whom I had already called upon for strength and courage.

I visited several local rural churches in the Wessex area, to
better appreciate the subtle surviving relics of former belief
systems. I started noticing Templar crosses, the green man,
dragons and serpents in churches all around Dorset and

Somerset, as well as relics of Templar foundations, such as at Templecombe. On one occasion, whilst changing trains on my way to Birmingham, I was struck by the naming of Bristol's main railway station, Temple Meads. And, standing on platform 13, I could see a church with a bright green spire on a nearby hillside, with a round structure at the east end - a Templar design?

Some amusing things happened, too. At the church at Hazelbury Bryan, I stood next to a tomb monument in the churchyard, just yards from the porch, which bore the description: Sacred to Mary, Wife of Joseph. *Now that's a bit of a strange coincidence*. More fantastic was that the surname I spied beneath was in fact – *'Strange'*. I smiled to myself, and felt that the Goddess had also seen the funny side. On the top of the tomb was a small Templar cross, and I noted other similar crosses on other gravestones.

Inside the same church, I was attracted to three stunning stained glass windows at the east end, behind the altar. In the centre was Jesus, in red with a glorious sun-like halo. He was indeed the solar deity of ancient religions. To his right stood a knight in armour - St George no less! On his chest was the traditional red cross, and I thought how familiar it was to those worn by the Knights Templar. He stood on a scaly dragon, but the beast was not dead, or blooded, but had open eyes and was still breathing fire. There was a symbiosis between knight and dragon, a sense of cooperation and balance, not opposition or subjugation. The third window depicted Elizabeth, mother of John the Baptist. I had only ever seen her alongside Mary the Mother and Mary Magdalene in windows depicting the Crucifixion. But here she was opposite St George, the Templar knight. I then remembered how the Templars held in high regard the skull of John the Baptist, which they had allegedly once possessed as a holy relic. I had also seen the glorious symbolism based on Templar designs and ideals at Rosslyn Chapel, on the Net and, of course, in *The Da Vinci Code*. It seemed to me that it was not just at Rosslyn that one could find vestiges of esoteric Christianity.

In front of the altar stood a small card on a wooden shelf. It bore verses from Act 1, Scene 2 of Shakespeare's Richard II. Some words from the passage jumped out at me: *This Earth of majesty... this blessed plot. This Earth. This Realm. This England.* As with other genius's before and since, Shakespeare clearly connected with the spiritual side of nature, and the sacredness of England in particular. Another feature of Hazelbury church were the numerous roses carved on the arches, and I remembered that they were the symbol of Mary Magdalene.

Ah ha! Mary and Joseph in the tomb outside was just a red herring - it actually contains the body of Mary Magdalene. Mystery solved! I wish.

On one of my regular visits to Avebury I stopped off at the church of Mary Magdalene at Woodborough, south of Alton Barnes. It was the dedication that drew me and I was not to be disappointed. My attention was immediately caught by two stained windows. At the west end of the church was a window depicting Jesus being baptised by John the Baptist. But standing immediately behind Jesus was a woman holding out a towel to him. She looked just as a dutiful wife might, waiting to dry off her husband. She also wore a simple headband, in the centre of which was a white orb. This looked very Pagan to me, similar to those I had seen worn as symbolic of the Full Moon. Was this Mary Magdalene?

Behind the altar were windows depicting the Crucifixion. The mourning figure to the left of the prophet was obviously Mary the Mother. To the right was Mary Magdalene, whom the Bible tells was present at the Crucifixion. But to me she looked to have just a hint of pregnancy about her. It wasn't obvious or pronounced, but her tummy was defiantly slightly swollen. More than this, her face was very androgynous, reminding me of the controversial appearance of John aka Mary Magdalene in Da Vinci's *Last Supper.* OK, the tummy and androgynous features were open to interpretation, and perhaps I was seeing what I wanted to, but I now had the appetite to find out more.

I also noticed that a Dorset village not far north of where I lived was called Fifehead Magdalene. Bearing in mind what had transpired in *The Da Vinci Code*, and on my trip to Brittany, I simply had to go. The church was hidden by a circle of huge yew, beech and pine trees, and stood on a knoll that seemed to betray that it had been an ancient site. I walked up a gently sloping path composed of large stone slabs and paused in front of the porch. The exterior was pleasing to the eye, composed of blocks of natural stone, and the tower was embellished with slit windows.

To my right I could see a stone cross in the corner of the churchyard and felt drawn to it. The shaft and top were obviously modern but the octagonal base was much older and worn, and looked similar to medieval cross bases I had encountered elsewhere. Two shallow steps that underpinned the whole structure caught my eye. Both steps formed the shape of an eight-pointed star. How unusual was that - sacred geometry in a memorial, which was, according to words carved into one of the steps, dedicated in the last Century to a certain Colonel Percival? What a wonderful coincidence that symbols of Masonic knowledge should be incorporated into a monument erected in memory of a namesake of one of the Grail Knights!

Funky!

My attention was grabbed further by a tomb that stood close to the porch. The roof of it was not a slab of finely cut and carved stone, but was heavily pitted and only roughly hewn. It looked for all the world like a modified megalith! A closer inspection revealed many deep conical depressions, which bore a remarkable similarity to the celebrated cup marks, which decorated rocks elsewhere in Britain. Was it possible that this was an ancient stone that was later customized for Christian burial? It would certainly lend weight to my suspicion that a sacred site was there prior to Christianity. I ran my fingers over the stone, pushing fingers into the enigmatic depressions. There were no inscriptions at all on the entire tomb, only a diamond at each end, adding to the mystery.

The interior of the church of the Magdalene also held treasures. The old wooden door creaked open and I noticed that it was dated 1637 – old indeed. The interior was as appealing as the outside, with naked stonework exposed on all the walls, a far cry from the monotonous Victorian whitewashing I so often encountered. I made my way to the altar, behind which was a wooden screen decorated with three fine paintings, dating from 1904. On the left was the biblical scene of Mary Magdalene anointing the feet of Jesus. She had so much love and tenderness in her eyes and gestures. But I thought it peculiar that she was wearing a light blue robe, a colour usually reserved for the mother of the prophet. My eyes moved to the central painting, which was a powerful depiction of the Crucifixion. Two middle-aged women stood to the left of the cross - the Holy Mother and Elizabeth. At the foot of the cross was the younger figure of Mary Magdalene, her face distraught with grief. She held centre-stage with Jesus and looked like a wife mourning the death of her husband. Again, she was wearing blue. The right-hand painting depicted Jesus' appearance to Mary Magdalene after his resurrection. Again, she was garbed in a pale blue garment. *How strange!* It made me wonder how many of the images supposedly of Mary the Mother were actually Mary Magdalene! *Wow!* Projecting that still further, how many images of Mary holding the infant Jesus were really that of Mary Magdalene holding Sarah, the child she had allegedly had by Jesus? *Mind-blowing thought for the dayf!*

But the greatest wonder awaited me inside the church at Child Okeford, the Dorset village where I had watched the Morris Men dancing at Beltaine, back in May. Two walls near the altar where inlaid with marble, displaying elaborate and grand depictions of the six-pointed Star of David (enclosed within a vulva-like vesica surround) and other esoteric symbols. But it was a window in the Lady Chapel that stopped me in my tracks. It showed Jesus flanked by two women. The church guide said they were Mary of Bethany and Martha. What caught my eye was that Jesus was directing his gaze to the lady wearing blue to his right, who not only held a jar, but who was heavily pregnant! There was no doubting it, for she was actually resting the jar on her enlarged belly, which protruded well beyond her upper body. Was it indeed Mary Magdalene, clutching her alabaster jar, and carrying Jesus' unborn child? I knew that some researchers regarded Mary of Bethany and Mary Magdalene as one and the same. So had the 19th Century craftsman left a coded message for future generations to appreciate? Her face seemed to portray both serenity and sadness, perhaps mourning the fact that she had been denigrated from being Jesus' wife and bearer of his child, to a prostitute. I stood looking at the mother-to-be:

'Is that you, Mary Magdalene, is that really you?'

She did not answer, maintaining her devoted, soulful gaze towards her husband. He would not live to see the birth of his child, whom she carried in her sacred womb. And the world was surely a worse place as a result.

27. Twelfth Moon (Part 1) – January: London Lesson – Towards an Earth-Conscious Future

© P Knight

Come to the edge, he said.
We are afraid, they said.
Come to the edge, he said.
They came to the edge.
He pushed them… and they flew.
(Guillaume Apollinaire)

Before long it was a just week before the forthcoming Full Moon on January 31st. I sat in front of my laptop and brought up the words spoken by the Goddess at Rosslyn:

'… proceed to the temple of Knights in the City of the Dragon. You will see visions of the past and of possible futures from the all-seeing preceptor, at sunset and moonrise'

I was pretty sure that the first part was guiding me to one of the surviving churches of the Knights Templar. They had been the subject of many books, concerning their alleged discoveries of the Grail and the Ark of the Covenant, as well as their understanding of sacred geometry and Gnosticism. But where was it to be? Which church or ruined temple? *'… in the City of the Dragon.'* Hmm. Now where could that be, then? I decided that Google might be able to help, so I keyed in *City of the Dragon*. This lead to the realisation that both Hong Kong and Ho Chi Minh City shared that title! I was pretty sure that the Knights Templar had not been that far east! *Oh well, never mind.* I then narrowed my search to UK websites. This was more promising. One of the first

295

leads I followed up took me to London, to a picture of a statue of a dragon sporting a shield embellished with a red cross, the heraldic symbol of the Knights Templar! The photo had the tall building known as the *Gherkin* in the background, as well as what looked like the masts of boats. It was next to the Thames. I then asked Google to do a search for *City of London coat of arms.* There it was again: a red cross and a dragon, sometimes two.

Then a light bulb went on. I remembered from *The Da Vinci Code* that Langdon, Neveu and Sir Leigh Teabing had had an encounter in an ancient church in London that housed effigies of some of the Knights Templar. But where was it? I punched in *Knights Templar London* as fast as I could. The first two pages of hits all pointed to just a single place - Temple Church, London – *'... **the temple of Knights in the City of the Dragon.'*** I stood up from my PC desk and gave out a resounding yell, simultaneously punching the air.

Over the next week, I soaked up all I could about the church from the Net, which turned out to be considerable. It was a very special, mysterious and ancient place, a fitting locality for Dan Brown's epic. It was 900 years old and was said to be the only surviving Romanesque church in London. It had been consecrated in 1185 by no lesser person than Heraclius, Patriarch of Jerusalem, confirming the close connection between the Templars and the City, where the order was founded following the success of the First Crusade. The chapel once served as the London headquarters of the Knights Templar, and the round section was in fact modelled on the Church of the Holy Sepulchre. This was the oldest part of the church and was typical of Templar churches. And within it were housed the effigies of the patrons of the Templars, dating from the 12th and 13th centuries. The choir area of the church came later, but was heavily bombed in the Blitz. The columns and roof were restored and the church was rededicated in March 1954. On the alternative side, I found some references to ley lines passing through the church, and clearly it was one of the most important ancient sites to survive in the capital. I also found a reference that Shakespeare's *Twelfth Night* was first performed in the district of Temple. This seemed further confirmation, as it was to be my twelfth conversation with the Goddess!

Prior to the big day I contacted my newfound friends from Newgrange and Stonehenge, Ken and Diana. We arranged to meet up mid-evening on the night of the Full Moon, for the Goddess had said,

'... you will see the past and visions of possible futures, from the all-seeing preceptor, at sunset and moonrise.'

Now sunset was around 4.00pm, so I would have plenty of time to get across London to Cannon Street Station, where I was to meet them. Ken said he wanted to show me an ancient surviving megalith, as well as the remains of a Roman temple, both of which were close to the station. Diana had added that I did not need to look for anywhere to stay that night! It promised to be another magical Full Moon!

So the day of the Full Moon came, and after an uneventful two-hour journey, I left the car at Richmond around 1.00pm and went into Central London via the Underground train. The District Line led me to Temple Station, and I was filled with anticipation as the sliding doors opened and I saw the station sign. After negotiating the crowds and a long flight of stairs, the crisp air was more than welcome. The day was overcast and cool, yet it was dry and the forecast said there was a chance of clearer skies later in the afternoon. The urban air was not exactly fresh but it was better than that of the Underground.

I set off along the Embankment, street map in hand, along pavements busy with shoppers who were no doubt taking advantage of the January sales. I tried to focus myself midst the noise of the traffic and the hoards of shoppers. They came at me like stampeding wildebeest, occasionally bumping into me without apology; I was on a sacred mission and no one I passed had the slightest idea - I was just another anonymous Joe impeding their progress. I passed Somerset House and crossed Temple Place. The sight of that street sign made me more excited and focused, enabling me to block out the intrusive hubbub. London was full of statues and monuments, but I soon came upon one that stopped me in my tracks. Mounted on the pavement, as if awaiting my arrival, was a huge stone dragon, holding a shield embellished with a red cross. *'... **the temple of Knights in the City of the Dragon.'** Here was the dragon, holding the icon of the Knights Templar.

'Good afternoon, Oh noble dragon! I am here on a sacred quest. I beseech you that I may pass, as I seek the Temple of the Knights.'

My words were almost drowned out by the traffic but I knew the dragon had heard me and at least two other passers-by, judging from the looks on their faces. I bowed to the noble beast and moved on through the mêlée. My map showed Temple Gardens

297

just ahead, which offered both a shortcut to Temple Church, as well as a respite from the scrum. To be suddenly surrounded by greenery, be it rhododendron bushes, was most welcome and my pace slowed as I made the most of the breathing space. I soon came upon a statue of a child, a girl, holding out a bowl in front of her, Oliver Twist style. The quote at the foot of the plinth caught my eye as I passed: *'I was thirsty and ye gave me drink.'* It seemed so appropriate considering what I had experienced; I had been thirsty and the Goddess had quenched my mind and my soul.

I soon turned left off Victoria Embankment and passed beneath an elaborately decorated archway, which would lead me to Middle Temple Lane. Either side of the arch stood two stone figures, one male, the other female, symbolising the balance of Nature, the equilibrium of yin and yang that drove the Universe. The contrast between the Embankment and the environment the other side of the arch could not have been greater. Tarmac and paving slabs were replaced by cobbles and quiet, narrow passageways. I had entered the district of Temple, where solicitors, barristers and lawyers plied their craft – you could almost smell the money! I eventually came to an alleyway on my right bearing the sign *'Pump Court Cloisters and Temple Church'.* The walk became reduced to a narrow passage with small trees down the centre. One of these was interesting, as it's trunk was decidedly bent over in a long arch. This was a sure sign of an energy node, which had affected the tree's growth. *Surely the church is near!*

Without warning the alley opened into a large, paved area and there, immediately to my left, was Temple Church. The rounded structure at one end was unmistakable and magnificent. The apex of the courtyard was a tall column, with a statue at its summit. Closer inspection revealed it to be of two knights on horseback – Templars! I did not enter the church immediately, as I was compelled to walk around the outside, a feeling I had felt before at Stonehenge. At the Round, there was a large wooden door, framed by intricately carved dogtooth design stonework of Norman age, which included a foliated head. My dowsing rod confirmed what I was feeling in my stomach - the presence of a powerful energy flow coming out through the door, aligned with the axis of the church. Other than this, the outside was mainly devoid of carvings and I had the impression that this was purposeful, and not through the lack of either funding or the availability of skilled masons. The design was powerful, yet at the same time humble.

I entered the church and was greeted by a pleasant lady of middle years who offered me a leaflet, which provided me with a brief guide to the church's features and history. I looked around to see that there were only three other visitors.

'I seem to have picked a good day to come – nice and quiet', I commented.

'Oh, indeed', she replied, '… in season we were packed out on many days. Since *The Da Vinci Code* the number of visitors has quadrupled. A couple of coaches rolled up earlier today, but you are right, you've picked a good time.'

'I'm glad. I wanted to feel the sanctity of the church.'

She smiled and seemed to appreciate the fact that I wasn't just another soul suffering from ODVCD - Obsessive Da Vinci Code Disorder!

The 13th Century choir was impressive, mainly due to its stark simplicity and tall dark, polished marble columns, which leaned peculiarly outwards. Dan Brown spoke of the church's 'stark grandeur', and there was certainly a world of difference between Temple Church and the elaborate richness of Rosslyn. But the church possessed a timeless atmosphere, which had survived Victorian embellishments, the Blitz and post-war restoration. The east end was dominated by brilliant, iridescent stained glass windows, in deep purple and blue hues, similar to Salisbury Cathedral, which strikingly contrasted the plain stonework. One window displayed a winged Pegasus – symbol of Inner Temple Order. Was this the *'… all-seeing preceptor'*, a horse that flew over the Land, and saw the bigger picture?

No, it just doesn't feel right.

I did not spend much time at that end, for I felt magnetically drawn to the Round, with its ancient prone effigies of Templars and their patrons. Although damaged by enemy bombing during the Blitz, they were nevertheless striking, made of dark polished stone and adorned with armour, helmets and various weapons. Some had animals at their feet, one being a dragon. Nearby was the font, which featured knights fighting mythical beasts, one of which again resembled a dragon. Then I spied a series of life-size stone heads, I counted sixty of them, decorating the walls of the Round. I passed them one by one, and saw that most were human caricatures, although some were bestial, and that all were unique. Was one of these the, *'all-seeing preceptor'* spoken of by the Goddess? I retraced my steps until I had re-scrutinized them all, but I did not feel drawn to any of the enigmatic images. I stood back and looked upwards, and I spoke a supplication to the vaulted roof:

'Where are you, My Lady?' There was silence, save for footsteps echoing on cold stone elsewhere in the church.

'I know, you are me, you are looking through my eyes and experiencing what I am, but is this the place of our dialogue?'

'Indeed, it is. Greetings, my son. Welcome to the temple of my noble Knights. Once again you worked out correctly where we would talk. This is an ancient hallowed place, which was sacred even before the Templars built here. My pulse surges through the Land, as you dowsed earlier, and the effect of which you saw in the tree. The Templars knew of this ancient sanctuary and came here to worship me, in the form of Mary, Sophia, and Jesus, the Solar Logos incarnate.'

I sat down in one of the stone seats of The Round, framed each side by a duo of carved heads. I whispered my reply, as my earlier words had echoed around the dome.

'It is good to hear your voice, my Mother, as always.'

'Thank you. I too rejoice our interchanges. I do so enjoy talking to myself!'

'Indeed,' I replied with a smile.

'It is sunset and moonrise in just over one hour and we have much to do. Today I wish to get across to all people about the crossroads at which you are standing. Mankind has a choice right now as whether to continue as part of my journey of self-discovery, or go the way of the dinosaurs and the Atlanteans.'

'Wow. Talk about hitting the ground running! OK, I know we're screwin' the planet up, so lay it on me.'

'Your comment is partially true. I would start by stating that you are also damaging yourselves, for you and I are one, remember? I am here to ask you all whether or not you wish to continue as part of my evolution, for you have free will to do so or not. Either way, I will evolve. You are at the moment the most evolved beings, mentally and spiritually, in physicality on the planet, and I am proud of you. You have been an essential part of my growth, or else I would not have dreamed you. But I can continue without Mankind, if that is the way things evolve. Should you disappear as a result of your own folly, your level of consciousness and intelligence will be repeated again, in some other physical form. I will eventually create all possible variations that are achievable in

all dimensions. Do you wish to be part of that potential, of that miracle? For I say to you now - as a species you have vast potential to help me grow and to further know myself, but I will get there eventually, with or without Mankind. I am in no hurry. Time means nothing to me. I am eternal. Mankind in physical form is not.'

'Gulp! You make it sound as if Mankind is expendable. That scares me. I thought you said we were part of you. How can we become extinct?'

'Take the human body. An growing infant constantly discards outmoded and outgrown cells. As a child grows toward adulthood, it further changes and evolves, and does not hang on to outmoded parts, such as milk teeth. And when an adult eventually reaches elder, parts of the body no longer used as often, or those that are worn, such as muscles and teeth, are discarded or reduce in size. It has to be so for the body to continue to survive for a while longer. Yes, you are all part of my being, of my body, of the Land, but that which is no longer serving a purpose in Nature becomes obsolete. This has always been the way of things. Dinosaurs, the mammoth, Neanderthal Man - they all had their day and were replaced by newer life forms, in my constant effort to create and maintain balance. Yin and yang in perfect harmony is the way of the Universe, the way of Wyrd, and that which does not serve this end will naturally wither and die out, be it an individual or a whole species. There have been many cycles of extinction, and there may be more to come.'

'I feel a little depressed, and also a little ashamed. But some may say that Humanity to you is just another disposable commodity in your evolution, and that you will discard us and move on to the next phase, to something higher and purer.'

'This may well be true. I know not yet. But the road Man has come along has been long, and at times savage and dark. Yet all too often it has also been a road of nobility, love and inspiration, of artistic creativity and compassion. The polarities of dark and light, love and fear, the strong and the weak, are an essential part of Nature, of my nature, and will always be so. That is the balance. The key is to see beyond the surface appearance of what you call darkness, fear, Hell, evil and despair, and see them for what they really are – aspects of Nature, aspects of yourselves. For this is where

you have the power to survive and start to heal the planet. You only really need do two things to survive and flourish.'

'And they are?'

'Firstly, you must connect once more in a spiritual way with the Land, with my body. Then it will be impossible for you to do further harm to your fellow beings or the Land itself. And secondly, realise that you really do possess the power not only to change yourselves, but also to change the world into the place you wish it to be. As you desire, so I will create, so we will create together.'

'So can you give us some ways to initiate Earth healing, and of healing ourselves? What are the bottom lines?'

'Next month, the final month, I shall give you Thirteen Insights by which Mankind can connect with the Land and, as a consequence, to me. These will be based on the previous months' lessons. They will be your bottom lines. But at this stage I will suggest some practical ways for you to move forward. I hope you can succeed, for you are part of who I am, and have been for some time, and to lose you would be like having a limb amputated. But make no mistake, an amputee will usually survive the necessary severing of a deceased or injured limb.'

'OK. I understand. This is the point of no return, isn't it?'

'It is, believe it. Here are the main points I wish you all to absorb into your lives. By following these guides I feel you may well endure and flourish:

You must cease cutting down the rain forests forthwith. They are my physical lungs and I feel shorter of breath every year and may not be able to feed my children with the oxygen they need for much longer. And with fewer big trees, the carbon levels rise, leading to a heating up of my body. Stop deforestation of the rainforests now! If you must use wood, and I accept this to be the case, then use trees cut down from sustainable forests. When a tree is cut down, ensure that two or more are planted in its place. For this is also important for your spiritual growth, for when you plant a tree, you plant part of yourself. Furthermore, you must not fell any more ancient trees, no matter where they are in the world. They are holders of ancient wisdom and their wizened bodies and souls hold the myths of the Land. Mugna spoke of this in the New Forest. Few appreciate today that Mankind and trees have an intimate relationship going back thousands of years.

302

When you nurture a tree, and love it, cuddle and respect it, you also cultivate your own soul.'

'Yes, I understand.'

I looked at the effigy of the dead Templar Knight stretched out on the floor in front of me and wondered if Man was destined for the same fate.

'Next. You must cease the exploitation of fossil fuels, replacing them with nature energy sources, such as wave power, wind turbines, solar panels and so forth. You have raped and pillaged my body for too long, and what should have remained deep within my body is now polluting the air my children need to breath. Every lump of coal, every crystal, every litre of gas, every natural element that you have gouged from my body has been painful to me. Such operations have been against the natural order. You have not replaced what you have taken – how could you? The sea levels are rising as you heat up my body, and I cannot stop this without your help, although I can slow down the process to a certain extent. Will you only stop polluting the planet when the ocean waters reach the White House lawn, or wash away the Houses of Parliament? Living with a global consciousness requires preventions not cures. And you need to do this NOW.'

'I understand.'

'Next. You must develop non-polluting means of travel at a much faster pace. Cars are the biggest source of greenhouse gas emissions. Each driver produces tons of carbon pollution each year. You must develop electric, solar-powered and alternative fuels. The technology is with you now and could be adopted globally in a very short time. Use public transport use your bicycle more, and your car less. Walk whenever you can and share your car with others whenever possible.

You must recycle most of the waste you produce. All your cans, garden refuse, cardboard, paper, batteries, tyres, wood, metals and much more can all be recycled. This saves energy and trees. It also reduces landfill – do you know how it feels when you scrape away my skin and dump millions of tons of toxic waste and rotting refuse into my pores? I am saddened and also have to compensate the detrimental effects on local earth energies, by drawing positive energy from elsewhere to balance the Land's energies. This means diverting it away from elsewhere, which in turn suffers in a domino effect. As well as recycling, you ought to buy consciously. Less

303

packaging, less waste, and less throwaway consumables means less energy consumption and less damage to the environment. The supermarkets are key here.'

'OK. Although I already recycle most of my unwanted stuff, I know I can do better. What else?'

'Get involved politically. Many think that being 'spiritual' means you do not get involved in political debate, that you 'drop out', as the saying goes. At one time that was fine and indeed necessary for many. But the time has come when people who know better need to act. You and your children can join bodies such as Greenpeace, Friends of the Earth, Rainforest Action Network, World Wildlife Fund, the Wildlife Trust, Men of Trees, English Nature, and a host of other groups doing good work to heal the Land.'

'And what about politics?'

'Political parties can also be examined regarding their environmental policies. More than this, environmental issues ought to be your key requisite as to which party, if any, you put your cross next to. Ask yourself this question: What is ultimately important - how much is being spent on education, the armed forces, hospitals, transport and so on, or whether or not your children's children will survive the irresponsible excesses of your generation? Do you care about the future and the quality of life that your children, grandchildren and great-grandchildren will have? When you vote, vote consciously not for today's issues, but for the legacy today's issues will leave on the future of all of Mankind and the planet. Voting green does not mean you are green in a naïve sense. It shows wisdom and foresight.

Next. Take care of your fellow creatures on the planet, for they are your brothers and sisters, and fellow travellers on the road to a higher consciousness. Eat only organically and wherever possible be vegetarian. If you must eat meat choose only from free-range and organic sources. Again, I feel the pain of your fellow souls as they are mistreated. Although everything has a higher purpose, that is no excuse for knowingly incurring pain. We are all part of the Land, and the harm you have caused your brothers and sisters of the animal kingdom has sent negative energy out along the Web of Wyrd and far out into the cosmos. This is now coming back to haunt you.'

The Goddess fell silent. I was the first to break the silence after a few moments, having got my breath back!

'Well, that's quite a lot to get our teeth into. Could you put it in a nutshell, a tenet to live our lives by?'

'Certainly. It is this: Live life in a conscious way, valuing and appreciating all life, respecting the views of those who hold different spiritual ideals, and act only in ways that benefit the Planet as a whole. The time has come for you to see the bigger picture with eyes and hearts wide open. Think about the Earth you will leave behind on your physical death, for in future incarnations you will personally reap what you are sowing today.'

'Phew. Thank you. You sound as if you were almost pleading with Mankind. Some may say that this is hardly the act of a Divine being, of a God or Goddess.'

'I think this is exactly how it ought to be. Would you rather I was a vengeful God, of brimstone and lightning and of thunderbolts, the God of the Book of Revelations? Shall I lay waste cities and wipe the slate clean in a demonstration of my power and dissatisfaction? Would this be the action of a Goddess of Love, of one who sees all and who regards all as part of herself?'

'Of course not. I hope all this gets through to people. Action groups like Greenpeace have been drawing attention to this stuff for years. I get so depressed sometimes when I see how very little seems to improve.'

'Oh, but it is improving. Just a few years ago it would have been almost impossible to buy organic, vegan, recycled and lead-free items from mainstream shops and supermarkets. Things are getting there, but not quick enough for Mankind and the animal kingdom. The foundations have been laid, but the rate at which you are building the Temple of Conscious Living needs to accelerate.'

'So there is hope?'

'Why, of course there is, or else you would not be sitting in the company of Knights on this Full Moon. Hope moves mountains, and may yet do so.'

'I will do my best, My Lady, to play my part.'

'I have no doubt of that. Tell me, did you solve the last part of the riddle I left you?'

'You know I haven't! Let me see, you said something about the, *'... all-seeing preceptor.'* I continued in a whisper, 'There are

305

enough all-seeing eyes here…', I paused as tourists passed me by, whilst at the same time looking around at the sixty heads decorating the walls of the Round.

'… but I can't see anything relevant. I don't feel drawn to anyone in particular.'

'Hmm. Well how about we retrace the steps that led you here. Off we go!'

'OK. I'm up for it.'

I left the church and stepped into the crisp late January air. The sky was still mainly overcast, but with one or two small breaks, giving hope that I might see something of the sunset and moonrise after all. I returned via the leaning tree, Temple Place and the arch. I turned right into the Embankment and it took only a few steps to realise what the answer to the riddle was. I was walking in the opposite direction than before and the solution loomed high in the sky, towering over the icy waters of the Thames.

The London Eye!

'There, you have it.'

'Of course, of course. The *all-seeing preceptor!*'

I laughed out loud, to the puzzlement of passers-by.

28. Twelfth Moon (part 2) – Visions from the All-Seeing Eye

© P Knight

*"They have killed their Mother,
and now they want to kill ours".*
From the movie *Avatar*.

I increased my pace, passing the dragon statue and onward over the Golden Jubilee Bridge. I had never been to the London Eye and stood in awe at the foot of it. An information board provided me with some impressive statistics: 1,700 tonnes of steel; higher than St Paul's Cathedral; thirty-two giant capsules that turned 360° as the wheel rotated and, which impressed me greatly, that the whole gigantean structure rotated using only 500kw of power, or six light bulbs per person per thirty minute experience.

'I guess I'm going up, right?'

'But of course!'

'Yes! I was hoping so! Beam me up Scottie!'

But as Scottie was on leave, I obtained a ticket by waiting my turn in a thankfully short queue. Only about a dozen people were in front of me and I appreciated the fact that it was a cold, overcast, out-of-season day. There were rows of stalls to hold the many throngs that must descend on the Eye in season and weekends, but today they were redundant. As I approached the capsules I could appreciate their size, as each was capable of holding up to fifteen people. Within a couple of minutes I was at the front. Incredibly, there was no one behind me.

'Any chance I could have one to myself?' I enquired to the attendant, who was busy scanning me with a security device.

He looked behind me and then over his own shoulder.

'No problem, mate, it's quiet. Go for it.'

I thanked him and stepped into my own, personal pod. It slowly rose from the ground, steadily rising above the River Thames. Even half way up the view was spectacular, the glass walls of the capsule enabling a 360° vista. To the north rose the resplendent dome of St Paul's and the infamous 'Gherkin', and below me the Golden Jubilee Bridge and the Temple gardens, through which I had walked. Coming around to the east I could see the ugly, invasive sprawl of Waterloo Station and beyond it Greenwich and Canary Wharf. I turned my attention to the south, where Westminster Bridge lay below, with St Thomas's Hospital on this side of the river. The Houses of Parliament and Westminster Abbey both rose out of London's bustle on the other side. Beyond them, the four distinct chimneys of the abandoned Battersea Power Station loomed up into the sky. After about fifteen minutes I was approaching the zenith of the journey and looked west, across the river to Downing Street, the Ministry of Defence, Buckingham Palace and the green oasis that was St James's Park. All the time, people were mere dots below, with cars and buses resembling model toys as I floated silently above the choppy, moody waters of the Thames.

'The view from up here is spectacular, is it not? It's amazing how Mankind can fashion the most uplifting creations such as this, whilst at the same time produce devices of death and suffering. Are you ready, my son?'

'Ready? Ready for what, My Lady?'

'This is the all-seeing preceptor, is it not? From here you can see the geography of the present. But I am also able to show you not just today, but also what you call the past, as well as possible futures I have dreamed. Come. Sit down on the seat. Look southwest, for sunset is approaching.'

I did not know what to expect, but got comfortable nevertheless on the seating in the centre of my glass bubble. I knew something was about to happen, but was not prepared for the visions that would sear themselves into my mind forever. I could see the cloud thinning to the southwest, above the Houses of Parliament, and felt hopeful of seeing a memorable sunset. It was already a month past solstice so I figured that the sun was already journeying northwards along the skyline and might set in alignment with Big Ben and Westminster Abbey. I was just settling down when it began.

It was almost imperceptible at first, a sort of misting up of the windows of the capsule, as if it were steaming up. But I then realised that it was the landscape below me that was fading from view. A mist that soon shrouded even the highest buildings was consuming London.

'We are going on a little journey through that which you call time. Look again at London now.'

I blinked and in an instant the mist had disappeared and with it London! The scene before me now was one of marshes and inlets and woods. Not a piece of concrete in sight! I was speechless and sat open-mouthed.

'We are looking at London as it was in the Bronze Age. As you can see, much has changed.'

I could make out a couple of wooden craft on the river, which was now wider, with grassy banks. On the far bank stood a small collection of round houses, made of wood with straw roofs. Beyond these was a forest, with occasional shafts of smoke that betrayed other settlements. I looked to my right and could follow the great right bend in the Thames, but the banks of the river were more ill-defined and marshy in places, and other tributaries flowed into the river from the north. More small boats were sailing downstream and beyond them I could discern another settlement, with grazing cattle nearby. I could also just make out what looked like a stone circle, at the summit of a small rise, more or less where St Paul's had stood moments before. Looking back left, a large island occupied the land where Westminster Abbey had been, and on it stood tall standing stones.

'Let us fast forward a thousand years, shall we?'

'OK... I think!'

In another blinking of an eye the scene changed again. The area was still marshy and the banks of the river amorphous but now there was a bigger collection of more substantial buildings to the north, a small town in fact, surrounded by a wall.

'Behold the Roman town of Londinium.'

I could make out what appeared to be a round amphitheatre, like the Coliseum, and just beyond it what looked like a garrison fort. The town comprised about two hundred or so buildings, mostly with red-tiled roofs, many with plumes of smoke rising into the air. One building, however, stood out above the others. Its sheer size, the tall columns and the arches could mean only one thing – it was a temple.

'It is the Temple of Mithras, the Mithraeum to be exact.'

Just this side of it, close to the river was another grand structure, which looked very high status, like a palace or governor's residence. I also noticed that a wooden bridge now spanned the river, close to where Waterloo Bridge now stood, and a smaller collection of red-tiled buildings stood on the south bank. Several large galleons were moored near to it, and they would surely have been large enough to sail from Italy or at least across from the Channel from Roman Gaul.

'Wow, this is so cool!'

The town wall was punctuated by several gates and, scanning the areas outside these, I could follow a network of diverging straight roads, the arteries of the Empire. To my left were some outlying settlements of wooden huts, with occasional, isolated red-tiled structures, which I took to be rural villas.

'Hold tight, we are off to Saxon London!'

In two shakes of a toga the scene changed again, as if time was being fast-forwarded, as on a DVD. To my surprise the Roman town had virtually disappeared. The temple looked in ruins and the amphitheatre had gone. Only a few vestiges of the walls remained, along with the bridge. There remained a mixture of rectangular and round huts, but the number of dwellings was less than in Roman times. I then noticed that to the west, to my left, a large settlement had established itself where there had not been one before. Smoke rose in abundance from a tight-knitted collection of wooden buildings and in the foreground there was a bustle of activity as boats were being loaded and unloaded.

'It is the Saxon port of Lundenwic.'

I scanned left towards the southwest to where the large island had been and saw that on it there was now what looked like a monastery, more or less on the site where Westminster Abbey stood today. Around it was a gathering of smaller buildings and wooden huts, presumably serving its needs. But before I could say, 'fire up the Tardis, Rose, we're off!' the scene had changed and this time it was quite a shift.

'Where, or rather when, are we now?'

'How about 1300AD? Does that sound OK?'

The first thing I noticed was that the centre of London seemed to have reverted back to the old Roman site, with only a scattering of houses and a few churches where the Saxon settlement had been. The big additions were the presence of the original St Paul's Cathedral, at about the same spot where I had seen the Bronze Age stone circle moments before, and what looked like a church or temple to the west of it. I could make out the rounded end. Yes, it was, it was Temple Church. Another big change was that the bridge, which was undoubtedly London Bridge, was now made of stone, whilst to the right of it stood the Tower of London, resplendent and surrounded by a moat. Numerous churches now peppered the skyline and as well as other high-status buildings. I panned left and came upon the splendour of Westminster Abbey, which dominated the landscape, accompanied by a grandiose building on the site of the Houses of Parliament. The island that I had seen earlier had been swallowed up by development. There was still no Westminster Bridge, yet I could see boats ferrying people across what was a busy crossing point.

Then I was off again, this time at an accelerated rate as I was fast-forwarded through centuries in seconds. The last thing I remember was London ablaze, and lights arcing across the skies – it was the Blitz! Then without warning the scene before me went dark, as if the sun had set. I could make out London again, as if I were once again in the present day. But something was wrong, for it wasn't night at all, but daytime and the sun was high in the sky. But it was pale, shining through dense layers of smog and pollution. It was awful. I could smell the stale air and I felt almost physically sick. All the buildings were caked with soot and pollution and the river was jet black and littered with rubbish, which floated on a thick, oily scum. The streets were devoid of any moving vehicles, although I saw rusting abandoned ones here and there. And there were people down there, right below the Eye, walking along the embankment. As I looked down at them I could see that the Eye itself was rusting and in a bad state of repair. The whole of London was in a state of terminal decay. There were no birds. No noise from traffic. No planes coming into land at Heathrow. The city was dying. It was like a nuclear winter, and all seemed lost.

'What's happened? Has there been a nuclear war, or a plague or something?'

'Nothing so melodramatic. No, this is a scene I have imagined, of what may beset Mankind in about 100 years

311

time. Not long, is it? No war, no meteorite impact, no 1984, no pandemic, but apocalyptic none the less. This is what I dream London to be like, along with other cities across the world, if Mankind does not change its ways. And I will tell you what lies beyond this dying metropolis. The Amazon Rainforest is no more – all wasteland. The Sahara Desert has now consumed the antiquities of Ancient Egypt. There are no coral reefs left around the world. Africa has been declared a quarantined no-go area because of famine and new incurable diseases. The crops are failing all over the world, as the sun cannot penetrate polluted skies. The Antarctic ice has now all but withered away, and there is no longer any annual winter freezing within the Arctic Circle. Melt waters have already submerged Florida, the Mississippi Delta, New Orleans, many Pacific Island nations, as well as Holland, and much of East Anglia. Very soon the waters will breach the defences that have been erected in desperation around the cities of London and New York. Need I go on, my son?'

I sat in disbelief and horror. A tear rolled down my check and I felt a mixture of guilt and deep remorse.

"And the sun became black as sack cloth and the moon became as blood.' That passage is from the Book of Revelations. Although its texts are a portent for the Second Coming, many of it's disturbing depictions could be heeded, as they paint a picture akin to what you see before you, do they not?'

It was all too much. I rose to my feet and smashed my fists against my glass cocoon. My cries of despair momentarily echoed around the capsule.

'You idiots did it. You didn't heed the warnings! You stupid bastards - you're killing the planet!'

'It is a sorrowful state of affairs. William Blake spoke of such circumstances:

'The Eternal Female groan'd!
It was heard all over the Earth,
Albion's coast is sick, silent.'

Blake was a man of vision, a man great sensitivity, who sensed the pain inherent in the Land.'

I sank down to my knees, slumped against the glass. All seemed hopeless.

'Fortunately, this is but one possible future that I have dreamed. My dreams can, of course, become nightmares for Mankind, should they be manifested. But there are many possible futures. It is up to you which road you choose to go down – planetary healing and the survival of mankind... or Armageddon. One Hopi Indian prophecy has already spoken of that which I speak:

'... total annihilation or total rebirth. The choice is ours. War and natural catastrophe may be involved... The degree of violence will be determined by the degree of inequity caused by the peoples of the world and the balance of Nature.'

The choice the Hopi speak of is the choice now facing your generation.'

'We don't really have any choice but to change our ways, do we?'

'No, you do not. But the problem is that most people do not realise they personally have to make the choice; they bury their heads ostrich-like in the sands of apathy. It would sadden me not to have Mankind's physical manifestation as part of my body and my growth. We have come far together and I feel that we are only just scratching the surface of our mutual potential. There are many souls awaiting incarnation, many souls who are eager to share the physical journey. They have long been part of my evolution and are keen to be here at the pinnacle, at the climax of Herstory.'

'I suddenly feel the heavy weight of responsibility that rests on my shoulders, personally, and on the shoulders of this and future generations.'

'But it is good that you feel this. You are all part of the cancer that is eating away at my body, and which could be fatally infecting you as a species too.'

I sat in silence, as the dark, sordid scene remained before me - sombre and utterly depressing. After a few more minutes, it was with some relief that the scene returned to the present day, and my eyes winced at the blinding light of the setting sun. Streaks of blue mixed with straggling black clouds - the sun was low in the sky. Astonishingly, but fittingly, it was in perfect alignment with both Big Ben and Westminster Abbey in the foreground. My spirits lifted slightly.

'Yes, it is fitting, indeed. The Houses of Parliament, that great symbol of democracy where your Government could help secure Mankind's survival, aligns with the sun. You need

to change the way governments ride roughshod over my body, and must ultimately elect leaders who think globally and environmentally when debating all issues of legislation. The perceived enemies you now focus on, be they Jew, Muslim, Christian, fundamentalist and so on, are not your real adversaries. All world leaders now have a common enemy – the destruction of natural resources and global warming. And the Abbey, symbol of the Church, stands below the Sky Father, bathing beneath its light and ultimate power. Religions must once again, as they once did, advocate a spirituality that nurtures Nature, revering the Earth as a living, divine spirit, and put aside all dogmatic differences, to unite and heal Mankind. There are many, many roads to the top, but there is only one Divine mountain. You are all flowers in my garden, and you share a common ancestry – that of the Earth Spirit. The garden is beautiful because it contains many different colours. I seek not to destroy or dilute religions or cultures, but to once again connect them with their common roots.'

My capsule was almost at the end of its revolution and the ground was approaching fast. What had gone before seemed to take longer than the thirty-minute official 'flight', but it was not the first occasion that time itself had slowed down when the Goddess was around. Just before the distant skyline was lost to view, the sun sank below the horizon, not far right of the power station. Its huge chimneys stood out in stark silhouette against the blazing sky behind. Then it was gone, replaced within seconds by a beautiful sky full of various shades of purple and oranges, whilst the undersides of black clouds were a blaze of red and salmon pink. But where was the moon? It was Full at 12.30am tonight, so it should have risen just before sunset. I stood up and looked anxiously in the opposite direction, concerned that my capsule might now have been too low to see it. But there she was, already risen and hanging over the dome of St Paul's Cathedral. The Moon, symbol and object of reverence for thousands of years before the coming of the Church, was perched over one of Christianity's iconic buildings.

'Religions may come and go, but some things never change. The Moon, along with its power to both heal and move the waters of the planet, is eternal. Man's icons, dogmas, ideals, ideologies, loves and hates, trials and tribulations, are but transient things, compared to my eternal

Nature. If Mankind destroys itself, along with many of his fellow beings, the moon and the sun will still rise and set every day, and I will still be here. For I am the 'here' - I am the all.'

'Amen to that, My Lady.'

The moon was lost from sight behind anonymous office blocks as my capsule reached the bottom of the gigantic wheel. I stepped out into the early evening January air, and the background rumble of London's rush hour traffic assaulted my ears. I stood watching the tides of commuters rushing by and it struck me how they were either oblivious or devoid of opinion or concern for the crisis that was unfolding around them.

The Goddess had not yet said her goodbyes so I knew there was more to follow. Yet I was to meet Ken and Diana early that evening and wanted to see Westminster Abbey before then. I walked south along the embankment, passing the Dalí Universe exhibition. I thought it fitting that Dalí was a surrealist – after my totally surreal experience up the Eye! Various metal sculptures stood outside, next to the river. One caught my eye and I stood transfixed before it. It was a huge copy of Dalí's masterpiece *Nobility of Time*. Its huge features towered over me: the centre piece was a huge melting clock, elongated and deformed, looking as if it were about to terminally slither from the branches of a dead tree, from which it hung. Either side were two figures at the foot of the tree. On the left was a female nude, whilst the other was a winged male angel, in a sorrowful pose. I soon noticed the time displayed on the misshapen clock. It was 12.30 – the exact time of the Full Moon!

'Wow. Now that's really neat.'

'I thought so too! So what does the sculpture say to you in the context of what you have just witnessed?'

OK. Right. I guess that the clock is the central thing. Time is an illusion? It can be distorted and replayed, as up in the Eye? I guess, also, that time is running out for Mankind. It is dripping off a tree – the Tree of Life? The tree is almost bare, save for a couple of leaves clinging to it. It represents Nature and life itself!

'Excellent. Go on.'

OK, Hmm. The figures either side are male and female. Yin and yang, the polarities - balance and harmony. The male is sad, distraught even. He perhaps represents Mankind itself. The female is beautiful and resplendent and sensual and noble. She is you, yes, she is you!

315

'And?'

And she is about to pull a shawl or shroud over herself. She is about to be covered. Nature is retreating into herself, for she is being stifled. My God, all this in a Dalí statue after what has just happened. Did he mean it to represent this?

'Does it matter? It's what it says to you that counts. This is how to perceive any work of art, individually, just as you can learn to perceive the Land and Nature.'

'Indeed, indeed! Brilliant, just brilliant, and magical!'

'Yes, we are aren't we?'

It was starting to get dark and I rested my arms on the wall behind the sculpture with my head on my hands, staring at the other side of Westminster Bridge – soon to be my destination.

'You must go and our dialogue will cease for now. A dear old soul and a beautiful young lady await you. Next month is a momentous occasion, for it is to be our last dialogue. I will give you the Thirteen Insights, based upon the lessons of the previous Full Moons. Meet me at the Grail Well, where the two circles meet and holy waters flow from my body. Again, you have done well. Goodbye, my son.'

'Goodbye, My Lady. And thank you.'

I set off across Westminster Bridge, in search of new adventures with old friends. The night was yet young, and young at heart was how I felt.

29. Reunited in Londinium

© P Knight

Omnia vincit amor
(Virgil, Roman poet, 37 BC.)

I reached the other side of Westminster Bridge just as the streetlights came on. The traffic was heavy, noisy and intrusive and I was about to carry on when I noticed a statue on the other side of the road. Mounted on a huge stone plinth was a figure riding a chariot, pulled by two noble steeds. It was Boudicca! And rising behind her was the huge illuminated London Eye. What a sight; my heart was moved and I was close to tears again. Boudicca, symbol of Britain's independence and of native people rising up against tyranny, and the illuminated Eye, overseeing the capital like the eye of Saurun in *The Lord of the Rings*. It stood as a magnificent technological achievement, yet also symbolised how millions could be spent on tourism and prestige projects whilst half the world starved. I looked back at Boudicca and felt hope, perhaps the sort of expectancy that she had once instilled in her people. Britain, Albion, would survive. Mankind would survive.

I gave Boudicca a big smile and a nod.

'Go get 'em, girl!'

My words were drowned out by the rush-hour traffic, but I felt she had heard me all the same. They say that the pen is mightier than the sword. Boudicca's sword had not been able to save her people. I hoped that the Goddess's words would.

The Abbey had closed for public access, except for those going to Evensong, which, in all good faith, I did not feel inclined to attend. In the yellow lights that bathed the outside I could make

317

out gargoyles, including dragons, which returned my gaze with a timeless majesty. Some appeared more than a little bewildered, perhaps grimacing at the changes they had witnessed since being fashioned by the masons' hands hundreds of years ago.

'We'll meet you outside Cannon Street Station at 7.00pm...' Ken had said, '... We've got a couple of special places we want to show you.'

I had two hours to spare so I thought I would walk there, via Whitehall, the Strand and St Paul's – for a bit of unashamed sightseeing. I picked up a bite to eat on the way, for although my stomach was still churning with excitement, it gave me a respite from the din and mêlée of London's jostling streets.

My watch said 6.50pm as I arrived outside Cannon St Station. The traffic was still hectic and with it the pedestrians, who pushed past as I waited under the station sign. I did not have to wait long.

'Greetings, pilgrim of the Great Mother, greetings!'

The words were loud and unmistakable. I turned around to see Ken coming up the sidewalk and, just a few paces behind, Diana. Ken was just how I would have expected him, sporting a baggy rainbow jumper and combat trousers, whilst Diana wore a long black coat, which was swinging open, betraying a tight fitting, low-cut black velvet top, black trousers and purple DM's. Her bright red, shoulder-length hair flashed under the streetlights. Within seconds we were all locked in a three-way embrace. It was fantastic, with pats on the back, smiles and exchanges of genuine friendship and love. After a few moments Ken backed away, and I was face-to-face with Diana. We exchanged kisses on cheeks, as well as eye contact, which was as potent and emotive as it had been at Stonehenge all those months ago.

'It's good to see you,' she said softly.

'Divine!' I replied and we smiled, and smiled and hugged and....

'Oh, come on, you two, plenty of time for all that stuff!' interrupted Ken with a wry smile, '...we've got things to show our pilgrim friend, haven't we, Di?'

'We sure have, Ken.'

They took hold of one hand each and we virtually skipped across the main road, the traffic opening up before us as if Moses had had a hand in it. We walked west along Cannon St, passing the *London Stone* pub (big clue), continuing for about twenty-five yards until Ken brought us to an abrupt halt. We all stood looking down at an iron grille, which protected a pane of glass, behind

318

which a spotlight shone, illuminating what looked like a large, square-cut stone. Yes, it was a stone, and it looked old.

Ken announced it was, '... *The London Stone*, the prehistoric Pagan omphalos of London. It had stood on Roman Watling Street. It is also known as the Brutus Stone, for legend says that so long as the stone is safe, so shall London flourish. It was possibly taken from a stone circle that once stood at the top of Ludgate Hill. Others think it a temple altar stone. Blake thought it a Druidic altar. Others regard it as the very stone from which Arthur pulled Excalibur. Quite a CV, hey?'

I kneeled down before my encapsulated stone brother. He seemed to cry out to be released from his imprisonment. Beer cans and litter occupied the space between the iron rails and the glass behind. I pushed my hands between the bars and gently stroked the glass case.

'It *is* from the stone circle,' I replied, my eyes remaining transfixed by the stone. 'I mean, I saw the circle, from the top of the London Eye. I saw it. The Goddess replayed history. I went through thousands of years of London's prehistory and history in minutes. The circle was there, and I think St Paul's was built on the site.'

'You saw that...?' whispered Diana, as she squatted to join me, interlocking her arms around mine, '... Cool.'

'Well, that makes sense,' said Ken, 'It was the power spot of Londinium and later London. The site of the circle was later developed by the Romans, who built a temple there dedicated to the goddess Diana. Christopher Wren knew of it, and that's why St Paul's has its dome – feminine symbolism – it's the belly of the Goddess. But there is another sacred place close by, which has also miraculously survived. Come, my friend.'

With reluctance, I pulled myself away, relieving the stone of some of the litter as I rose. We walked back past the station and into Walbrook, stopping to look at a large blue sign on an ancient-looking wall.

The heading read *St Stephen's Walbrook*. Information that followed said it was the site of a Saxon church, built on the foundations of a 3rd Century Mithras Temple, which was preserved in Queen Victoria Street. Other info about later history of the site followed but I had already seen the relevant part, and Ken knew it.

The Mithras Temple!

'Want to see the temple, then?' he enquired. My answer came in the form of a beaming smile and a nod. I wondered, however, if he knew why I was smiling.

We carried on around the corner and on our left, opposite a new office/shopping complex, there it was, the remains of the Mithraeum. Even under street lighting the site was impressive. Low runs of stone marked out rooms and doorways and I could make out one much larger room. Some lights dimly illuminated the site, but low railings restricted access.

'You'll... you'll never guess what, guys.' I said, staring at the ruinous foundations whilst shaking my head.

'You saw this too?', Ken interjected, '... amazing. We reckon this was *THE* place in Pagan times, along with the stone circle. Mithras was the central saviour solar god of Mithraism, and some writers claim that the Jesus story evolved from this myth. The birthday of Mithras was on December 25th and he was resurrected from a cave tomb – sound familiar? His cult was around from about the 1st Century BC to around the 5th Century AD, and so was widespread when the prophet came along. The sacrifice of bulls was involved and the temples were usually windowless, thought to be an attempt to mimic caves. As well as images of Mithras, sculptures of Dionysus and Minerva were also found here. Many think that the all-male sect was the origin of the Masons and other male mystery schools that followed. Mithras' popularity with the Roman military invites comparison with the Templars and their ideals. We may have here the remains of a dress rehearsal for esoteric Christianity. Tell me, what was the temple like?'

'Well, I was looking at it from a mile or so away, and it was partially obscured by buildings, but it was pretty spectacular. Tall columns and a large door and, above that, huge images carved in stone.'

Diana looked into my eyes and then back to the ruins. 'Cool.'

I could feel the energy of the place, despite the fact that every stone had been moved. It was as if the energies had sought the stones out, following them to the new site. The stones themselves, and perhaps the design, were still attracting energies today. I took out a dowsing rod and began to walk around the perimeter. At several places my rods were swung this way and that by energies flowing both in and out of the temple ruins.

'Even now,' I pronounced to my watching friends, '... the place is alive. Midst all this noise, crowds, traffic and development, this holy ground still channels the life-force of the Mother. She once told me that even in the biggest city She could be found. Even here her love flows. Long may it continue.'

'So mote it be', said Ken and Diana almost simultaneously.

'Omnia vincit amor', Ken added, in uplifting tones.

'Pardon me?' I queried.

'It's Latin. *Love conquers all.* Ultimately, the love of Our Lady will conquer all!'

I smiled and nodded in agreement.

'And these places', Ken continued, 'not only mark flows of energy. Many of London's churches, former ancient sites and holy wells mark out complicated geometrical shapes, such as five, six and eight-pointed stars, plus circles and pentagrams. Wren incorporated the ancient knowledge of geomancy into his *New Jerusalem,* and the tradition continues today in secret societies and orders.'

'The Goddess told me', I replied, 'that the whole of Nature is based on geometrical principles and that elders and shamans, and later the Templars and Masons, sought to incorporate these principles into their architecture, but not just out of imitation, but because they knew the energies would be enhanced if they followed the sacred geometry they observed in Nature.'

'Too true,' exclaimed Ken.

The three of us spent the next few hours back at Diana's flat in Hampstead. We exchanged views and experiences and I told them of some of the wondrous things that had happened since I had seen them last, promising them copies of the book when it came out. After we had all sat out on the balcony to experience the Full Moon over London, watching it play hide-and-seek with scudding clouds, Ken left around midnight. Diana and I united again that moonlit night, as we had done four months before. The magic was no less than before: a bedroom illuminated by two dozen candles, burning incense, the moon coming in through the windows, and Diana, the most perfect incarnation of the Goddess I could ever wish to hold in my arms. Our bodies and souls united on the night of the twelfth Full Moon. It was a sacred *Hieros Gamos* no less.

Next morning Diana took me to a sacred place near her flat. She had felt drawn to live in the area because of a Bronze Age round barrow, known as Boudicca's Grave, that stood on Hampstead Heath. It was an atmospheric place, a large mound situated on open ground, yet shielded from the outside world by a ring of tall trees. She had taken part in solitary and group rituals there in the past. Dowsing confirmed it to be a powerful place. We sat on the ancient mound in the bright January sunshine and all seemed well with the Universe.

'We must do this more often', she said, smiling and entwining her fingers around mine.

'Yes, we must.'

'You know, at first I wanted to connect with you because of who you were, the messenger of the Goddess,' she continued, '... I guess it was a sort of ego thing. But last night and this morning, it was because of who you have become, because of who you now are. You have grown, as if finding the Goddess enabled you to find yourself.'

'You're also pretty cool yourself, you know. Last night I made love to the Goddess.'

'We both did,' she replied, 'for when we look into each other's eyes, it is She who returns our gaze. Knowing that makes life both bearable and magical. And whilst there are people thinking like us, like Ken and the others, spreading the message, there's gotta be hope for Mankind.'

'That's just what the Goddess said, at Wayland's Smithy I think it was, that there was hope for Mankind. Looking into your eyes I have no reason to doubt her words.'

We embraced on the top of that ancestral mound, united in our mutual love for the Goddess.

30. Thirteenth Moon – February: Glastonbury The Thirteen Insights

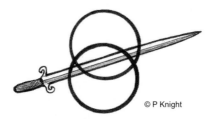

© P Knight

*The holistic picture implies that everything is organic
and alive - the Earth is alive…
it is a spiritual awakening to the reality of
something greater beyond us.*
(Sir George Trevelyan)

On my return from London, I spent the next week mulling over what had taken place and inputting into the *13 Moons.doc* file in my laptop. The beginning of February heralded the ancient festival of Imbolc, reminding me that it had been twelve months since I had sat in the wind and the rain at Arbor Low. It had all started with those words of Bel:

Who is it that walks on this hallowed ground, the temple of ancestors, on such a wearisome night?

Little had I known what I was to be catapulted into. *Has it really been a year?* Twelve full moons of wonder and awe, plus numerous magical moments in-between. Occasionally, I still had to pinch myself. I also had thoughts of the enormity of the task that still lay ahead. Getting the book published might be daunting, although I hoped that my previous publishing and editorial experience would hold me in good stead. I had contacts in the publishing world, and intended to call in a few favours.

Imbolc marked the lengthening of the days and shortening of the long winter nights. Spring was dawning, snowdrops were out, catkins were decorating alder and wych elm, and playful lambs were prancing around the fields, full of innocence and the promise of new life. I noticed the changes in the landscape more than ever before, acutely aware now that the Land never really slept and was constantly changing. I found myself appreciating the smallest facets of Nature, be they the intricacy of a spider's web, the geometry of a spiralling shell on a beach, or the awakening of tiny horse chestnut buds and their metamorphosis into gigantic five-fingered leaves. It became an obsession for me to know what phase the moon was at on a daily basis, to the extent that I printed out the phases for the whole year and pinned them up on my kitchen notice board.

The thin crescent moon appeared in the dusk skies around the middle of February. Each night I watched it grow little by little, and came to realise that I had mixed feelings as the Full Moon got nearer. It was to be my last verbal dialogue with the Great Mother. Although it was to be the climax of the whole journey, with the gift of the Thirteen Insights, it would also be the end of the most memorable part of my life to date. Before that, however, I still had to work out where I was to go.

'Meet me at the Grail Well, where the two circles meet and holy waters flow from my body.'

The Grail Well? Hmm. There were hundreds of sacred wells to choose from across Europe and no doubt plenty of sites associated with the Grail. *The Grail Well:* I reverted to my old saviour - Google. The results showed candidates in Cornwall that were associated with King Arthur, and several other sites around the country where Excalibur had allegedly been returned to the Lady of the Lake. But there was only one holy well that was linked with Grail legends, and that was the one at Glastonbury.

Chalice Well nestled at the foot of the Tor and was linked with various legends surrounding Arthur, including those that said the Grail chalice lay at the foot of the well. Glastonbury was a major centre for alternative seekers and Christians alike. Its myths and famous places were well known and its Tor dominated the Somerset Levels. In the *Sun and the Serpent,* Miller and Broadhurst had shown how the Michael and Mary currents flowed through the Chalice Well Gardens, bestowing its waters with curative properties. *Hmm, the Chalice Well - it somehow feels right.* Although I had been to Glastonbury previously, I had never visited the well, but it now felt right to do so. The culmination of my own Grail quest towards the Goddess and the Land would take place at a holy well associated with the sacred goblet.

During the next few days I re-read all I had on Glastonbury, as well as surfing the Net for new info. I particularly enjoyed one quote from the 12th Century, made by no less a person than the sovereign, Henry II:

> ... the town of Glastonbury, in which the vetusta ecclesia [ancient assembly] of the Mother of God is situated.

The Mother of God! Why didn't he just say *The Goddess* and be done with it? Not PC in his day no doubt – nor today for that matter. Well, the *Mother of God* was awaiting me there, and I would certainly not disappoint her. As to the rest of the conundrum, *'... where the two circles meet and the holy waters flow from my body',* it just had to be at the well head itself, where a metal well cover was endowed with the two interlocking circles of the vesica piscis. I found that it was not only a Christian icon but also an ancient sacred geometrical symbol, representing the Goddess, the balance of the male and female forces of the Land. The area created by the overlapping of the circles was symbolised the vulva of the Earth Mother. A fitting meeting place indeed for the thirteenth and final Full Moon.

And so the day arrived. The exact time of the Full Moon was in the afternoon so I travelled up to Glastonbury in the morning, arriving there around midday. After a sandwich and a cuppa at the Blue Note Café, I explored some of the funky shops on the High Street. Pausing in front of bookshop windows, I visualised *Thirteen Moons* sitting alongside *The Sun and the Serpent* and *The Da Vinci Code.* Was it to be but a dream, or was it going to be for real? I had to have faith, and up until then I had had direct monthly contact with the Mother to encourage me. But what about when I no longer had her to support me? There would soon come a time when I would have to remind myself that She was always with me. She was all of us. It was the Goddess, in fact, who would be the author, publisher, printer, reader and critic of the book.

There was one sacred place, however, I wished to visit before I went to the Chalice Well. That was the parish church of St John the Baptist, half way up the High St. I had read that the 'male' current of the St Michael Line flowed through the church before it continued to both the Abbey and the Well. The tall tower of the church was impressive and as I approached the porch I saw the image in stone of St George slaying a dragon. As I entered the doorway I felt a flow of energy, surging across my path from left to right. A few steps further it faded. I had walked in and out of the Michael flow, which was very strong as the Full Moon approached. I was particularly interested to see the tomb of Joseph of Arimathea, which was housed within the church. Legend had it that he was great-uncle to Jesus and was a member of the Sanhedrin in Jerusalem, and that he brought the young Jesus to Glastonbury, and was eventually the one who buried him after the Crucifixion. I had encountered ancient connections between England and Jerusalem before, at Temple Church and at Rosslyn.

I located the tomb in the North Transept. It was grand yet worn smooth by pilgrims, and on it now rested a case containing old embroidery from the Abbey. Closer inspection revealed a caduceus at one end, a sacred symbol, and one that Miller and Broadhurst had taken to represent the two major flows of energy, in balance, around a central axis, the ley line no less. Behind the monument was Joseph himself, immortalised in stained glass. His cloak and hood were deep purple and in his right hand he held a mighty staff. But it was his left hand that caught my attention. He held two golden cups, emanating rays of light. What did these represent – two Grails? They might be the ampullae in which Joseph collected the blood of Jesus at the Crucifixion. These sacred objects reputedly had healing powers. To me the cups had added meaning, representing the balance needed to achieve enlightenment, the equilibrium of yin and yang, male and female. Joseph was depicted facing forward and his eyes looked directly into mine. I wondered what secrets this man held.

'Well, Joseph, our paths cross. Mine is a holy quest, as was yours. Did you ever come this way? Did you drink from the sacred waters? I'll have a drink for you and toast your good soul, wherever you are now.'

I gently stroked the top of his tomb, before making my exit into the cool early Spring air.

The gardens that enclosed the Chalice Well were about fifteen minutes walk from the town centre, and I decided to go via the southern route, along Magdalene Street. I passed the ruins of the Abbey on my left, through which I knew the Mary and Michael currents flowed. On my right I soon walked by a church dedicated to St Mary, noting a sculpture of her holding the infant Jesus. It reminded me so much of the statues I had seen in Egypt – those of Isis, the Earth Mother, nurturing Horus, her Solar son. I could see from where the Christians had obtained this potent image.

Further on down the street I spotted a narrow alley on my right, which attracted my attention. In front of it was a round plaque inlaid into the pavement, which read *Glastonbury Millennium Trail - 19*. A wooden notice board informed me that down the alley I would find a *13th Century Chapel and St Magdalene's Almshouse*. I was powerfully drawn to follow. The alley opened up into a delightful and peaceful garden. At one end was the chapel. Two small windows, both of which had old, cracked, supporting beams, framed an old wooden door. Two yew trees stood nearby, one of which was bedecked with ribbons and other votive objects, left by those who had passed that way before me.

The door opened with a creak and I entered. The atmosphere and sacredness of the interior was immediately felt. At the far end was a long, narrow window, surrounded by a wall from which plaster was flaking off, revealing ancient stonework. The room was illuminated only by a few nightlights and candles that decorated a stone step in front of a simple wooden altar. A larger candle was surrounded by pieces of paper. Closer inspection revealed that on these had been written a collection of handwritten prayers, wishes, poetry and invocations. It was clear that this place was well-frequented by the people of Glastonbury as a holy shrine, and I could feel why. My heart filled with the love of the place and I sat down on a chair, my eyes closed to absorb it all. I felt empowered and humble, energised and calm. I could have stayed there for hours, but had to reach the Chalice Well Gardens well before the winter closing time of 4.00pm. I made my way back to the door, turned and bowed in the direction of the altar. I knew I would return to that hallowed place.

Moments later the quiet sanctity of the chapel was replaced by the noise of the busy road. I somehow tried to block out the imposition, focusing on both the chapel I had left, and on the Tor that I periodically saw before me. Thankfully, the din of the traffic was soon replaced by another, more tranquil world as I passed through the gates of the Chalice Well Gardens. Even in early spring there was blossom, colour, and all manner of delights to both uplift and calm a pilgrim. As I approached the pay booth I walked over a Vesica Piscis, formed of pebbles inlaid into the path. On entering the gardens I could see that although the sun illuminated the higher areas, the heart of the garden was mainly in shade, due to hedges and ancient walls, which obscured the low sun. To my right was a pool that was fed by a waterfall that was organic in design. The pool itself was in the shape of another vesica, and a sinuous stream drew its waters away. Walking across the lawn I came to a huge yew tree, which had split in two half way up, forming a gaping hole.

Behold the yoni of the Great Mother.

Continuing on, I passed through a doorway, above which was metalwork depicting yet another vesica piscis, this time pierced through the centre by a sword, which I took to be Excalibur. The sun was piercing the vulva of the Goddess, symbolic of both the sun coming down to earth, and the merging together of male and female polarities - the consummation of the God and the Goddess no less. The doorway opened up into a courtyard with a pool to my right. At the far end was a beautiful cascade of water, about 10ft deep, the iron-rich waters of which had stained the rocks an orangey-red. Symbolically, had this been seen as the blood of the Earth Mother? Later, Christians took it to be symbolic of the blood spilt by Jesus at the Crucifixion.

I continued onward and upward. The gardens were virtually empty, save for a small group of women who were washing crystals in water that poured from the mouth of a lion's head. As they receded to a nearby grassy area with their pieces of jasper, amethyst and quartz, I sampled the water using a glass tumbler left there for the purpose. The water was pure and cold and instantly refreshed my body and soul. I could feel the life-force flow through me, and could also feel her presence.

'Cheers to you, Joseph of Arimathea, and cheers to you to, My Lady.' I held the glass to the air before partaking another refreshing mouthful of the elixir of life.

'And good health to you too.'

'I knew you were here. I could feel your energies flowing through the whole place.'

'Indeed. The flows of the Archangel and Mary pass through this hallowed town, and through this garden of peace. The waters that issue from my body here have been revered and used for healing for thousands of years. This place has been continuously acknowledged as sacred regardless of which spirituality or religion was in vogue, much like Jerusalem.'

'That reminds me of William Blake's vision of Britain becoming the New Jerusalem. How does the song go?'

'I will not cease from mental fight,
Nor shall my sword sleep in my hand,
'Til we have built Jerusalem,
In England's green and pleasant land.'

'That's it. Will the New Jerusalem be built here?'

'It has already begun. In the eyes of the Templars and Masons, London was to be the New Jerusalem – they even built 12 gates into the city, mirroring that of the Holy City. But nowadays it is perhaps time to look for the New Jerusalem within, rather than without, one of the characteristics of the Grail, I would suggest. Glastonbury shares many similarities with the holy city. It has the potential to give people of all faiths and persuasions what they come here seeking.'

'That it surely does.'

'The spot where you stand, at the lion's head, is where the yin and yang, the Mary and Michael flows of my life-force converge. The water is sacred and very healing at this place and behind the lion stands a holy thorn. It can often be in flower and fruit at the same time, symbolising both death and rebirth. Flower essences are made from a combination of the blossom, the sacred water and sunlight, and are sent all over the world to facilitate healing.'

'Yes, the waters taste and feel divine indeed.'

'Come... to the wellhead.'

I put down the tumbler and wended my way past the thorn tree, from which hung ribbons and crystals, on through the serenity of the gardens, which gently ascended to the well. The wellhead nestled beneath tall yews and the well lid was open. The vesica piscis ornamentation was fashioned from solid strips of wrought iron and painted black.

'The vesica is indeed multi-layered with meaning. The space created by the two circles is symbolic of my vulva and of balance, created as it is by the circles of yin and yang. The vesica also displays Man's relationship with his soul and spirit. If you turn the two circles on end, then the top circle represents Spirit, whilst the bottom one the physical body. The area where the two circles interact is the individual Soul, the conduit between your physical body and Spirit.'

I looked down into the waters below. Although the water was calm, I could hear a more vigorous flow gushing somewhere beneath my feet. The energy was palpable and my heart filled with a sense of deep peace. I looked around and seemed to have the garden to myself. It was sunny, yet the wind still blew with the last sting of winter. I sat down on one of the stone seats next to the well, gazing down at the inlaid ammonite fossils.

'We shall not be disturbed for a while. We have almost reached the end of our journey. You have been an admirable student, and now you can go out into the world as my emissary. And my final words I will lay down before you now, in such a manner that they may be easily comprehended. I offer the world Thirteen Insights, each one based on our Full Moon discourses. Are you ready?'

'I am.' I shuffled on the cold stone, readying myself.

'In the book, please list them in big bold letters, so they are easily accessed and appreciated. I shall begin.

At the first Full Moon at Knowlton I spoke to you of how physicality was the manifestation of consciousness.

The First Insight –
Seek to perceive that every part of Planet Earth possesses consciousness on some level.
Everything is energetic, everything is alive and you are all students of a planet seeking to know itself.

At the second Full Moon we met in Cornwall, and I spoke of the human experience, the birth of fear, and how physicality creates duality, the illusion that you and spirit are separate.

The Second Insight –
The way you choose to perceive your experiences is the key to life and that nothing is constant except change.
You are always choosing between love and fear. Fear witnesses only its own expectations.
Beyond fear is where I wait with open arms.

And so at the third Full Moon I spoke of how you can connect with the living landscape that is my body, and you perceived the energetic forces that bind the world.

The Third Insight –
To connect with the spiritual essence of the Land is to connect with your own Divinity.
Love for the Land is Man's surest way to self-love.
When you go out into the Land, you really go within.

At Loughcrew in Ireland, on the fourth Full Moon, I spoke of how everything in the Universe is connected to all else, via the Web of Wyrd. In this respect you have power over your lives, as you and I will create in physical form whatever your beliefs dictate.

The Fourth Insight -
You are connected to everything that exists. More than this, you are *part* of everything that exists. What you send out will come back to you in manifestation. Through the Web of Life you create your own reality, so you may as well do it consciously.

You returned to Avebury for the fifth Full Moon and sat in a crop circle, my sacred artwork, where I told you of sacred geometry and how it forms the basis for all physical forms.

The Fifth Insight -
Sacred geometry is present in every aspect of the Universe, and expresses pure consciousness. It manifests the thoughts and dreams of Divinity. The principles you see in the Universe are within you.

Are you all right?'
'Yes, my Mother. Please continue, although I do feel like Moses receiving the Ten Commandments.'
'Yes, I know. He felt just as you do. The tenets I gave him were suitable for the world as it was then, suitable for those times and his culture. Now it is time for a new dialogue, appropriate to these times. I shall continue.
At the following moon we met at Dartmoor, and you walked across its hallowed ground and connected with the Land, and were introduced to your totems.

The Sixth Insight –
It is not necessary for you to understand the Universe. What is required is that you fully experience it. Be at one with the Land and recognise yourself to be part of it, for then you may find many of the answers you seek.

At the seventh Full Moon, in the autumn, we spoke at Stonehenge, the holy temple on the Plain. I spoke of sacred sites, both natural and man-made, and how they are an integral part of the Land, and that such places reflect the beliefs of those who built them.

The Seventh Insight -
Ancient sacred sites are not *ON* the landscape, but rather *WITHIN* it. Your imaginations and your spirit can be projected into them, and through them you may find your own divinity. Sacred sites are portals of infinity.

At the October Full Moon we talked at length at Wayland's Smithy, tomb of ancestors, about how ley lines and earth energies connected all sacred sites and how healing and positive energies can be transmitted to where it is needed.

The Eighth Insight -
Focus on sending out your love from a sacred place to wherever in the world it is needed.
In being at one with the Land, you can instigate healing.
Just send out your love, pure and sincere.

At the ninth blossoming of the moon you met the mighty tree spirit Mugna, King of the Duir, who told you of the plight of his brethren and how you need to reconnect with nature and, in particular, with trees.

The Ninth Insight -
Be as a tree: by connecting to the Land you shall remain grounded, yet your soul shall reach up to the heavens. Trees are wise – spend time with them.
In planting a tree you plant yourself.
In destroying forests you destroy yourselves.

We met in Brittany, at the sacred womb of Kercado, for the December Full Moon. I spoke of your ancestors, ancient and recent, and how vital it was to honour them, remember them, and even to seek their council. You saw visions of ancient ancestors in that primordial place and realised the debt you owe to your own father.

The Tenth Insight -
By remembering and honouring from where, and through whom, you have come, you shall enrich your life today and the world you will create tomorrow.
Honour your ancestors, for one day you shall be one.

You then travelled to Rosslyn Chapel for the eleventh Full Moon, where I recounted to you what the Grail really is, or rather what the many Grails can be.

The Eleventh Insight -
Ask not whether a myth is historically sound, but rather is it spiritually true.
The Grail is the journey into the unknown, but not just a journey into the past, for it creates your future.
It is ultimately a journey to your true Self.

In London, on the twelfth moon, you saw visions of the past and a harrowing dream of a possible future. I then gave you the means of Mankind's salvation, through conscious, environmentally friendly co-existence with the Planet.

The Twelfth Insight –
Live life in a conscious way, valuing all life, respecting the views of those who hold different beliefs.
Act only in ways that benefit the Planet as a whole, living always out of need, rather than greed.'

There was then silence. I looked up to the sky, my head reeling, my body immersed in rapture. The air was electric as I prepared myself for the culmination of my journey with the Goddess. I was silent for about a minute, until I could wait no longer.

'And the final Insight, Mother. *Please*, what is the final one?'

'The final Insight, if comprehended fully, and acted upon, and used as the basis and tenet for your lives, in conjunction with the other twelve, has the potential to save Mankind. They are but a few simple words, yet they contain much wisdom, and the means of your salvation is woven into them. Please absorb the words into your very being:

The Final Insight -
Look upon time as an eternal unfoldment as Now
moves from Now to another Now.
Do not see the world how you believed it to be,
but rather as it really is.
For you are both the lock and the key.
You are not only the shadow on the wall, but also the
hand that creates it, and the source of the light.
For you have always been and you shall always be.
For you are eternal. You are pure consciousness.
You are pure love. You are the Land.
You are God. You are the Goddess.

There was again silence, but this time it persisted. I could not speak, for I was breathless and tearful, filled with the immensity of her words. It was as if She had dotted the I's and crossed the T's on the new tablets. I wondered if Moses had felt like this.

'You will be fine. I could not have chosen anyone more suitable. If there had existed such a person, then our journey together could not have taken place.'

'Is this the end then, My Mother?'

Tears rolled down each check as the finality of the situation struck home.

'You know the answer to that, my son. Whenever you wish to hear me, just listen to birdsong, or the crashing of waves on the shore, or my soft whispers in the wind as it rustles through the trees, or my shout in a crash of thunder. More than this, you will find me in the silence of an ancient tomb, in the tranquillity of a still pond, or in the stillness of your sleep. I am always with you. How can I not be?'

'I know. I know. And that is the whole point, isn't it?'

'It surely is. You must go now, for people are approaching this sacred spot, and someone is closing in on you along the Web of Life. The summit of the Tor is where the strands of your lives may well entwine. Go quickly. Follow your heart always. I am always with you, as I am always with the one you are to meet. Go play with the joy of life. Rejoice with the Land. You and I are one, as I said the first time we spoke. For now it is surely goodbye. These thirteen moons have been magical, and more magic is afoot as 2012 cometh. Finally, I urge everyone to come and stand on that edge, looking across the

precipice. For if you do I will surely push you off – so be prepared to fly! The healing has begun. Yes, it has begun.'

'Yes, it surely has begun - and the book *will* be published. But please tell me, My Mother, one last thing. What will we do when we have eventually reached our highest form, when you and I shall at last know ourselves?'

'What will we do? Why, we won't have to do anything – we shall simply BE. Goodbye, my son – for now!'

'Good bye, my Mother…'

I looked to the heavens. My emotions were mixed. On one hand I knew this would be the last verbal interchange between the Goddess and myself. On the other, I felt enormous pride for what had been achieved. Tears continued to trickle down my face.

'… And I thank you - with all of my heart.'

I had felt it before, the feeling that a cord had been severed. Yet somehow it was different. The lessons were over, the dialogue done. My sadness was mixed with elation, for in my heart I knew that She would always be with me. And I knew that my totems would also be there too, as would Ken and Diana. No, I would never be alone again. I never had been, of course, not once in my whole life, I just hadn't realised it. We are all part of the Goddess. The key to life was to never forget our divinity.

I left the Chalice Well Gardens just as I detected the first tiny flakes of snow falling and I hastily zipped up my weatherproof coat and donned my gloves. As I ascended the Tor via the well-trodden south path, my mind replayed many of the events of the past year, events that I still could barely comprehend: At Kercado in France I had seen spectral ancestors parade before me; in the New Forest the Oak King had conversed with me in the dead of night; at the top of the London Eye I had seen three thousand years of history unfold before my eyes; I had met my two totems on a moon-lit moor. But above all, I had grown to know the Land and, in doing so, had grown closer to knowing myself. I had received insights from the Spirit of the Earth, which I was to send out to all people, to help make the world a safer and more tolerant place. She had gently cajoled and schooled me, never scolding, never putting me down. She was the ideal parent. If only we, her children, could become worthy of the unconditional love She had for us.

By the time I was half way up the Tor the flakes had become larger and were falling more frequently. The sky was grey and featureless - it looked as if we were in for a big fall. *Fantastic!* On arriving at the tower on the summit I was surprised to see that I was again alone. But it was, after all, getting cold, and it would soon be dark, and it was snowing!

For the next half hour I sat leaning against the south side of the tower, sheltering from a cold north wind. The snowflakes settled around me, dusting my waterproofs as if a mischievous child had sprinkled me with flour. The scene unfolding before me was a synthesis of *Narnia* and *Lord of the Rings*. Before my very eyes the landscape was transforming into one of primeval enchantment. Avalon was quietly settling down to a night of slumber beneath a blanket of snow, and I felt the Goddess was pleased with her gift to us, just as I was to receive it.

I looked at my watch - it was 4.35pm, which meant that the sun had already set, although this was betrayed only by a slight darkening of the leaden, snow-filled sky. After a further five minutes I saw someone approaching the summit through the snowflakes. She was a funky-looking woman, in her late-forties, I would have said, decked out in a black shawl, rainbow-painted jeans and DM's with flowers printed on them. She had long blonde hair and a cute pixy-like nose. *You're cool!* She approached with a great sense of purpose in each stride.

'Hi,' she said. She was English but with not a hint of regional accent. 'It's great up here, isn't it? Been up here so many times, but never when it's been snowin', so I didn't wanna miss it.'

'Yes, I know what you mean...' I replied, '... they've forecast a heavy fall. It's gonna be beautiful – although it already is.'

She stood in front of me, eyeing me intently.

'Oh, I'm sorry. Please, join me,' I requested.

I beckoned her to sit with me, against the sheltering buttress of the tower. She accepted my invite, nestling down beside me.

'Hi. I'm Maggie. I'm into the Old Ways, as you can probably tell.'

She looked down at her pendants, which were of various designs, such as pentacles, crescent moons, and a clear quartz crystal that dangled perfectly between the curves of her exposed cleavage. She was very attractive, but not just physically, for she also possessed a powerful spirit and an air of confidence that led me to believe she could tackle whatever came her way.

'Yeah, I kinda guessed.' We exchanged a chuckle, before returning our gaze to the ever-whitening landscape spread before us. The possible relevance of her name struck me.

Maggie... now is that short for Margaret, or Magdalene?

'Maggie, eh? As in Magdalene – wise companion of Jesus?' I said, with tongue very much in cheek.

336

With an impish grin and a flash of her elfish eyes, she replied, 'Well now, that's up to me to know and you to wonder at, isn't it! I don't have a daughter, but I do have a cousin called Sarah, if that counts!'

We both laughed aloud, before eventually settling down to look out again across the whitening landscape below.

'This may sound a bit crazy,' she continued, 'but last night I had the weirdest dream. Can I share it with you?

'Please do.'

'Well, amongst other things, I dreamt I was walking in a wood and I met my totem, which is a buzzard, but also a friendly stag and a white wolf. Then I heard the voice of an elderly woman, gentle and wise. She said that I needed to come up the Tor today, for I may well meet someone with whom I could move forward, someone who would walk with me on my path and help me connect to the Spirit of the Land as 2012 approaches.'

My heart welled up with excitement and an acknowledgement at what the Goddess had communicated to her – the white wolf and the deer were surely my totems - and the buzzard had been there too! Our eyes met, and there was a meeting of souls and hearts. We were transfixed, as if some bridge of ancient knowing were passing between us, unseen but deeply felt. I had the distinct feeling that we had crossed paths in a previous life.

'Tell me', she enquired with a wry smile, 'do **you** follow the Goddess?'

I looked down at the ground, smiling from ear to ear. I raised my head, and gazed into her knowing eyes.

'Do I follow the Goddess? Well, you could say that... yeah, you could say that!'

'Tell me then,' she continued, 'what's the most sacred place you've ever visited?'

I thought about it for a few moments, but there was really only one answer I could give to her.

'The most sacred site I have ever been to is... Planet Earth. Yes... Mother Earth.'

The End

'You must be the change you wish to see in the world.' (Gandhi)

Resources

Thirteen Moons Localities and Further Reading

You too can retrace the footsteps of our hero by visiting the locations. Within each section the localities are listed in alphabetical order. The inclusion of a locality does not imply public right of way, or permission to enter, so please check.

Chapter 1 - Genesis
Arbor Low. Derbyshire. Henge and stone circle, ¾ mile east of Parsley Hay Station, near Youlgreave. Grid ref: 161636. Car park at Upper Oldham Farm.
Further reading:
John Barnett, *Stone Circles of the Peak,* 1978, Turnstone Books.

Chapter 2 – First Moon
Knowlton. Dorset. Knowlton church and henges are 3 miles south of Cranborne on the B3078, at grid ref: 024103.
Further reading:
Peter Knight, *Ancient Stones of Dorset*, 1996, Power Publications.
Peter Knight, *Sacred Dorset – On the Path of the Dragon*, 1998, Capall Bann.
Peter Knight and Mike Power, *Dorset Pilgrimages – A Millennium Handbook,* 2000, Power Publications.

Chapter 3 – Second Moon
Hurlers and Cheesewring. Cornwall. North of Minions, 1½ miles west of Upton Cross, grid refs 258714 (Hurlers) and 258724 (Cheesewring).
Lanyon Quoit. Cornwall. Next to the Madron road, grid ref: 430337.
Men-an-Tol. Cornwall. Neolithic dolmen, 1½ miles east of Morvah (B3306), ½ mile north of Lanyan Farm, grid ref: 427349.
Trethevy Quoit. Cornwall. Neolithic dolmen, ¾ mile NE of St Clear, behind cottages between Tremar and Darite, grid ref: 259688.
Zennor Quoit. Cornwall. 1 mile SE of Zennor, grid ref: 468380.
Further reading:
Ian Cooke, *Journey to the Stones,* 1987, Men-an-Tol Studio.
Hamish Miller and Paul Broadhurst, *The Sun and the Serpent,* 1989, Pendragon Press.
James Redfield, *The Celestine Prophecy,* 1994, Bantam.
Cheryl Straffon, *Pagan Cornwall: Land of the Goddess,* 1993, Meyn Mamvro.
Craig Weatherhill, *Cornovia – Ancient Sites of Cornwall and Scilly,* 1985, Alison Hodge.

Chapter 4 – Beltaine Clogs
Saxon Inn, Child Okeford. Dorset. On the road going west out of village. Grid ref: 830133. Morris Dancers sometimes perform outside the pub.

Chapter 5 – Third Moon
Avebury. Wiltshire. The Avebury complex covers a wide area, including the henge in the village of Avebury, the stone avenue south of it, West Kennet long barrow (grid ref. 104677), Silbury Hill (ref: 100685), and other sites. See both the Henge Shop and Museum at Avebury for information. Parking for Avebury, Silbury and West Kennet is signposted.
Further reading:
Peter Knight, *West Kennet Long Barrow.* Stone Seeker. 2011.
Michael Dames, *The Avebury Cycle,* 1996, Thames and Hudson.
Peter Knight and Toni Perrott, *The Wessex Astrum,* 2008, Stone Seeker.
Terence Meaden, *The Secrets of the Avebury Stones,* 1999, Souvenir.
Hamish Miller and Paul Broadhurst, *The Sun and the Serpent,* 1989, Pendragon Press.

Chapter 6 – Newgrange and a Meeting with Einstein
Newgrange, Knowth and Dowth. Co. Meath, Ireland. North of Dublin lies the Boyne Valley, in which the monuments and the Visitor Centre stand. Guided tours, a shop, toilets and a museum are on site. Admission charge. Dowth is not included in tours and can be reached by car or foot.
Further reading:
Liam Mac Uisten, *Exploring Newgrange,* 1999, O'Brien Press.
N L Thomas, *Irish Symbols of 3500 BC,* 1988, Mercier Press.
Martin Brennan, *The Stones of Time,* 1994, Inner Traditions.

Chapter 7 – Fourth Moon
Loughcrew. Co Meath. 2 miles east of Oldcastle, 51 miles NW of Dublin. An incredible group of over 30 mounds and chambered cairns, some with carvings, and most with scenic views.
Further reading:
Brian Bates, *The Way of Wyrd,* Hay House, 2004.
Jean McMann, *Loughcrew: The Cairns,* 2005, After Hours Books.
N L Thomas, *Irish Symbols of 3500 BC,* 1988, Mercier Press.
Martin Brennan, *The Stones of Time,* 1994, Inner Traditions.

Chapter 8 - Chasing Rainbows
Castleruddery. Co Wicklow. South of Dublin, just off the N81 at Lower Castleruddery, 6 miles NE of Baltinglass. The circle is signposted.
Fourknocks. County Dublin. North of Dublin, west of Naul, grid ref: 109621. Keys available at a cottage in Davidstown at grid ref: 093616.
Tara. Co Meath. A complex of sacred sites. Toilets and shops nearby.
Further reading:
N L Thomas, *Irish Symbols of 3500 BC,* 1988, Mercier Press.

Chapter 9 – Fifth Moon

Avebury. Wiltshire. The field containing the crop circle is just NE of the henge, at grid ref: 105702. It had been the site of formations previously.

Barge Inn. Alton Barnes, Wiltshire. With crop circle room in the rear.

Grey Mare and Her Colts. Dorset. 1½ miles NW of Portesham, just south of path going west to Kingston Russell stone circle, grid ref: 584871.

Further reading:

Michael Dames, *The Avebury Cycle,* 1996, Thames and Hudson.

Peter Knight and Toni Perrott, *The Wessex Astrum,* 2008, Stone Seeker.

Peter Knight, *Ancient Stones of Dorset*, 1996, Power Publications.

John Michell, *The New View Over Atlantis,* 1983, Thames and Hudson.

Freddy Silva, *Secrets of the Fields,* 2002, Hampton Books.

Tim Wallace-Murphy, *Cracking The Symbol Code,* 2005, Watkins.

Visit: www.temporarytemples.co.uk for crop circle reports and images.

Chapter 10 - Dreaming a Crop Circle

County Museum. High West Street, Dorchester, Dorset. Exhibits of fine collections from local archaeology and geology. Admission charge.

East Kennet. Wiltshire. The field that contained the hero's crop circle is just outside West Woods, east of East Kennet, at grid ref: 137661.

Nine Stones. Dorset. Fine Bronze Age stone circle, on the A35 west of Winterbourne Abbas, grid ref: 611903.

Old Sarum. North of Salisbury. National Trust. Admission charge and restricted opening. Fine views of Salisbury along ley line.

Further reading:

Karen and Steve Alexander, *Crop Circle Year Books.* Annual reviews of crop circles. Website: www.temporarytemples.co.uk for up-to-date reports and photos of formations.

Freddy Silva, *Secrets of the Fields,* 2002, Hampton Books.

Chapter 11 - Dartmoor, Deer and Dowsing

Corringdon Ball. Neolithic long barrow, 1½ miles NW of South Brent. Access via Fairy Glen (see above). Grid ref: 669613.

'Fairy Gully'. ¼ mile west of Didworthy, NW of South Brent. The small glen at the beginning of the bridle path to Corringdon Ball long barrow, that leaves the road just south of Zeal Cottage at grid ref: 679623.

Merrivale Stone Rows. 2 miles west of Princetown, on open ground south of the B3357. Car parks available. Grid ref: 554747.

Nine Stones. Dorset. Fine Bronze Age stone circle on the A35, west of Winterbourne Abbas, near Dorchester. Grid ref: 611903.

Further reading:

Peter Knight, *Sacred Dorset – On the Path of the Dragon*, Capall Bann

Peter Knight and Mike Power, *Dorset Pilgrimages – A Millennium Handbook*, 2000, Power Publications.

Paul White, *Ancient Dartmoor – An Introduction,* 2000, Bossiney

OS Explorer Map, OL28 *Dartmoor* sheet is essential for detailed exploration of the moor, including its many isolated sacred sites.

Chapter 12 - Sixth Moon

Scorhill circle. Dartmoor. On Scorhill Down, 1 mile SW of Gidleigh. Take footpath from Scorhill Farm to circle, grid ref: 654874.

Tolmen Stone. Dartmoor. 1 mile SW of Gidleigh, on the north bank of the North Teign River, just east of two clapper bridges. Grid ref: 657870.

Further Reading:

Paul White, *Ancient Dartmoor – An Introduction,* 2000, Bossiney.

OS Explorer Map, OL28 *Dartmoor.* Essential for walking on the moor.

Chapter 13 - Shamanic Moon - Wolf and Stag

Longstone and Stone Rows. Chagford Common, 2 miles SSW of Gidleigh. Reached via footpaths from Batworthy. Grid ref: 660856.

Scorhill Circle. Dartmoor. On Scorhill Down, 1 mile SW of Gidleigh. Take footpath from Scorhill Farm to circle. Grid ref: 654874.

Thornworthy Tor. ½ mile north of Fernworthy Reservoir. Reached via open moorland from several directions. Grid ref: 665852.

Further Reading:

Paul White, *Ancient Dartmoor – An Introduction,* 2000, Bossiney.

OS Explorer Map, OL28 *Dartmoor.* Essential for walking on the moor.

Chapter 14 - Dartmoor – Open and Closed

Drizzlecombe. Dartmoor. 4 miles south of Princetown, 1½ miles east of Sheepstor. Stone rows march across the moor at grid ref: 592670.

Fernworthy circle. Dartmoor. In clearing of forest plantations ¼ mile west of Fernworthy Reservoir. Reached via bridle way. Grid ref: 655841.

Grey Wethers. Dartmoor. Stone circles, 1 mile west of Fernworthy Reservoir. Reached via bridleway from reservoir. Grid ref: 638832.

Spinster's Rock. Dartmoor. On edge of Dartmoor, 2 miles north of Chagford. In field near road junction next to Shilstone. Grid ref: 702908.

Further Reading:

Paul White, *Ancient Dartmoor – An Introduction,* 2000, Bossiney.

OS Explorer Map, OL28 *Dartmoor.* Essential for exploring the area.

Chapter 15 - Seventh Moon

Belas Knap. Gloucs. Neolithic barrow. 1¾ miles S of Winchcombe, west of road to Charlton Abbots. Signposted. Grid ref: 022254.

Durdle Door. Dorset. Just west of Lulworth Cove, grid ref: 805802.

Hetty Pegler's Tump. Gloucestershire. Neolithic chambered long barrow. Shown on some maps as Uley Longbarrow. West of B4066, 1 mile north of Uley church. Grid ref: 789001. Signposted.

Stonehenge. Wiltshire. This world heritage site stands 2 miles west of Amesbury, off the A303, and well signposted. Admission charge and restricted opening. Shop, refreshments and toilets. Grid ref: 123422.

Further reading:

C Chippendale, *Stonehenge Complete,* 1983, Cornell University Press.

Peter Knight and Toni Perrott, *The Wessex Astrum,* 2008, Stone Seeker.

Terence Meaden, *Stonehenge – The Secret of the Solstice,* 1997, Souvenir.

Chapter 16 - Drumming, Didges and Diana

Stonehenge. Wiltshire. This world heritage site stands 2 miles west of Amesbury, just off the A303, and is signposted. Admission charge and restricted opening. Shop, refreshments and toilets. Grid ref: 123422.

Chapter 17 - Eighth Moon

Knowlton. Dorset. Knowlton church and Neolithic henge complex is 3 miles south of Cranborne on the B3078, grid ref: 024103.

Ogbourne St Andrew. Wiltshire. 2 miles north of Marlborough, just west of the A345. Church, mound and a megalith. Grid ref: 188723.

Wayland's Smithy. Oxfordshire. Next to the east-west ridgeway track to the Uffington White Horse, 1 mile NE of Ashbury. Signposted. Grid ref: 281854.

Further reading:

Hamish Miller and Paul Broadhurst, *The Sun and the Serpent,* 1989, Pendragon Press.

Gary Biltcliffe, *The Belinus Line.* In preparation. E-mail the author at: Albion111@aol.com for further details.

Chapter 18 - Walking with Mary and Michael

Avebury. Wiltshire. The Avebury complex covers a wide area, including the henge that surrounds the village, the Kennet Stone Avenue running south from it, West Kennet long barrow (grid ref: 104677), Silbury Hill (grid ref: 100685), and several other sites. Visit both the Henge Shop and Museum at Avebury for more information. Car park, pub, cafe and toilets in the village.

Cucklington. Somerset. Church and well in village. Between Gillingham and Wincanton, grid ref: 755277.

Little Bredy. Dorset. Church, megaliths in churchyard and lake. 3 miles north of Abbotsbury, grid ref: 587890.

Milborne Port. Somerset. 2 miles east of Sherborne, on the A30. The church of St John is at the west end of main street, at grid ref: 677185.

Stoke Trister. Somerset. Church and megalith nearby. 1½ miles east of Wincanton, south of A303, grid ref: 737287.

Toller Porcorum. Dorset. Church and megaliths near gate. 2½ miles west of Maiden Newton, just south of A356, grid ref: 563980.

Winterborne Monkton. North of Avebury, Wiltshire. Church and megalith in churchyard at grid ref: 097719.

Further reading:

Peter Knight, *Ancient Stones of Dorset*, 1996, Power Publications.

Peter Knight, *Sacred Dorset – On the Path of the Dragon*, Capall Bann.

Peter Knight and Mike Power, *Dorset Pilgrimages – A Millennium Handbook,* 2000, Power Publications.

Hamish Miller and Paul Broadhurst, *The Sun and the Serpent,* 1989, Pendragon Press.

Chapter 19 - Stones, Secateurs and Samhain
Goddess Stone. Dorset. On bridle path between Grey Mare and Her Colts and the Kingston Russell stone circle. Grid ref: 583873.

Hampton Hill Circle. Dorset. The circle is next to an east-west public footpath, ¾ mile NW of Portesham, on crest of hill. Grid ref: 596865.

Knowlton. Dorset. Knowlton church, henge complex and megaliths, 3 miles south of Cranborne on the B3078, at grid ref: 024103.

Moot Stone. Gorwell, Dorset. 1 mile NE of Abbotsbury, next to cattle grid entrance to Gorwell Farm, which is just off the road going north from Abbotsbury to the Hardy Monument. Grid ref: 588868.

Muckleford. Dorset. Three miles west of Dorchester. Megalith on north side of bridge over River Frome, north of village centre. Grid ref: 643936.

Nine Stones. Dorset. Bronze Age stone circle, on the A35 west of Winterbourne Abbas. Grid ref: 611903.

West Lulworth. Dorset. Megaliths along rough track going west from Burngate. The stones are south of where a north-south footpath meets this track, at grid refs: 829815, 829814 and 827812.

Whitcombe. Dorset. Church, Saxon cross and megalith, 2 miles SE of Dorchester, on the A352 Wareham road, at grid ref: 717883.

Further reading:

Peter Knight, *Ancient Stones of Dorset*, 1996, Power Publications.

Peter Knight, *Sacred Dorset – On the Path of the Dragon*, 1998, Capall Bann.

Peter Knight and Mike Power, *Dorset Pilgrimages – A Millennium Handbook,* 2000, Power Publications.

Chapter 20 - Ninth Moon
Burley. New Forest, Hampshire. Church in village, gird ref: 214032.

Clay Hill. New Forest, Hampshire. Our hero parked at grid ref: 223023, on the east side of crossroads. The parking area and the road east are sometimes open in the summer. Follow the hero's route east along track.

Naked Man. New Forest, Hampshire. 2 miles east of Burley. The tree is marked on OS maps, just east of A35 at Wilverley Post. Grid ref: 245017. Nearby is **Wilverley Inclosure,** where Mugna was encountered.

Further reading:

Paul Broadhurst, *The Green Man and the Dragon,* Mythos, 2006.

The special OS 1:25 000 map *New Forest* will enable you to follow the route of our hero, and explore this beautiful area.

Chapter 21 - The Coven and the Dragon Tree
Dragon Tree. Woodlands, Dorset. ½ mile north of village centre, at junction of the B3081 and the road south into village, at grid ref: 051100. It is known locally as the Remedy Oak, and is marked by a plaque.

Hod Hill. Dorset. Roman Fort. Near Blandford, grid ref: 854107.

Long Crichel. Dorset. The church, on a ley, is at grid ref: 977103.

The Naked Man. New Forest, Hampshire. 2 miles east of Burley. The tree is marked on OS maps, just east of A35 at Wilverley Post, at grid ref: 245017. Mugna was encountered in the adjacent Wilverley Inclosure.

Further reading:

Peter Knight, *Ancient Stones of Dorset*, 1996, Power Publications.

Peter Knight, *Sacred Dorset – On the Path of the Dragon*, 1998, Capall Bann.

The OS 1:25 000 map *New Forest* will enable you to follow the route of our hero, as well as explore this beautiful area.

Chapter 22 - Tenth Moon

Dorset Cursus. Cranborne Chase, Dorset. Neolithic processional way and long barrows. The south terminal with its attendant long barrows are 1 mile east of Chettle, off the A354. Access via stile. Grid ref: 969125.

Kercado. Brittany. Neolithic passage grave. In grounds of Kercado Château, E of Carnac, off the D196. Access allowed and signposted.

Menec. Brittany. Hundreds of stones in avenues, near Carnac. Access restricted to certain fields. Visitor Centre and toilets nearby.

Further reading:

Aubrey Burl, *Megalithic Brittany,* 1985, Thames and Hudson.

Julian Cope, *The Megalithic European,* 2004, Element.

Martin Green, *A Landscape Revealed,* 2000, Tempus.

Peter Knight, *Ancient Stones of Dorset*, 1996, Power Publications.

Peter Knight, *Sacred Dorset - On the Path of the Dragon*, 1998, Capall Bann.

The detailed 1:25 000 maps that cover the Carnac area are IGN sheets 0821 OT and 0921 OT. They show all the sites in *Thirteen Moons.*

Chapter 23 – Madeleine, Prêtres and Prejudice

Chapel de la Madeleine. Chapel, megaliths and holy well. Between Carnac and Aurey, Brittany - off the D186, North of Kerguéarec.

Dolmen de la Madeleine. Between Carnac and Aurey, Brittany - off the D186, North of Kerguéarec. In field north of chapel (see above).

Dolmen des Pierres-Plats. At the southern end of the Locmariaquer Peninsular, Brittany, yards from beach. Signposted - car park nearby.

Le Grand Menhir Brisé. Locmariaquer, Brittany. Massive megalith. Restricted opening and admission charge. Visitor Centre and toilets.

Le Table Des Marchands. Locmariaquer, Brittany. Restricted opening times and admission charge. Visitor Centre and toilets.

Further reading:

Aubrey Burl, *Megalithic Brittany,* 1985, Thames and Hudson.

Julian Cope, *The Megalithic European,* 2004, Element.

Lynn Picknett, *Mary Magdalene - Christianity's Hidden Goddess,* 2003, Robinson.

Dan Brown, *The Da Vinci Code*, 2003, Bantam Press.
1:25 000 maps that cover Carnac are IGN sheet 0821 OT and 0921 OT.

Chapter 24 – Returning my Father to the Land.

Avebury, Wiltshire. The Avebury complex covers a wide area, including the henge in the village of Avebury, the stone avenue south of it, West Kennet long barrow (104677), Silbury Hill (grid ref: 100685), and other sites. Visit both the Henge Shop and Museum at Avebury for information. Parking for Avebury, Silbury and West Kennet is signposted.
Further reading:

Aubrey Burl, *Prehistoric Avebury,* 1979, Yale.
Michael Dames, *The Avebury Cycle,* 1996, Thames and Hudson.
Peter Knight, *West Kennet Long Barrow.* Stone Seeker. 2011.
Peter Knight and Toni Perrott, *The Wessex Astrum,* 2008, Stone Seeker.
Terence Meaden, *The Secrets of the Avebury Stones,* 1999, Souvenir.
Hamish Miller and Paul Broadhurst, *The Sun and the Serpent,* 1989, Pendragon Press.

Chapter 25 – Eleventh Moon

Rosslyn Chapel. Rosslyn, south of Edinburgh. Bus and taxi services. Restricted opening times and admission charge.
Further reading:

Dan Brown, *The Da Vinci Code*, 2003, Bantam Press.
Tim Wallace-Murphy, *Cracking The Symbol Code,* 2005, Watkins.
Philip Coppens, *The Stone Puzzle of Rosslyn Chapel,* 2004, Frontier.
Lynn Picknett, *Mary Magdalene – Christianity's Hidden Goddess,* 2003, Robinson.

Chapter 26 – Finding Mary

Child Okeford. Northwest of Blandford Forum, Dorset.
Fifehead Magdalene. North of Sturminster Newton, Dorset.
Hazelbury Bryan. West of Blandford Forum, Dorset.
Woodborough. Wiltshire. Church of Mary Magdalene, near Alton Barnes, south of Avebury.
Further reading:

Peter Knight, *Sacred Dorset – On the Path of the Dragon*, 1998, Capall Bann.
Peter Knight, *Ancient Stones of Dorset*, 1996, Power Publications.
Peter Knight and Mike Power, *Dorset Pilgrimages – A Millennium Handbook,* 2000, Power Publications.
Peter Knight and Toni Perrott, *The Wessex Astrum,* 2008, Stone Seeker.
Lynn Picknett, *Mary Magdalene – Christianity's Hidden Goddess,* 2003.

Chapter 27 – Twelfth Moon

Temple Church. London. Situated off Temple Place, in the Temple district of Central London. Nearest underground is Temple.
Further reading:

Temple Church, 1997, Pitkin Guides.

Dan Brown, *The Da Vinci Code*, 2003, Bantam Press.

John Matthews and Chesca Potter (editors), *The Aquarian Guide to Legendary London*, 1990, Aquarian Press.

Chapter 28 – Visions from the All-Seeing Eye

Boudicca Monument. London. West side of Westminster Bridge.

Dali Exhibition. Just south of London Eye, near Westminster Bridge.

London Eye. This stands on the South Bank, close to Westminster Bridge. See www.ba-londoneye.com for details and on-line booking.

Further reading:

John Matthews and Chesca Potter (Eds.), *The Aquarian Guide to Legendary London*, 1990, Aquarian Press.

Chapter 29 – Reunited in Londinium

Boudicca's Grave. Hampstead Heath, London. Bronze Age mound.

London Stone. Cannon Street. The stone is set behind iron railings opposite Cannon Street Station (although it is to be temporarily moved to the British Museum, pending a new development).

Temple of Mithras. London. At Poultry, near Bank Station.

Further reading:

John Matthews and Chesca Potter (Eds.), *The Aquarian Guide to Legendary London*, 1990, Aquarian Press.

E O Gordon, *Prehistoric London – Its Mounds and Circles*, 1985 edition, Artisan.

Chapter 30 – Thirteenth Moon

Glastonbury. Somerset. Chalice Well, Tor and Abbey. Opening restrictions and admission charges at Chalice Well and Abbey.

St Margaret's Chapel. Magdalene St, Glastonbury. Opening hours restricted. Atmospheric, sacred chapel and gardens.

Further reading:

Frances Howard-Gordon, *Glastonbury – Maker of Myths*, 1982, Gothic Image.

Kathy Jones, *The Goddess in Glastonbury*, 1990, Ariadne.

Kathy Jones, *In the Nature of Avalon*, 2000, Ariadne.

Peter Knight and Toni Perrott, *The Wessex Astrum – Sacred Geometry in a Mystical Landscape*, Stone Seeker Publishing, 2008.

John Michell, *The New View Over Atlantis*, Thames & Hudson, 1983.

Hamish Miller and Paul Broadhurst, *The Sun and the Serpent*, Pendragon Press, 1989.

Philip Rahtz, *Glastonbury: Myth and Archaeology*, 2003, Tempus.

About the Author

Peter Knight is well known for his lively and enthusiastic workshops, lectures and field trips on topics relating to our ancient heritage, sacred sites, leys and dowsing. He is co-founder of the Dorset Earth Mysteries Group, is an Adult Education Tutor on archaeology and earth mysteries subjects, and has spoken at international conferences in the USA, UK and Malta. He is a freelance magazine writer, and has appeared on radio and TV, such as on Channel 4's *Don Roamin'* with Monty Don. Peter is the founder and organiser of the *Convention of Alternative Archaeology and Earth Mysteries*, held annually in Wiltshire, which give platforms to new and leading researchers. In 2006 he founded Stone Seeker Tours, promoting holistic tours to sacred sites across the UK and Europe. He also envisioned and hosts the *Ancient Ambient Chill-Out*, combining funky world music with large-screen images of sacred sites and tribal cultures.

His interests include walking, travel, drumming, world music, dowsing, prehistoric art, shamanism, experiencing sunrises and sunsets at sacred sites, and photographing nature. He is a father and grandfather, a vegetarian, and follows a Goddess-orientated spirituality, whilst honouring the wisdom of other spiritualities and religions. He recently co-founded the Calne Environmental Network.

Contact the author by e-mail: stoneseeker@waitrose.com
Web site: www.stoneseeker.net

Thirteen Moons Tours and Workshops

Peter Knight runs *Thirteen Moons Tours* to many of the locations in this book. He outlines the archaeology, architecture, ley lines, dowsing and other qualities of each sacred site and re-enacts some of the profound moments that our hero experienced, with readings from the novel. He also facilitates drumming, meditation and ceremony, to help seekers connect with the Land and experience some of the adventures of our hero in *Thirteen Moons*.

Peter is also available for group workshops, which go into the principles outlaid in the book in more depth, including how these can lead to more fulfilling lives, by living in an ecological and positive way. These include meditations, visualisations, visual presentations as well as drumming, sometimes at sacred sites.

For more details email: **stoneseeker@waitrose.com**
or visit the website: **www.stoneseeker.net**

Stone Seeker Tours
with Peter Knight

Are you planning to bring a group to visit sacred sites in the UK, or are you looking for a magical private tour? Do you wish to truly experience places like Stonehenge, Avebury, West Kennet, Glastonbury, Dartmoor, Ireland, Malta or Dorset?

Stone Seeker Tours specialises in tailor-made excursions. You bring the pilgrims and we will provide the expert guide, and the unforgettable experiences. The following subjects will be expertly covered, and individual topics can be included or excluded, depending on the focus and requirements of the group:

Sacred archaeology - Ancient astronomical alignments
Ley lines and sacred geometry - Myth and folklore
Earth energies and dowsing - Crop circles
Church symbolism - Drumming and healing circles

Peter Knight is the main guide of Stone Seeker Tours, and has been taking groups around sacred sites for over ten years, including a wide variety of 'alternative' groups, such as dowsers, healing circles, and self-growth groups. He has a relaxed manner, a good sense of humour and is very enthusiastic, making for entertaining and informative tours. His trips are a spiritual experience, as he helps you interact with the Goddess landscape.

List of localities:
Stonehenge (can include Woodhenge) – Avebury (bigger than Stonehenge and hands-on!) – Dartmoor (stone circles) – Glastonbury (Tor, Abbey, Chalice Well, etc) – Dorset stone circles – Neolithic Jersey – Ancient Winchester – Megalithic Brittany – Sacred Cornwall – Ancient Dorchester and Cerne Abbas – St Michael Line – Da Vinci Code and Templar localities - Prehistoric Ireland – Shamanic Drumming in West Kennet. Peter also has in-depth knowledge of other areas, so please enquire! School, retirement and disabled parties can be catered for with special wheelchair-friendly itineraries. The tours can be accompanied by illustrated talks on a variety of subjects.

www.stoneseeker.net
stoneseeker@waitrose.com

Other Books by Peter Knight

Ancient Stones of Dorset
Published in 1996 by Power Publications
Still the most comprehensive work on Dorset's megalithic sites. Maps of ley lines and map/grid references of sites. Earth energies, astronomy, and ancient crosses.

Sacred Dorset ~ On the Path of the Dragon
Published in 1998 by Capall Bann
A thorough work on Dorset's ancient spiritual heritage. Includes hillforts, wells and springs, Cerne Giant, sun & moon, green man, fairies, dragons and more.

Dorset Pilgrimages ~ A Millennium Handbook
(with Mike Power)
Published in 2000 by Power Publications
Newly envisaged day-long pilgrimages across Dorset
Churches, stone circles, megaliths, wells, etc visited en route

Earth Mysteries ~
An Illustrated Encyclopaedia of Britain (CD-ROM)
Published in 2003 by Stone Seeker Publishing
Over 350MB of information. 250 colour and b&w illustrations, maps and line drawings. A-Z format, plus resources, like a huge web site – over 1000 hyperlinks!

The Wessex Astrum –
Sacred Geometry in a Mystical Landscape
(with Toni Perrott)
Published in 2008 by Stone Seeker Publishing
The story of the discovery of the huge landscape hexagram, involving Stonehenge, Avebury, Glastonbury, the St Michael Line and more!

West Kennet Long Barrow – Landscape, Shamans and the Cosmos.
Published in 2011 by Stone Seeker Publishing.
The definitive guide to this Neolithic monument near Avebury. Includes the excavations, astronomy, alignments, acoustics, earth energies, shamanism etc.

The Cerne Giant – Landscape, Gods and the Stargate
Published in 2013 by Stone Seeker Publishing.
Groundbreaking, definitive guide to the iconic Dorset hill figure. Includes Giant's probable age, his identity, alignments, folklore, astronomy and much more!

Calne – Gateway to Ancient Wiltshire
(with Sue Wallace)
Published in 2014 by Stone Seeker Publishing
16 walks encompass the history and prehistory of this North Wiltshire town and the surrounding villages and landscape, including Avebury.

Signed and dedicated copies of the above available direct from Peter.

www.stoneseeker.net

Dorset Earth Mysteries Group

Peter Knight is the co-founder of this active group who meet for regular monthly meetings, hosting lectures by prominent people in the earth mysteries field. Its members organise field trips to sacred sites, such as our annual pilgrimage into the inner sanctum of Stonehenge to experience the sunset, and also hold social events. Members are entitled to reduced entrance rates at talks, as well as generous discounts on the author's field trips. Membership is open and a warm welcome awaits you. For membership enquiries, or to obtain a list of forthcoming events, visit the DEMG website at:

www.dorsetmysteries.org

Wessex Research Group

The Wessex Research Group is a coalition of local groups, societies, centres and organisations, founded by the late Nigel Blair. It networks and exchanges information about talks, available speakers, events and field trips. It issues a monthly newsletter about forthcoming events across Wessex and other areas.

For further information, please visit their website:

www.wessexresearchgroup.net